Geology of the country around Leighton Buzzard

This memoir describes an area centred on Leighton Buzzard, some 70 km north-west of London, which includes parts of Bedfordshire, Buckinghamshire and Hertfordshire. The mainly rural landscape is dominated by the escarpments of the Woburn Sands and the Chalk; the major population centres are Luton, Dunstable and part of Milton Keynes. Jurassic and Cretaceous rocks crop out at the surface, but about a third of the area is covered by varied drift deposits.

The district has been important in terms of mineral extraction for over a century. Active working of sand and fuller's earth from the Woburn Sands and of chalk for cement and lime manufacture continues. Formerly, brick clays were dug from the Gault, Oxford Clay and drift deposits, and 'coprolites' at several horizons in the Cretaceous rocks were used for the manufacture of superphosphate fertiliser. The recent surveys will assist in assessing the remaining mineral reserves.

An appraisal of the structure of the concealed Palaeozoic basement rocks of the district has been made from the interpretation of regional geophysical and borehole data, and an attempt is made to relate this to structures and depositional patterns in the Mesozoic rocks. Full stratigraphical accounts of the exposed formations are presented with due emphasis on their mineral potential and possible geological hazards. Briefer accounts of the concealed rocks are based on limited borehole information.

During the Quaternary period, the district was overridden by the Anglian ice sheet, which reached the Chilterns escarpment and left behind extensive spreads of chalky till and associated glaciofluvial deposits. Deep subglacial valleys were cut at this time and infilled with varied glacial deposits including laminated lake clays. The groundwater needs of the district are met from the Chalk and Woburn Sands aquifers, which are discussed herein.

Cover photograph
8 m face in 'Red Sands' division of the Woburn Sands in Pratt's Pit, Leighton Buzzard [SP 931 240] (Joseph Arnold & Sons Ltd). Large-scale cross-bedding typical of sand waves in shallow tidal waters is picked out by concentrations of dark clay and goethite ooliths on the foresets (A14488)

Plate 1 'Carstone reef' in 'Silver Sands' division of the Woburn Sands, Mundays Hill Quarry, Heath and Reach [SP 937 282] (George Garside (Sand) Ltd). The 'reefs' are linear features, 3 to 10 m wide and 2 to 3 m high, formed by the local ferruginous cementation of the sands. They have been shown to extend for hundreds of metres in an east–west direction by observations over many years in the quarries around Shenley Hill (A11479).

BRITISH GEOLOGICAL SURVEY

E R SHEPHARD-THORN
B S P MOORLOCK
B M COX
J M ALLSOP
C J WOOD

Geology of the country around Leighton Buzzard

Memoir for 1:50 000 geological sheet 220
(England and Wales)

CONTRIBUTORS

Stratigraphy
D T Aldiss
J P Colleran
R D Lake
R J Wyatt

Biostratigraphy
H C Ivimey-Cook
A W A Rushton
I P Wilkinson

Hydrogeology
N S Robins

LONDON: HMSO   1994

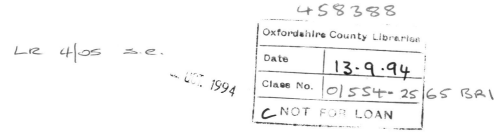
© NERC copyright 1994

First published 1994

ISBN 0 11 884503 9

Bibliographical reference

SHEPHARD-THORN, E R, MOORLOCK, B S P, COX, B M, ALLSOP, J M, and WOOD, C J. 1994. Geology of the country around Leighton Buzzard. *Memoir of the British Geological Survey*, sheet 220. (England and Wales).

Authors

E R Shephard-Thorn, BSc, PhD
B S P Moorlock, BSc, PhD
B M Cox, BSc, PhD, CGeol
J M Allsop, BSc, CGeol, MIScT
British Geological Survey, Keyworth

C J Wood, BSc
formerly British Geological Survey

Contributors

D T Aldiss, BSc, PhD, CGeol
R D Lake, MA
R J Wyatt, MBE
H C Ivimey-Cook, BSc, PhD
A W A Rushton, BA, PhD
I P Wilkinson, MSc, PhD, CGeol
British Geological Survey, Keyworth

N S Robins, MSc, CGeol
British Geological Survey, Wallingford

J P Colleran, MSc
formerly British Geological Survey

Other publications of the Survey dealing with this and adjoining areas.

BOOKS

Memoirs
Geology of the country around Huntingdon and Biggleswade (187 and 204), 1965
Geology of the country around Hitchin (221), in preparation
Geology of the country around Thame (237), in preparation

British Regional Geology
London and the Thames Valley (3rd edition)
East Anglia and adjoining areas (4th edition, 1961, reprinted 1982)

Reports
The geology of the new town of Milton Keynes (1974)
The geology of the Leighton Buzzard–Ampthill district (1988)

MAPS

1:625 000
Solid geology (south sheet)
Quaternary geology (south sheet)

1:250 000 Chilterns
Solid geology (1991)
Aeromagnetic anomaly (1980)
Bouguer gravity anomaly (1983)

1:100 000
Hydrogeological map of the area between Cambridge and Maidenhead (1984)

1:50 000
Sheet 204, Biggleswade (reprinted 1976)
Sheet 238, Aylesbury (reprinted 1990)
Sheet 239, Hertford (reprinted 1978)
Sheet 221, Hitchin (in preparation)
Sheet 237, Thame (in preparation)

1:25 000
Milton Keynes New Town (1971)

Printed in the UK for HMSO
Dd 292046   C8   3/94

CONTENTS

FIGURES

PLATES

TABLES

PREFACE

The Leighton Buzzard district, which lies some 70 km north-west of London, is of national importance as a source of industrial sand and fuller's earth products, won from the Woburn Sands Formation of early Cretaceous age. This memoir, with the new 1:50 000 sheet it describes, provides the first comprehensive modern account of the geology.

The landscape is for the most part rural, with mixed and arable farming, and sizeable tracts of woodland, but has been locally scarred over the past century by quarrying activities. The major population centres are the Luton–Dunstable conurbation and a part of Milton Keynes new town. Jurassic and Cretaceous formations crop out at the surface and dip in a general south-easterly direction. The escarpments of the Woburn Sands and Chalk are the dominant topographical features.

Full stratigraphical accounts of the exposed Jurassic and Cretaceous formations are given, with due regard to their mineral potential and geological hazards. Briefer descriptions of the concealed formations are based on limited borehole information. The deep geology has been interpreted from regional geophysical and borehole data, and an attempt is made to relate basement structure to structural and depositional patterns in the Mesozoic rocks. The district includes the type localities for the Woburn Sands and Ampthill Clay formations, and the Totternhoe Stone and Shenley Limestone, for which revised accounts are given. It also has the most northerly outcrops of the Portland and Purbeck formations in Britain.

Quaternary drift deposits, of glacial, periglacial and fluvial origin, cover about 30 per cent of the district. Drift deposits and periglacial processes have considerably modified the landscape, and are linked to potential hazards such as solution collapse features in the Chalk and landslips in the clay formations. A deep buried channel infilled with till, fluvioglacial and lake deposits underlies the floodplain of the River Ouzel. Improved understanding of the properties and three-dimensional relationships of the drift to the solid geology will greatly assist the planning of civil engineering projects.

Peter J Cook, DSc
Director

British Geological Survey
Kingsley Dunham Centre
Keyworth
Nottingham
NG12 5GG

September 1993

ACKNOWLEDGEMENTS

The greater part of this memoir has been written and compiled by E R Shephard-Thorn. He has received major assistance from the following: Beris M Cox has written Chapter 3 on the geology and biostratigraphy of the exposed Jurassic formations; Chapter 4 on the Woburn Sands is largely the work of B S P Moorlock; Jenny M Allsop has written on aspects of concealed and structural geology incorporated in Chapters 2 and 7, and J D Cornwell has provided helpful advice on some aspects of the geophysical interpretation; C J Wood's work on the Chalk stratigraphy of the district appears in Chapter 6. The biostratigraphy of the Lias in the Tattenhoe Borehole has been reviewed for this memoir by H C Ivimey-Cook, and A W A Rushton has similarly dealt with the Tremadoc rocks of this borehole. I P Wilkinson has contributed on aspects of Chalk and Gault micropalaeontology. The description of the Chalk sequence around Totternhoe and of the Totternhoe Stone in its type locality have been contributed by D T Aldiss. The Sundon Borehole was logged by J P Colleran; and calcimetry studies were carried out by G E Strong and A Connell. The hydrogeological account of the district in Chapter 9 has been prepared by N S Robins. This memoir has been edited by Drs R A B Bazley and A A Jackson.

The completion of this survey has been assisted by many organisations and individuals. Grateful acknowledgement of financial support in the form of jointly funded contracts is made to the Department of the Environment and the National Rivers Authority, Thames Region. Our thanks are also especially due to a number of quarrying concerns within the district, who have facilitated access to their properties and in some cases supplied useful information from their programmes of trial boreholes. These include: George Garside (Sand) Ltd, Joseph Arnold and Sons Ltd, Ready Mixed Concrete Ltd, Buckland Sand Ltd, L B Silica Sand Ltd, P Bennie Ltd, Steetley Minerals Ltd, Blue Circle plc, Laporte Absorbents, Totternhoe Lime and Stone Co Ltd and Rugby Cement Ltd.

Local government bodies have also been most helpful in supplying copies of borehole data from their archives and other assistance. These include Bedfordshire, Buckinghamshire and Hertfordshire county councils, Luton Borough Council and Luton Museum Service. Several scientific colleagues have been generous in making personal communications and in providing access to theses and other unpublished work. These include: Dr C R Bristow, Dr R G Bromley, Prof J H Callomon, R A Carter, Prof J A Catt, Dr K L Duff, Dr A S Gale, S E Hollyer, Dr M K Howarth, Prof R J N Mortimore, Dr K N Page (formerly of the Bedford Museum Record Centre), Dr A H Ruffell, P J Smart and Dr D J Wray. Geoffrey Walton and Partners have co-operated in providing access to borehole cores and logs at Kensworth Quarry (on behalf of Rugby Cement Ltd).

Finally, our thanks are due to the land owners of the district for their co-operation in providing ready access to their property during the course of the surveys.

NOTES

Throughout the memoir the word 'district' refers to the area covered by the 1:50 000 geological sheet 220 (Leighton Buzzard).

National Grid references are given in square brackets; they lie within 100 km squares SP and TL and are prefixed accordingly.

Zonal nomenclature: zones and subzones in the Lower Jurassic and the Cretaceous are considered to be defined and recognised exclusively on the basis of fossil (often ammonite) taxa. They are thus treated as biozones and their names are italicised.

In the Upper Jurassic, on the other hand, while the zones and subzones are also based on ammonite faunas, they are often recognised by other characters and are defined at specific horizons in type sections. Such zones and subzones are therefore considered to be chrono-stratigraphical rather than biostratigraphical units and their names are not italicised.

HISTORY OF SURVEY OF THE LEIGHTON BUZZARD SHEET

The district covered by the new 1:50 000 Leighton Buzzard geological sheet formed part of the Old Series Sheet 46, which was surveyed at a scale of one inch to the mile (1:63 360) between 1863 and 1868, and published in four quarters between 1864 and 1869. The surveyors were H Bauerman, F J Bennett, A H Green and W Whitaker, of whom Green was the major contributor. Additional surveys of drift deposits and revisions of solid boundaries were carried out by A C G Cameron and A J Jukes-Browne on six-inch field slips between 1884 and 1894; these were incorporated in revised editions of the Old Series quarter sheets issued between 1884 and 1898. No descriptive memoir was prepared for Sheet 46, although some reference to the district was made in the regional memoir for the London Basin (Whitaker, 1872).

The 'Old Series' one-inch maps were never reissued in the 'New Series' format, so that the new 1:50 000 Leighton Buzzard (220) sheet published in 1992 is the first geological map of the district to appear for over 90 years. Primary mapping at the 1:10 560 and 1:10 000 scales was carried out between 1967 and 1968 and between 1985 and 1990. The surveys carried out between 1967 and 1968 were part of an investigation of the Milton Keynes new town area, which overlaps the north-western corner of the district. A colour-printed 1:25 000 scale geological map of the new town area was published in 1971 and a descriptive report in 1974. The later 1:10 000 scale surveys were in part jointly funded with BGS by the Department of the Environment and the Thames Water Authority (latterly the National Rivers Authority, Thames Region). A report on the work for the Department of the Environment is available (Wyatt et al., 1988).

The following is a list of the six-inch or 1:10 000 geological maps included wholly or in part within the 1:50 000 Leighton Buzzard (220) geological sheet, with the initials of the surveyors and the date of the survey for each map. Sheets SP83NW, NE, SW and SE are at the scale of six inches to the mile (1:10 560). The surveyors were B S P Moorlock, E R Shephard-Thorn, R J Wyatt, R D Lake, J P Colleran, A Horton, R G Thurrell, D T Aldiss, A J M Barron, M G Sumbler and B J Williams.

Manuscript copies of the maps are deposited for public reference in the library of the British Geological Survey at Keyworth. Uncoloured dyeline copies of these maps are available for purchase from the British Geological Survey, Keyworth, Nottingham NG12 5GG.

SP81NW	Bierton	AJMB	1988
SP81NE	Wingrave	RJW	1985
SP82NW	Mursley	RJW, MGS	1988–90
SP82NE	Soulbury	ERST	1985–86
SP82SW	Whitchurch	RJW, MGS	1988–90
SP82SE	Wing	RDL	1985
SP83NW	Loughton	AH	1961–68
SP83NE	Woughton-on-the-Green	ERST, AH, BJW	1967–68
SP83SW	Tattenhoe	RGT	1967–68
SP83SE	Bletchley	AH, RGT	1967–68
SP91NW	Mentmore	RJW	1985
SP91NE	Edlesborough	DTA	1989
SP92NW	Heath and Reach	ERST	1985
SP92NE	Hockcliffe	RDL	1986
SP92SW	Billington	RJW	1985
SP92SE	Totternhoe	DTA, RDL	1986–89
SP93NW	Woburn Sands	RGT, BJW, ERST	1968
		BSPM	1985
SP93NE	Ridgmont	BSPM	1985
SP93SW	Great Brickhill	RGT	1968
		BSPM	1985
SP93SE	Eversholt	RJW	1985
TL01NW	Kensworth	JPC	1988
TL01NE	Caddington	ERST	1989
TL02NW	Toddington	RDL, BSPM	1987
TL02NE	Streatley	BSPM	1987
TL02SW	Dunstable	JPC	1988
TL02SE	Luton	ERST	1988
TL03NW	Ampthill	BSPM	1986
TL03NE	Clophill	BSPM	1986
TL03SW	Flitwick	RDL, BSPM, RJW	1986–87
TL03SE	Barton-le-Clay	BSPM	1986
TL11NW	Luton Hoo	ERST	1987–88
TL12NW	Great Offley	JPC, ERST	1987
TL12SW	Luton East	ERST	1987–88
TL13NW	Shefford	BSPM	1986
TL13SW	Shillington	JPC	1987–88

ONE
Introduction

LOCATION AND TOPOGRAPHY

Leighton Buzzard is situated about 70 km north-west of Central London. The surrounding district, which is depicted on the 1:50 000 geological map and described in this memoir, lies mainly in Bedfordshire, but includes part of Buckinghamshire in the west and a small area of Hertfordshire in the east (Figure 1). The district has good rail and road links with the capital and the Midlands. The main population centres are the Luton–Dunstable conurbation and part of Milton Keynes new town; in addition there are the smaller country towns of Leighton Buzzard, Ampthill and Woburn, and other scattered settlements. Beyond these urban areas the landscape is for the most part pleasantly rural, with mixed and arable farming, and extensive areas of woodland. There are several large estates, the most notable being the Bedford Estate centred on Woburn Abbey. Quarrying for chalk, sand, brick clay and fuller's earth has scarred the landscape in some areas, but several of the disused quarries are being reclaimed as landfill sites or restored as the work proceeds.

Jurassic and Cretaceous formations are exposed at the surface (Figure 2) and dip gently in a general south-easterly direction. The more resistant beds and formations give rise to positive features including dominant escarpments, while the more easily eroded clays give rise to areas of low relief. Drift deposits are present over about 30 per cent of the district and significantly modify the topography; glacial drifts and clay-with-flints are the most extensive deposits.

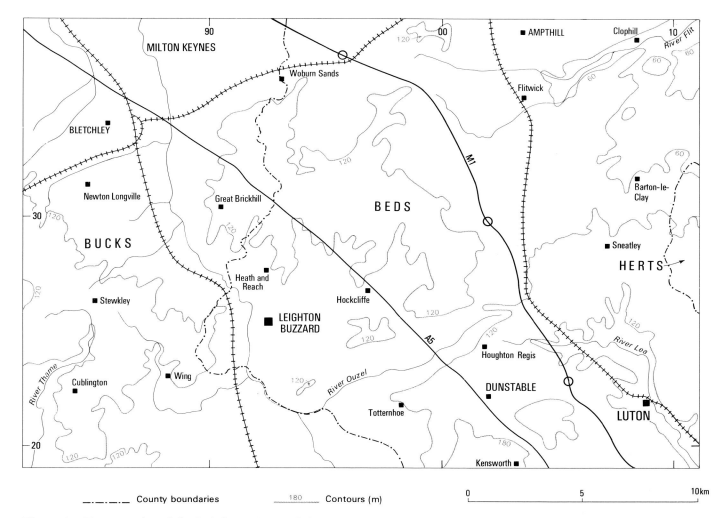

County boundaries   Contours (m)   0   5   10km

Figure 1   Topography of the Leighton Buzzard district.

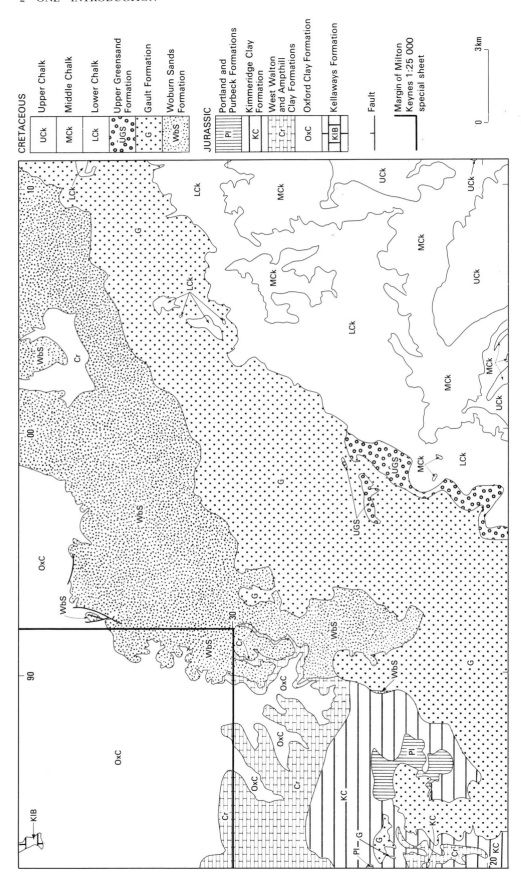

Figure 2 Outline solid geology of the Leighton Buzzard district.

CRETACEOUS

	Upper Chalk	UCk
	Middle Chalk	MCk
	Lower Chalk	LCk
	Upper Greensand Formation	UGS
	Gault Formation	G
	Woburn Sands Formation	WbS

JURASSIC

	Portland and Purbeck Formations	Pl
	Kimmeridge Clay Formation	KC
	West Walton and Ampthill Clay Formations	Cr
	Oxford Clay Formation	OxC
	Kellaways Formation	KlB

Fault

Margin of Milton Keynes 1:25 000 special sheet

0   3km

The district has a relief range of some 120 m, from just less than 60 m above OD in the Flit valley near Clophill to a little over 180 m on the crest of the Chilterns near Dunstable. The Chilterns Chalk escarpment is the dominant feature in the south-eastern corner of the district, with the lesser Woburn Sands escarpment in the north-central portion rising to over 120 m above OD. In the south-west corner, till and other glacial deposits, overlying Gault and Upper Jurassic formations, form a plateau rising to over 120 m above OD.

The western part of the district is drained mainly by the northward-flowing River Ouzel and tributaries, which join the River Ouse near Newport Pagnell. The south-western corner is drained by the headwaters of the River Thame. The River Flit, a tributary of the River Ivel, drains the north-eastern part of the district. The River Lea rises at Leagrave, north of Luton, and flows south-eastwards to the Thames.

The district remains important in terms of economic geology, being a national source of industrial sand and fuller's earth products. Chalk is still quarried for cement and lime manufacture, albeit less extensively than in the past. The working of the Oxford Clay for Fletton brick manufacture is now defunct in the district. Groundwater from the Chalk and Woburn Sands is exploited for public supply.

HISTORY OF RESEARCH

The district was first surveyed at a scale of one-inch to the mile between 1863 and 1868, as parts of 'Old Series' sheets 46NW, NE, SW and SE, published between 1864 and 1869. Revisions and additional drift mapping carried out between 1884 and 1894 were incorporated in later editions of these sheets issued between 1884 and 1895. No descriptive memoirs for Sheet 46 were ever published.

In the 19th century, the district was extensively exploited for sand, chalk and brick clay, providing numerous geological sections, which were studied by academic and Geological Survey workers. The construction of the railways likewise provided a number of important cutting sections, for example at Ampthill.

Initially, little was known about the age or depth of the Palaeozoic basement rocks underlying the Mesozoic formations at outcrop. An unsuccessful water well, sunk at Bletchley Station [SP 8684 3372] in 1886 to 1887, penetrated 'granitic rocks' beneath the Jurassic at a depth of about 40 m below OD (Jukes-Browne, 1889). It was not clear whether the igneous rocks were in situ or represented boulders lying on the Palaeozoic surface; they could not be dated at the time, but comparisons were drawn with the 'Charnian' rocks of the East Midlands. More recently, a borehole at Tattenhoe [SP 8289 3437] penetrated fossiliferous Tremadoc rocks below Lias at 47 m below OD (Horton et al., 1974). Further information on the concealed Palaeozoic rocks has come from boreholes in surrounding areas and from regional geophysical surveys, which are discussed elsewhere in this memoir.

A special survey of the area of Milton Keynes new town was carried out in 1967 to 1968 and a colour-printed map issued in 1971. The new town area overlaps with the north western corner of the district (see Figure 2). Some of the concealed Jurassic rocks of the district crop out in the adjacent new town area and have been reported on previously (Horton et al., 1974). The Jurassic sequence in the Tattenhoe Borehole is described in Chapter Two.

Upper Jurassic strata ranging from the Kellaways to the Purbeck formations crop out at the surface in the district. The Kellaways and Oxford Clay formations were exposed in the large brick pits near Bletchley until recently. Callomon (1968) gave the first detailed stratigraphical account of the Oxford Clay of the district, based on the Bletchley sections and those at Stewartby, a little to the north on the Bedford (203) Sheet. He subsequently reported on the Middle and Upper Oxford Clay, and the West Walton formations exposed in excavations for the General Motors proving track at Millbrook [TL 005 390] made in 1970 and logged for BGS by A Horton. The Ampthill Borehole [TL 0244 3804], drilled in 1970, penetrated the Ampthill Clay and West Walton formations, providing an alternative type section for the former to that described by Woodward (1895) in the now overgrown and inaccessible Ampthill railway cutting.

The outcrops of the Portland and Purbeck formations, near Stewkley in the south-west of the district, are the most northerly in Britain. They were first noted by Fitton (1836) and subsequently described by Davies (1901, 1915) and Bristow (1963, 1968).

The Woburn Sands formation has been extensively quarried for sand and fuller's earth over the past century, notably around Leighton Buzzard, and a voluminous literature has built up on various aspects of the formation. Fossil plants from the district were included in a catalogue of the Lower Greensand flora by Stopes (1915). The indigenous brachiopod fauna of the basal nodule bed of the Woburn Sands was described by Keeping (1883), and further researched by Middlemiss (1962). Casey (1961) referred to exposures within the district in his comprehensive review of the stratigraphical palaeontology of the Lower Greensand. Sedimentological and palaeogeographical aspects of the Woburn Sands have been studied by Allen (1982), Bridges (1982) and Buck (1985). Cameron (1892) gave an early account of the fuller's earth occurrences near Woburn Sands village; a more modern review was given by Cowperthwaite et al. (1972) in which a volcanic origin for the smectitic clays was propounded. This latter concept was supported by later work by Jeans et al. (1977).

Jukes-Browne (1900) briefly referred to the Gault and Upper Greensand of the district in his memoir on the Lower Cretaceous rocks. He included a description of the working of 'coprolites' (phosphatic nodules) from the Gault, Upper Greensand and Cambridge Greensand for fertiliser manufacture, in the 19th century. The lower 10 m or so of the Gault are often exposed as overburden above the Woburn Sands in the quarries around Leighton Buzzard. Some of these sections across the junction of the formations display the Shenley Limestone, the 'Cirripede Bed' and the 'Junction Beds', and have been described by various authors over the years including Cameron (1897), Kitchin and Pringle (1920, 1921, 1922), Lamplugh (1922), Toombs (1935), Owen (1962, 1972), Bristow (1963), Hancock (1958), Wright and Wright (1947) and Casey (1961).

The Chalk is, or has been, well exposed in a number of major quarries in the south-east of the district, but comparatively little has been written on them since early accounts by Whitaker (1865), Jukes-Browne (1875), Hill and Jukes-Browne (1886) and Jukes-Browne and Hill (1903). More recently, several authors have referred to sites within the district in papers of regional scope (see also Chapter Six).

The Quaternary deposits of the area have received scant attention over the years, although those in the portion of Sheet 220 lying within the Milton Keynes new town area were described by Horton et al. (1974). This included a study of part of the Ouzel valley and its underlying buried glacial channel. Various authors have written on the clay-with-flints capping the Chilterns dipslope in the south-east of the district. This work has been comprehensively reviewed by Catt (1986).

The hydrogeology of the Chalk and Woburn Sands aquifers in the district is illustrated by a hydrogeological map of the country between Cambridge and Maidenhead issued by BGS in 1984. The groundwater resources of the Lower Greensand (Woburn Sands) in Bedfordshire and Cambridgeshire have been reviewed by Monkhouse (1974).

The sand and fuller's earth resources of the Woburn Sands within the district are featured in recent BGS reports for the Department of the Environment (Shephard-Thorn et al., 1986; Moorlock and Highley, 1991).

OUTLINE OF GEOLOGICAL HISTORY

The oldest rocks proved in the district are the graptolite-bearing Tremadoc mudstones and siltstones penetrated in the Tattenhoe Borehole (see also Chapter Two). These were laid down in fully marine environments about 500 million years ago and, together with other Lower Palaeozoic rocks, were folded during the Caledonian orogeny, some 400 million years ago. Geophysical evidence and the doubtful proving of 'granitic' rocks in the Bletchley Borehole suggests that igneous rocks were emplaced locally during this episode.

Devonian rocks are inferred to be present beneath the eastern part of the district and to rest unconformably on folded and eroded Lower Palaeozoic formations. Limited records from surrounding areas suggest that the Devonian rocks are mainly terrestrial 'red-beds' of Old Red Sandstone aspect. These, and possibly Carboniferous rocks, were deformed during the Variscan orogeny approximately 290 million years ago. The structures of the pre-Mesozoic basement rocks subsequently exerted an important controlling effect on Mesozoic depositional patterns.

Erosion continued during the Permian and early part of the Triassic. Fluvial and lacustrine marls and sandstones of the Mercia Mudstone Group were proved in the Deanshanger Borehole a little to the west of the dis-

trict and appear to die out southwards. No strata of latest Triassic (Penarth Group) or earliest Jurassic age have yet been found in the district. The area was transgressed by the early Jurassic sea and beds in the Tattenhoe Borehole show that marine deposition recommenced about 195 million years ago. A thick sequence of calcareous mudstone and limestone was laid down during the Pliensbachian and ranges in age from the *Uptonia jamesoni* Zone to the *Amaltheus margaritatus* Zone. Shallower-water conditions are indicated by the overlying ferruginous and calcareous shell fragmental rocks of the Marlstone Rock Bed. The overlying silty and calcareous mudstone of the Upper Lias suggests a return to a deeper-water environment in the early Toarcian; only the lower Toarcian Zones (*Harpoceras falciferum* and *Hildoceras bifrons*) are represented.

A break in deposition and erosion of some of the Upper Lias, due to uplift or shallowing, is indicated by channels which cut deeply into the Upper Lias; these are infilled with sandstones and mudstones of the Grantham Formation. A slight pause in deposition probably separates the Grantham Formation and the overlying Upper Estuarine 'Series'; both laid down in shallow, tidal, brackish-marine environments with much evidence of plant colonisation marking periods of emergence. The overlying Blisworth Limestone and Blisworth Clay formations are a variable sequence of oolitic and shell-fragmental limestone and mudstone, partly of brackish origin.

The Cornbrash Formation, dominantly limestone with thin clays, marks a return to more widespread marine sedimentation. The overlying Kellaways Formation accumulated, at first, in quiet water conditions, which were later replaced by a current-swept sea. The thick mudstone sequence of the Oxford Clay marks a return to deeper marine sedimentation which continued throughout the deposition of West Walton, Ampthill Clay and Kimmeridge Clay formation in the late Jurassic. Bituminous shales in the lower Oxford Clay and the oil shales of the Kimmeridge Clay probably accumulated when bottom waters were oxygen deficient, although it has been suggested that the oil shale bands may represent widespread algal blooms in the ocean of the period. Towards the end of the Jurassic, the long period of clay sedimentation was terminated by slight uplift, shallowing of the seas, restriction of the depositional basin and erosion. The sandy clay with phosphatic nodules which marks the base of the Portland Formation records a period of minimal deposition. The limestone, sand and marl which makes up the remainder of the Portland Formation was deposited in a shallow marine environment. The basal limestones of the overlying Purbeck Formation is of shallow, brackish water origin, while the Whitchurch Sand has a fauna of more marine aspect. The end of the Jurassic period, about 145 million years ago, was marked by regional uplift and folding, which was influenced by earlier basement structures.

During the earliest Cretaceous, the district formed part of the London Platform, a land mass drained by rivers transporting sediment southwards into the Wealden Basin of south-east England. There was a gradual return to brackish and marine sedimentation with the deposition of the Woburn Sands, following a transgression in late Aptian times (*Parahoplites nutfieldiensis* Zone), about 115 million years ago. The sea transgressed over a deeply eroded surface to form a shallow enclosed shelf sea with strong tidal influences, in which sand waves were well developed. Seams of fuller's earth preserved in the formation represent reworked airfall ash ejected from volcanoes, elsewhere in north-west Europe. The Woburn Sands rest on various Upper Jurassic formations and thickness variations within the district are due partly to the irregular pre-Aptian surface and partly to contemporary movements on basement faults.

A break in sedimentation of some duration occurred between the deposition of the Woburn Sands and the 'Junction Beds' of the earliest Gault. A general shallowing and reduction in the rate of sedimentation occurred, together with local erosion. Around Shenley Hill, north of Leighton Buzzard, the Shenley Limestone, a condensed ferruginous phosphatic deposit with a rich brachiopod fauna, was formed in restricted environments, possibly on mounds on the contemporary sea bed.

Fully marine clay deposition resumed with a major transgression in Albian times. The complex and variable 'Junction Beds' at the base of the Gault Formation include a mixture of ferruginous, phosphatic and glauconitic material reworked from the Woburn Sands and other sources. The Gault oversteps the Woburn Sands to rest on Jurassic rocks in the west of the district. Phosphatic nodule beds within the Gault mark pauses in sedimentation and there is evidence of a considerable break between the Lower and Upper Gault, followed by a renewed transgression. In late Albian times there was an influx of silty and sandy material, the Upper Greensand, into the basin.

A break of variable magnitude separates the late Albian Upper Greensand and the early Cenomanian Lower Chalk, reflecting differential movements on basement faults. The Upper Greensand is preserved in the south of the district and in the Sundon Borehole sequence (see Chapter 6); it passes almost imperceptibly up into the Lower Chalk. Farther north-east, the Upper Greensand was totally removed by pre-Cenomanian erosion and, beyond Barton-le-Clay, the Gault–Lower Chalk junction is marked by a thin bed of glauconitic sand with reworked phosphatic nodules, known as the Cambridge Greensand. It is postulated herein that the incoming of the Cambridge Greensand to the north-east coincides with a basement fault (the Lilley Bottom Structure), which was active at this time and also affected the thickness of the Lower Chalk.

Chalk sedimentation commenced about 97 million years ago in clear open waters. The dominant calcareous components of chalk are submicroscopic plates of coccoliths (marine algae), fine shell debris, foraminifera and calcispheres. Initially, material of terrestrial origin was also transported into the basin including clay (often smectitic), silt and some fine sand. The lower part of the Lower Chalk, the 'Chalk Marl' is notably argillaceous, having up to 60 per cent of noncarbonate material. Sedimentation was cyclic, with marly units alternating with thin limestone bands. The 'Chalk Marl' was terminated by an erosional–depositional event in which channelling was followed by the deposition of a relatively coarse calcarenite: the Totternhoe Stone. The upper part of the Lower Chalk, the 'Grey Chalk', has a lesser proportion of clay and passes up into a thin but widespread group of marls and limestones known as the Plenus Marls, probably representing a regressive episode. Above this, the Middle and Upper Chalk comprise very pure limestone, with occasional thin bands of smectitic clay (or marl) and bands of nodular flint; nodular chalk or chalkstone beds represent periods of shallower water or standstill.

The Chalk was gently folded and eroded prior to the deposition of the Tertiary formations. These are believed to have been present in the district, but have been eroded away, prior to or early in the Quaternary, leaving only traces in solution pipes. The final tectonic imprint on the district is believed to have been in the mid-Miocene period; the inversion of the Weald, the formation of the Tertiary London Basin and of the Chilterns occurred at this time.

The Quaternary period saw the final evolution of the landscape to its present form. Remnants of Plio-Pleistocene marine deposits high on the Chilterns around Rothamsted to the south are the only record of the earliest Quaternary near the district. The clay-with-flints is believed to represent highly modified but in-situ remnants of the Woolwich and Reading Beds, of Paleocene age, resting on a sub-Tertiary erosion surface on the Chilterns dip slope. The Anglian glacial period, dating back about 400 000 years, had a profound effect on the landscape of the district. A sheet of till was deposited over much of the district and deep subglacial valleys and overflow channels were excavated. Extensive deposits of glacial sand and gravel, and lacustrine clays and silts, were formed. Ice did not return to the district after the Anglian glacial period, and for the remainder of the Quaternary the climate has oscillated between temperate interglacial periods and colder intervals when periglacial processes were active. Much of the final shaping of the landscape has occurred since the Anglian with erosion of parts of the till sheet, solifluction and landslipping, and the evolution of the rivers and their flood plains.

TWO
Concealed formations

The Mesozoic formations of the district rest unconformably on a basement of folded and faulted Lower Palaeozoic strata, at depths of 50 m to about 140 m below OD. The Palaeozoic rocks range from Tremadoc to Devonian in age, and there is evidence of igneous rocks in places. Jurassic formations from the Lias to Cornbrash are concealed within the district, while those from Kellaways Formation to Purbeck Formation crop out at the surface. Direct borehole evidence of the concealed Palaeozoic and Jurassic sequences is sparse, so that much of the interpretation of the Palaeozoic sequence given below is based on extrapolation from adjoining areas and on regional geophysical evidence.

Tremadoc mudstones and siltstones were proved below the Lias in the Tattenhoe Borehole [SP 8289 3437]. A borehole at Bletchley [SP 8684 3372] was reported to have penetrated 'granite rocks' below the Jurassic sequence (Jukes-Browne, 1889), but the chisel-drilling method then employed failed to provide adequate samples; it is thus unclear whether the igneous rocks penetrated were in situ or were perhaps derived boulders. A sizeable pebble of altered vesicular basalt incorporated in the basal conglomerate of the Lias, in the Tattenhoe Borehole, is seemingly not related to the Bletchley 'granite'.

North-west of the district, Tremadoc rocks were also proved in the Deanshanger Borehole [SP 7652 3880] about 8 km north-west of Tattenhoe, where 75.6 m of the Mercia Mudstone Group intervened between them and the Lias. It appears that the Triassic rocks occupy an embayment on the flank of the London Platform and wedge out between Deanshanger and Tattenhoe. The Ware Borehole [TL 3531 1398] to the east of the district, completed in 1879, entered Wenlock Shales below Lower Cretaceous rocks (Whitaker and Jukes-Browne, 1894).

The Jurassic sequence, from basal Lias to low Oxford Clay, was fully cored in the Tattenhoe Borehole (Table 1), and other boreholes in the Milton Keynes new town area (Horton et al., 1974). Some of the deep wells sunk to tap the Woburn Sands aquifer below Dunstable and Luton have penetrated a few metres of the underlying Upper Jurassic mudstones, but no material has been available for stratigraphical study to establish their age.

RECONSTRUCTIONS OF CONCEALED PRE-MESOZOIC GEOLOGY

The interpretation of the concealed pre-Mesozoic geology of the district is speculative because of the paucity of borehole and other evidence. However, some information can be obtained from interpretations of geological and regional geophysical data in adjacent areas, including resistivity surveys and a seismic reflection line [Shell (UK) Exploration] to the east of the district (Allsop, 1985b).

An east-north-east-trending ridge of pre-Mesozoic rocks crossing the northern part of the area is the eastern end of the Charlton Axis (Figure 4, Figure 29). The

Table 1 Outline sequence in the Tattenhoe Borehole.

Tattenhoe (Howe Farm) Borehole (1970)
NGR [SP 8289 3437]
Surface level 102.43 m above OD

			Thickness m	Depth m	Reduced level m
QUATERNARY		Till	29.38	29.38	
		Glacial lake deposits	9.67	39.05	+ 63.38 OD
JURASSIC	UPPER	Oxford Clay	17.02	56.07	
		Kellaways Formation	0.68	56.75	+ 45.68 OD
	MIDDLE	Blisworth Clay	1.10	57.85	
		Blisworth Limestone	11.12	68.97	
		Upper Estuarine 'Series'	6.39	75.36	
		Grantham Formation ['Lower Estuarine Series']	3.82	79.18	+ 23.25 OD
	LOWER	Upper Lias	6.91	86.09	
		Marlstone Rock [Bed] Formation	1.03	87.12	
		Lower/Middle Lias [Brant Mudstone Formation]	62.11	149.23	− 46.80 OD
ORDOVICIAN	TREMADOC		63.98	213.21	− 110.78 OD

End of borehole

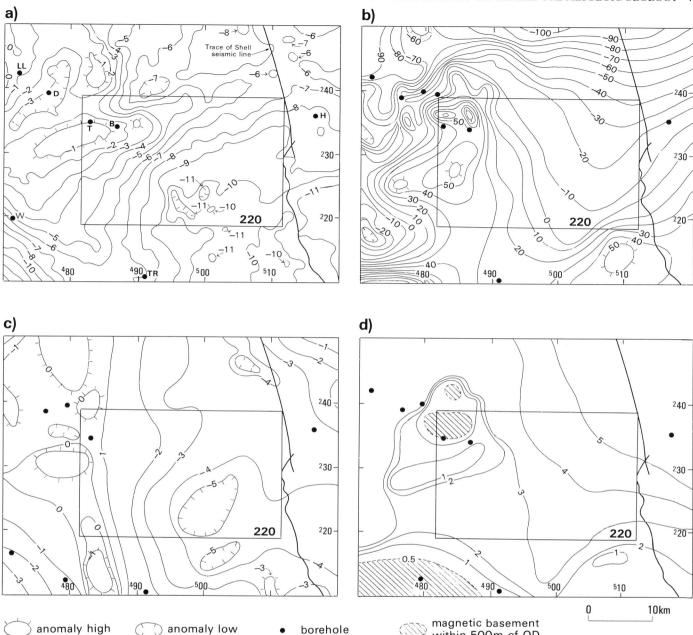

Figure 3 Regional geophysical anomaly maps.

a) Observed Bouguer gravity anomaly map.
    Anomalies calculated against the International Gravity Formula, 1967, and referred to the
    National Gravity Reference Net, 1973, using a surface density of 2.7 mg m^{-3}.

b) Aeromagnetic anomaly map (contours in nT (nanotesla)).

c) Residual gravity anomaly map after removal of Mesozoic effects (contours in mGal).

d) Depth to magnetic basement (contours at 1 km intervals below OD)
    (see Figure 30 for identification of boreholes).

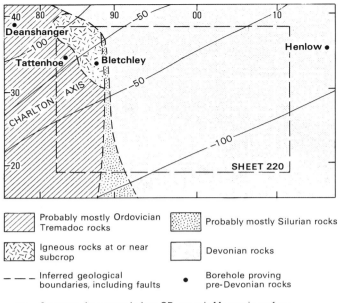

Probably mostly Ordovician Tremadoc rocks

Probably mostly Silurian rocks

Igneous rocks at or near subcrop

Devonian rocks

_ _ _ Inferred geological boundaries, including faults

• Borehole proving pre-Devonian rocks

—50— Contours, in metres below OD, on sub-Mesozoic surface

Figure 4 Reconstruction of pre-Mesozoic basement geology.

axis extends from the Bicester area of Oxfordshire, through Buckinghamshire and Bedfordshire towards Cambridge (Smith et al., 1985), where it appears to terminate against a major north–south lineament. To the west, boreholes at Noke Hill [SP 5386 1218] and Bicester [SP 5272 2081] situated on the axis show that Jurassic and Triassic rocks rest unconformably on rocks of Upper Devonian and Silurian (Llandovery) age (Wyatt and Ambrose, 1988). The base of the Mesozoic rocks lies at about 50 m below OD on the crest of the ridge dipping north-west and south-east away from the ridge to reach a maximum depth of about 140 m below OD.

The regional Bouguer gravity and aeromagnetic anomaly maps for the district and surrounding area are shown in Figure 3 (a and b respectively). Figure 3c illustrates the gravity field after the effects of the Mesozoic rocks and a regional, linear increase in gravity values eastwards have been removed (Allsop, 1985b). These residual gravity anomalies reflect the density variations within the pre-Mesozoic rocks; the amplitude and frequency characteristics of the majority of the closures and gradients suggest that the sources of the gravity features occur close to the basement surface.

Figure 3d shows the depth to magnetic basement derived from the aeromagnetic data using a combination of interpretive techniques based mainly on the method of Vacquier et al. (1951). Much of the area, particularly in the north and east, is underlain by deep magnetic basement in excess of 3 km below ground level; therefore any magnetic contrast within the basement is unlikely to be related to the more shallow density contrasts in the basement rocks indicated by the residual Bouguer anomaly map (Figure 3c). The exceptions to this are high ampli-

tude magnetic anomalies in the area around, and to the south of the Tattenhoe Borehole, which are also believed to be associated with the Charlton Axis.

The relatively near-surface magnetic anomaly in the vicinity of the Tattenhoe Borehole [8289 3437] suggests the possible presence of basic igneous rocks, such as a thick sequence of basic volcanic lavas or a large intrusion. These rocks could be related to those occurring more extensively in the Birmingham–Oxford Block (Reid et al., 1990), a magnetic basement ridge flanked to the west by the Worcester Basin and to the north-east by deep nonmagnetic rocks (Figure 29).

The steeply dipping Tremadoc mudstone and siltstone in the lower part of the Tattenhoe Borehole would be unlikely to cause the magnetic anomalies. However, a pebble of altered vesicular basalt, which is undated, was recovered from the basal conglomerate of the Lower Lias. This rock could possibly be indicative of the nature of the underlying source of the aeromagnetic anomalies. The presence of a significant low-density intrusion of acidic rocks, suggested by the 'granitic' rocks described from Bletchley Borehole (Jukes-Browne, 1889), is not supported by the geophysical evidence.

The eastern edge of the shallow magnetic basement is indicated by the coincident magnetic and Bouguer anomaly gradients which represent a major north–south-trending lineament (A–A' in Figure 30). This may mark a lithological and chronological break, representing the contact between the shallow magnetic basement to the west and the relatively nonmagnetic Palaeozoic rocks proved farther east. It is tentatively interpreted as a fault.

Evidence from boreholes farther east, including that at Ware [TL 3531 1398], indicate the presence of folded Silurian rocks (Allsop and Smith, 1988) which probably underlie most of eastern England. These are overlain unconformably by a succession of Devonian rocks which generally thicken to the east.

The interpretation of the regional geophysical and borehole data in this district and surrounding areas has resulted in the production of a generalised map of the basement geology shown in Figure 4.

THE TREMADOC ROCKS IN THE TATTENHOE BOREHOLE

The Tattenhoe Borehole [SP 8289 3437] penetrated 63.98 m of Tremadoc rocks (Table 1) above a total depth of 213.21 m, but steep dips, commonly about 80°, suggest that perhaps no more than 10 m of strata are represented. The Tremadoc rocks consist of centimetre- to decimetre-scale alternations of dark grey mudstones and siltstones, which were red stained in the upper 10 m of core and along joint planes. Cross-lamination and graded bedding are visible in the siltstone layers; they indicate that some, if not most, of the beds in the steeply dipping succession are inverted. There are many polished bedding planes and several levels at which the cored strata are crushed or brecciated. The beds yielded abundant fossils indicating a Tremadoc age; the following fauna has been identified:

Brachiopoda:	*Eurytreta sabrinae* (Callaway)?
	Lingulella sp. (small)
Conodonts:	*Westergaardodina bicuspidata* Müller
Graptolithina:	*Rhabdinopora* [*Dictyonema*]
	flabelliformis aff. *flabelliformis* [sensu Bulman]
	R. flabelliformis patula (Bulman)
	Transient forms between the same subspecies also occur
	R. flabelliformis cf. *anglica* (Bulman) (doubtful)
Worm (?):	cf. *Hirudopsis*
Trace fossils:	*Tomaculum problematicum* Groom burrows

The abundance of *Rhabdinopora flabelliformis* subspecies indicates a Tremadoc (early Ordovician) age, but the exact horizon is not known. Commonly the abundance of these *Rhabdinopora* indicates an early Tremadoc age, at least in Britain and Scandinavia. However, in the Tattenhoe core the particular forms of *R. flabelliformis* are very like those from the Deanshanger Borehole [SP 7652 3880], about 8 km to the north-west, where they were associated with a later Tremadoc trilobite fauna and an acritarch flora (Bulman and Rushton, 1973), which have been referred to the lower part of the *Shumardia pusilla* Biozone. It is thus possible that the Tremadoc rocks at Tattenhoe are older than those at Deanshanger, but they are unlikely to be younger. On the evidence presently available, the Tremadoc rocks in the Tattenhoe Borehole may possibly be referred to the lower part of the *pusilla* Biozone.

CONCEALED JURASSIC STRATA

The Kellaways Formation (p.00) is the oldest part of the Jurassic System seen at outcrop in the district. The underlying Middle and Lower Jurassic formations were cored in the Tattenhoe Borehole (Table 1), which serves as a convenient reference section for the concealed succession. Middle Jurassic formations, which outcrop a little to the north of the district in the Milton Keynes new town area, have been described elsewhere (Horton et al., 1974) so that only a brief summary of them is given here.

Lias Group

The Lower Jurassic rocks belonging to the Lias Group rest unconformably on folded Tremadoc rocks in the Tattenhoe Borehole. They were proved between depths of 79.18 and 149.23 m (23.25 m above to 46.80 m below OD) (Table 1). The sequence is dominated by uniform grey, commonly calcareous, mudstone and siltstone, with a number of phosphatic pebble horizons, several thin calcarenites and the chamositic limestone known as the Marlstone Rock Bed. The stratigraphy is summarised in Figure 5.

The zonation of the Lias Group is based on the occurrence of various ammonite taxa, so that the zones and subzones are biozones and biosubzones, which can be linked to the international system of chronostratigraphical stages.

The Lias has traditionally been divided into Lower, Middle and Upper divisions; the Marlstone Rock Bed and some underlying mudstone and siltstones (to the base of the *margaritatus* Zone) constitutes the Middle Lias. The lithostratigraphy of the Lower and Middle Lias in the Grantham area has recently been revised (Brandon et al., 1990). These authors argued that the division between Lower and Middle Lias was essentially biostratigraphical, and that there was little change of lithology across this junction. They proposed the adoption of two new lithostratigraphical formations within the combined 'Lower' and 'Middle' Lias strata below the Marlstone Rock Bed. The lower, Scunthorpe Mudstone Formation (see also Gaunt, Fletcher and Wood, 1992), includes beds of the latest Triassic to *obtusum* Zone age. The upper, Brant Mudstone Formation, includes beds of *oxynotum* to *margaritatus* Zone age.

In the Chilterns area the Lias onlaps onto the London Platform from the north-west (Donovan, Horton and Ivimey-Cook, 1979); in this district the Scunthorpe Mudstone Formation and the lower part of the Brant Mudstone Formation were not deposited, and most of the Upper Lias is absent, presumably due to erosion in late Toarcian times, prior to the deposition of the Grantham Formation.

The evidence for the zonal sequence in the Tattenhoe Borehole is summarised below (Figure 5). A full lithological log is available in BGS archives. Faunal lists for the identified zones and subzones of the Lias are given in Appendix 1. The fossils have been identified by Dr Ivimey-Cook with the exception of the Middle and Upper Lias ammonites which were dealt with by Dr M K Howarth (British Museum (Natural History)).

Brant Mudstone Formation [Lower Lias, Middle Lias Silts and Clays] 87.12 to about 149.23 m

Above a basal conglomeratic unit (about 7 m thick) the formation consists principally of pale grey calcareous mudstones except for two thin calcarenitic horizons between 114.19 and 115.17 m and thin horizons with phosphatic nodules between 88.82 and 99.60 m.

The base of the Lias is taken at about 149.23 m. However most of the overlying 6 m of core, recorded as conglomerate and calcarenite, was lost. The limestone conglomerates contain clasts of igneous rocks and of Palaeozoic shales. One large clast, about 7 cm across, is a highly altered vesicular basalt (Mr R J Merriman, personal communication). The conglomerate becomes finer grained upwards to about 142.50 m and is overlain by a thin calcarenitic limestone at about 142.40 m.

The age of the conglomerate is proved at 142.85 m, by the presence of the zonal and subzonal index fossil *Uptonia jamesoni*. Below this the beds yielded bivalves and brachiopod fragments including a lobothyrid and a *Piarorhynchia* sp,. There is no reason to postulate the occurrence of beds older than the *jamesoni* Zone. The calcareous conglomerates above, between 142.85 and 142.50 m, yielded fragments of *Cincta*?, *Piarorhynchia* sp., *Rimirhynchia* sp., *Chlamys*?, *Apoderoceras*? (at 142.77 m) and belemnite fragments. The junction of the *jamesoni* and *ibex* Zones is uncertain but it is placed here at the earliest liparoceratid fragments found at a depth of 142.50 m. Calcarenitic limestones with bivalves and ammonite fragments continue to about 142.40 m.

The basal beds are overlain by pale to medium grey calcareous mudstones up to 99.60 m; these are variably silty and fossiliferous with shell fragments in drifts and on partings. The mudstones contain scattered ironstone nodules, rare phosphatic pebbles and traces of pyrite. Between 113.9 and 115.17 m there are thin calcarenitic limestones. A diverse fauna was recovered (Appendix 1), with brachiopods, bivalves, scattered ammonites, belemnites, crinoids and echinoids. Bioturbation, with *Chondrites*-type burrowfills is common.

These beds are of *Tragophylloceras ibex* Zone age. The *Tropidoceras masseanum* Subzone is not proved in the lowest beds as the only ammonites are liparoceratid fragments at 139.5 and 142.50 m and the other fauna is not diagnostic. Between 122 and 139 m faunal diversity is very low with only *Discinisca holdeni*, a few bivalves, small *Tragophylloceras*, fish fragments and finely comminuted plant debris. A single *Androgynoceras* sp. juv. at 125.08 m could indicate the A. [*Beaniceras*] *centaurus* group as it has a wide whorl section, finely ribbed venter and strong almost tuberculate ribs on the flanks. This would suggest the Centaurus Zonule of Phelps (1985), in the *Acanthopleuroceras valdani* Subzone.

The beds between 99.60 and 119.09 m are asssigned to the *Beaniceras luridum* Subzone of the *ibex* Zone, yielding *Beaniceras* at 119.09 m, *Beaniceras* cf. *luridum* at 100.80 and 109.45 m. The calcareous mudstones continue upwards to a 14 cm thick bed of limestone above 115.17 m. They are locally rich in *Rimirhynchia anglica*, *Cardinia attenuata* and other bivalves but with no ammonites. The presence of *R. anglica* is of interest as the species is best known from the *jamesoni* Zone in the west of Britain, Ager (1958, p.64) commented that it was almost unknown in the east Midlands. A further calcarenite occurs between 119.9 and 114.34 m. Above this the fauna of the mudstones is again rather sparse but here with some variety of bivalves, some crustacean fragments, crinoid debris, ophiuroids and both test fragments and drifts of current orientated spines of *Eodiadema*.

A minor erosional nonsequence occurs at 99.60 m; it is marked by a thin fossiliferous conglomerate with pebbles resting on the erosion surface. The grey calcareous mudstones above contain several horizons with phosphatic nodules up to the base of the Marlstone Rock Bed at 87.12 m. The erosion surface and its infill appear to correlate with the '100 Marker' of north Oxfordshire (Horton and Poole, 1977), which occurs early in the *Prodactylioceras davoei* Zone. Ammonites at 99.27 m can be tentatively identified as *Androgynoceras* cf. *maculatum* and A. cf. *sparsicosta*, which would indicate an early *maculatum* Subzone age (Phelps, 1985). There is no faunal evidence to locate the junction with the overlying *Aegoceras capricornus* Subzone but the presence of the latter is shown by *Aegoceras* cf. *crescens* at 93.84 m. Phelps (1985) restricts this species to a particular Crescens horizon in the top of the *capricornus* Subzone. The junction with the overlying Zone of *Amaltheus margaritatus* is taken at the calcareous mudstone with phosphatic pebbles between 93.66 and

93.78 m; *Aegoceras* was found in the matrix at 93.66 m together with an amaltheid fragment. There is no faunal evidence for the *Oistoceras figulinum* Subzone so this pebble bed may be a *remanié* deposit representing both late *davoei* and earliest *margaritatus* Zone times. This boundary marks the top of the Lower Pliensbachian Substage and the approximate level of the traditional Lower–Middle Lias junction.

The highest part of the Brant Mudstone Formation (87.12 to 93.66 m) consists of pale grey mudstones which become more silty upwards and contain sporadic ironstone nodules. A phosphatic pebble bed occurs at the base of the unit and others occur between 88.78 to 88.82 m. The *Amaltheus stokesi* Subzone is proved by the subzonal index between 88.62 and 92.48 m, and the presence of an amaltheid at 93.66 m extends the subzone down to this level. Numerous, almost smooth, amaltheids, here referred to *Amauroceras*, and some *Tragophylloceras*, occur below 91.32 m. Between 88.62 m and the base of the Marlstone at 87.12 m the calcareous silty mudstones and siltstones are attributed to the *Amaltheus subnodosus* Subzone, there is no evidence of the youngest subzone of this Zone (*A. gibbosus*) which may have been removed prior to the deposition of the Marlstone Rock Bed. The *margaritatus* Zone yields a typical rich bivalve fauna and also belemnites and echinoderm remains.

MARLSTONE ROCK BED, 86.09 to 87.12 m

The Marlstone Rock Bed is a chamositic limestone, extensively developed in central and eastern England, where it was formerly exploited as an iron ore. At Tattenhoe it is represented by only 1.03 m of chamositic sandy limestone; in the log this is described as containing belemnites, rhynchonellids, bivalves and an ammonite, but only belemnite fragments are now available for study. In the borehole cores, the Marlstone is unoxidised and greenish in colour; this contrasts with the rusty orange-brown colours seen at outcrop. The fossils seen do not provide any clear indication of age but locally the Marlstone is assigned to the *Pleuroceras spinatum* Zone. The correlation of the Marlstone Rock Bed and the Upper Lias sequence of the Tattenhoe borehole with others in the Milton Keynes area was illustrated in Horton et al. (1974, Figure 5).

UPPER LIAS, 79.18 to 86.09 m

The Upper Lias consists principally of mudstone. The lowest part, the Fish Beds, are overlain by mudstones and argillaceous nodular limestones (Cephalopod Beds Member), and pass up into grey silty mudstones, which persist to the top of the Upper Lias. The Fish Beds unit is present between 84.82 to 86.09 m and comprises dark olive-grey and greenish grey laminated silty mudstones, usually markedly fissile and with abundant fish debris, bivalve fragments and ammonites. They show small-scale folds suggesting soft-sediment deformation. The lowest 0.09 m contains *Discinisca*, a rhynchonellid and fish remains with poorly preserved harpoceratid ammonites. Above this the fauna indicates the *Cleviceras exaratum* Subzone of the *Harpoceras falciferum* Zone with *Cleviceras elegans* and *Harpoceras serpentinum* at 84.78 and 84.80 m

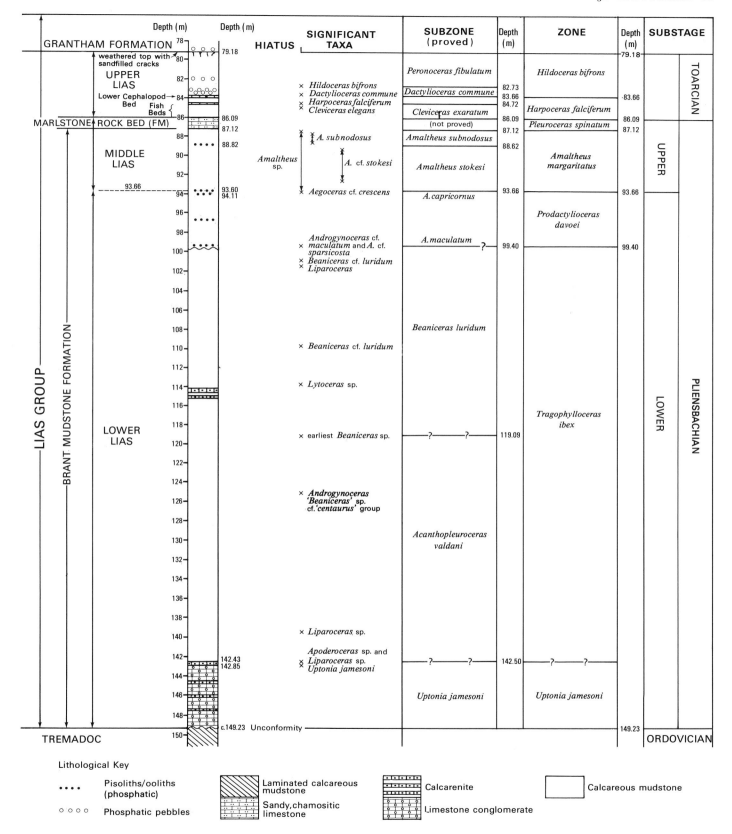

Figure 5 Stratigraphy of the Lias Group (Lower Jurassic) in the Tattenhoe Borehole.

respectively, *Dactylioceras* sp. crustacean and fish fragments also occur. Above the Fish Beds are calcareous mudstones with very thin limestones; the mudstones contain ooliths from 82.80 m up to about 83 m. An argillaceous, nodular limestone between 83.65 and 83.72 m can be correlated with the Lower Cephalopod Bed (Howarth, 1978). The overlying *Harpoceras falciferum* Subzone yielded the subzonal index at 84.56 and 84.70 m together with *Pseudomytiloides* sp., *Dactylioceras* sp. some bivalves and belemnites.

The oolitic mudstones extend into the base of the *Hildoceras bifrons* Zone; these small brown phosphatic ooliths are described from other sequences in central England (Horton, Ivimey-Cook, Harrison and Young, 1980) where they are shown to occur at three horizons, one in the *falciferum* Subzone, one across the *falciferum/commune* subzone junction and one within the *fibulatum* Subzone. Higher beds consist of grey silty mudstones. However, immediately below the base of the Grantham Formation these are weathered to a very pale colour with sphaerosiderite; they have a waxy or soapy texture comparable with seatearths. Oxidation is evident down to at least 82 m and is the result of later Toarcian erosion and weathering.

The presence of the *Dactylioceras commune* Subzone up to 82.73 m is demonstrated by the nominal species together with *Hildoceras* cf. *sublevisoni*; other *Dactylioceras* and bivalves are also present. The *Peronoceras fibulatum* Subzone is established by the presence of *H. bifrons* above 82.73 m, *Dactylioceras* and fish remains are also present. There is no evidence for the overlying *crassum* Subzone or any of the younger zones of the Toarcian.

Inferior Oolite Group

GRANTHAM FORMATION ['Lower Estuarine Series']

In the Tattenhoe Borehole the Grantham Formation is 3.82 m thick and is present between depths of 75.36 and 79.18 m. This is the only well recorded section available in the district. In the adjacent Milton Keynes new town area, to the north, up to 12.09 m are recorded (Horton et al., 1974). It was noted that in the Milton Keynes area the formation shows great lateral and vertical changes in thickness and lithology, and that it appears in places to occupy channels eroded into the underlying Upper Lias clays. It is locally absent in the north-west of the district and probably wedges out in a south-easterly direction towards the London Platform.

As its former name implies, the formation was laid down in a shallow freshwater to brackish environment, in lagoons and deltas, on the north-western flank of the London Platform. Grey mottled mudstone and silt are the dominant lithologies with subordinate fine-grained whitish sands. Sand-filled mud cracks were noted at the top of the formation in the Tattenhoe Borehole. Plant remains in the form of carbonaceous or pyritised root sheaths and drifted laths are very common; seatearth lithologies are well developed. Commonly the original sedimentary lamination of the deposits is disturbed or destroyed by the roots, giving a mottled appearance.

It is not possible to establish the zonal age of the formation because of the paucity of fossils, but the beds are generally correlated with the Inferior Oolite Group of the Middle Jurassic (Aalenian Stage) (Cope et al., 1980).

Great Oolite Group

UPPER ESTUARINE 'SERIES'

These beds are the lowest formation of the Great Oolite Group in this area. They consist of variable mudstones with a limestone, the Upper Estuarine Limestone, in the middle. The total thickness in the Tattenhoe Borehole is 6.39 m, proved between depths of 68.97 and 75.36 m, with the Upper Estuarine Limestone occurring from 70.92 to 74.57 m.

The basal contact with the Grantham Formation at 75.36 m is abrupt. The beds below the limestone comprise pale to dark greenish grey silty mudstones with wisps of fine sand and abundant carbonaceous plant traces; rootlets infilled with olive-grey clay are also present. Fossils are more abundant than in the Grantham Formation and include bivalves, rare gastropods and an echinoid spine; shells and plants often show pyritous preservation. The fauna suggests a brackish to marine environment, somewhat more saline than that of the Grantham Formation.

More marine conditions prevailed during the deposition of the Upper Estuarine Limestone. At Tattenhoe, the limestone comprises a number of thin beds of micritic, commonly shelly, limestone interspersed with greenish grey marls and mudstones, and with a basal bed of sand with very coarse shell debris. The shells include the oyster *Praeexogyra hebridica* which indicates a Mid to Late Bathonian age. The mudstone beds above the Upper Estuarine Limestone are generally similar to those below. They include grey and greenish grey mudstone with rootlet traces, of seatearth aspect, with bivalves. These beds probably record a reversion to brackish-marine conditions.

Within the district there is little further evidence of the nature and thickness of the Upper Estuarine Series, which is presumed to thin south-eastwards onto the flanks of the London Platform.

BLISWORTH LIMESTONE AND BLISWORTH CLAY FORMATIONS

These formations are proved only in the Tattenhoe Borehole, where they are 11.12 and 1.10 m thick respectively (Table 1). The combined thickness of the two formations is fairly constant at about 12 m (Horton et al., 1974) and where one of the formations is comparatively thick, as in the Tattenhoe Borehole, it is usually matched by correspondingly thinner developments of the other formation.

The Blisworth Limestone comprises beds of mainly micritic shell-fragmental limestones with occasional ooliths and pellets and some calcite cement or cavity fillings. Thin marl or mudstone partings account for about 8 per cent of the total thickness. Cross-stratification and other sedimentary structures are picked out by laminae of shell debris. The limestones are generally pale to medium grey in colour, while the intervening mudstones are darker grey or greenish grey. The basal contact with the Upper Estuarine Series at 68.97 m is sharply defined by an abrupt change of lithology from green mudstone to grey limestone with shell debris and ooliths; burrows infilled with shell debris extend down from the limestone into the green mudstone.

A similar sharp change in lithology marks the contact of the Blisworth Limestone and the Blisworth Clay at 57.85 m. The thin Blisworth Clay in the Tattenhoe Borehole comprises mottled dark purplish and greenish grey mudstones, with carbonaceous rootlet traces and common listric surfaces, of overall seatearth aspect. Small shells and derived limestone pebbles occur in the basal layers.

The Blisworth Limestone is broadly equivalent to the Great Oolite Limestone of Northamptonshire, but may be slightly younger (Torrens, 1968, pp.242–243), and of late Bathonian age. The shelly fauna is dominated by bivalves, with brachiopods and echinoids, suggesting a fully marine environment.

CORNBRASH FORMATION

This thin, but distinctive, limestone formation is absent in the Tattenhoe Borehole, where the Kellaways Formation rests directly on an eroded surface of Blisworth Clay. It was proved between depths of 24.07 and 24.79 m in the MK16 Borehole [SP 8908 3545] near Simpson (Horton et al., 1974), but the full thickness was not proved. The Cornbrash comprises hard, grey, shell-fragmental limestones with some pyrite and muddy wisps.

It crops out extensively in the Milton Keynes area (Horton et al., 1974) where brachiopods and ammonites confirmed the presence of both Lower and Upper Cornbrash. The formation probably extends south-eastwards, at depth below the present district, thinning onto the flanks of the London Platform.

THREE
Jurassic

The oldest rocks to crop out in the Leighton Buzzard district belong to the Jurassic System. Their outcrop occupies the western and northern parts of the district (Figure 2), but elsewhere they occur in the subcrop beneath Cretaceous strata, which overlie them unconformably. Seven formations are recognised—Kellaways, Oxford Clay, West Walton, Ampthill Clay, Kimmeridge Clay, Portland and Purbeck—although the West Walton and Ampthill Clay formations have not been mapped separately. These seven formations represent the Callovian, Oxfordian, Kimmeridgian and Portlandian stages.

KELLAWAYS AND OXFORD CLAY FORMATIONS

The outcrop of the Kellaways Formation is restricted to a small area in a valley near Loughton [SP 8337], whereas the overlying Oxford Clay occupies much of the northwestern quarter of the district (Figure 6). Along the southern margin of the outcrop, the Oxford Clay is overlain, probably conformably, by younger Jurassic deposits, but to the east, it is overstepped by the Woburn Sands (Lower Cretaceous). Much of these outcrops is masked by drift deposits and there is only minimal exposure. However, brickpits at Newton Longville, near Bletchley

(now closed), together with other temporary sections and cored boreholes, provide details of the local sequence (Figure 6).

Within the district, the Kellaways Formation may be divided into a lower unit of predominantly dark grey mudstone and an upper unit of sandstone, siltstone and subordinate mudstone with silt wisps. Although not differentiated on the geological maps, these two units have been termed the Kellaways Clay and Kellaways Sand respectively (e.g. Horton et al., 1974); the lower unit is the 'Cayton Clay Formation' of Page (1989). The overlying mudstone sequence of the Oxford Clay has traditionally been divided into three members (Lower, Middle and Upper Oxford Clay). Although these can be recognised in unweathered exposures and boreholes, they have not been mapped because of extensive drift cover in this district. The Lower Oxford Clay consists predominantly of brownish grey, fissile, bituminous mudstone with a calorific value sufficient to enable partial self firing in brick manufacture (Callomon, 1968). Both the Middle and Upper Oxford Clay consist predominantly of pale grey, calcareous, variably silty mudstones with subordinate calcareous siltstones. The junction between the Lower and Middle Oxford Clay is usually marked by a few metres of interbedded brownish grey and pale grey mudstone; these are included with the Lower Oxford

Figure 6 Leighton Buzzard and adjoining district showing Kellaways Formation and Oxford Clay outcrop and localities referred to in text.

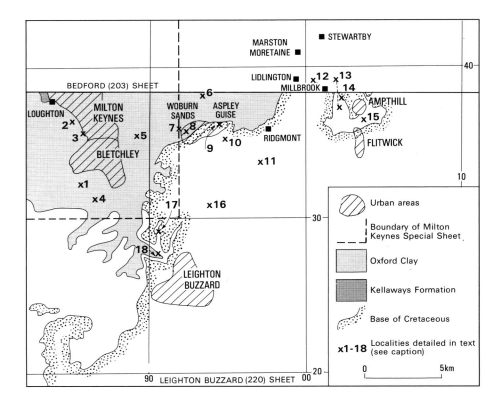

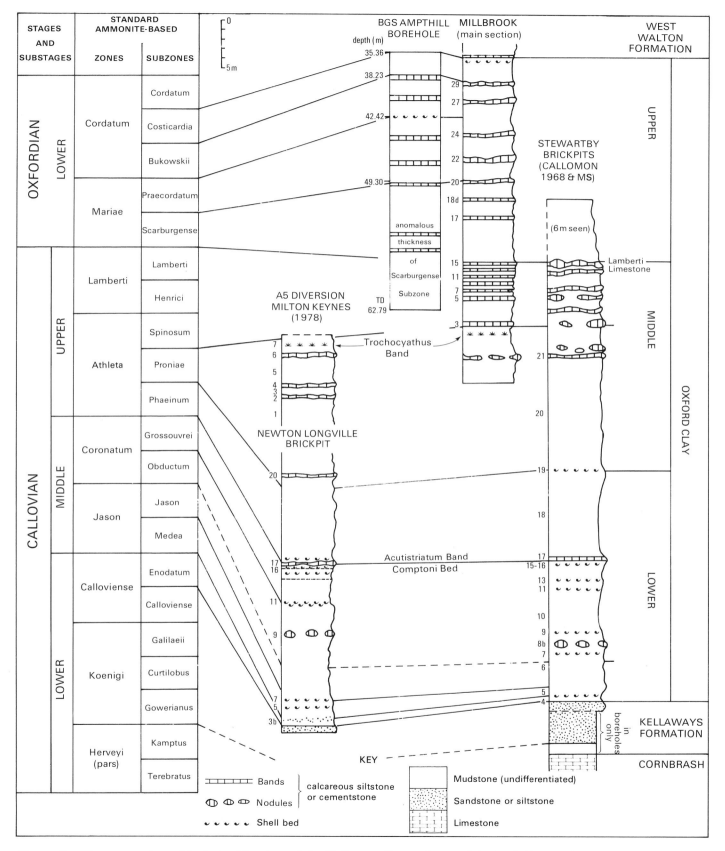

Figure 7 Chronostratigraphical classification of the Kellaways Formation and Oxford Clay, and reference sections for the Leighton Buzzard district.

Clay. Although, in this district and elsewhere in Bedfordshire and Buckinghamshire, there is a locally mappable marker bed (the Lamberti Limestone) at the boundary between the Middle and Upper Oxford Clay, they can most readily and conclusively be distinguished on the basis of their ammonite faunas, the Middle Oxford Clay has *Kosmoceras*, the Upper Oxford Clay has *Cardioceras* (see below).

Borehole MK16 [SP 8908 3545] (Horton et al., 1974) proved 4.51 m of the Kellaways Formation; a general thickness for this district of up to 5 m seems appropriate. No single section has proved a complete Oxford Clay sequence, but the total thickness is estimated at about 70 m. The thickness of the Lower Oxford Clay in the Bletchley pits is about 23 m (e.g. Callomon, 1968); an estimated total thickness for the Middle Oxford Clay, based on several sections, is about 20 to 25 m; a temporary exposure at Millbrook [TL 005 390], just to the north of the district, showed a complete Upper Oxford Clay sequence of 21.35 m (see Details). The thickness of Upper Oxford Clay recorded in the BGS Ampthill Borehole [TL 0244 3804] is 27.43 m.

Both the Kellaways Formation and Oxford Clay have a rich macrofauna dominated by bivalves and ammonites; the latter are used as the basis of the standard zonation (Figure 7). In the Lower Oxford Clay, ammonites are generally preserved crushed and with aragonitic shells; in the Middle and Upper Oxford Clay they are commonly pyritised with pyritic inner whorls. Ammonite species give their names to three important lithological marker horizons in the Oxford Clay—the Comptoni Bed, named after *Binatisphinctes comptoni*, the Acutistriatum Band, named after *Kosmoceras acutistriatum* and the Lamberti Limestone, named after *Quenstedtoceras lamberti* (Figure 7). At outcrop, the most likely fossil to be found is the oyster *Gryphaea* and if sufficient specimens are available from any one locality, they can be useful stratigraphical indicators: *Gryphaea dilobotes* (Kellaways Formation and Lower Oxford Clay), *G. lituola* (Middle Oxford Clay) and *G. dilatata* (Upper Oxford Clay). Like oysters, preservation of belemnites is also favoured because of their strong calcitic composition; *Cylindroteuthis* (particularly in the Kellaways Formation and Lower Oxford Clay) and *Hibolithes* (particularly in the Middle and Upper Oxford Clay) are characteristic. Gastropods, scaphopods, brachiopods, serpulids, echinoderms and crustaceans are also present amongst the invertebrate fossils; the distinctive serpulid *Genicularia vertebralis* is a useful indicator for the Lower and basal Middle Oxford Clay. Higher up in the Middle Oxford Clay, the small solitary cup coral *Trochocyathus magnevillianus* may be sufficiently abundant over a short vertical range to provide a useful marker horizon, here named the Trochocyathus Band (Figure 7). Marine microfauna and microflora, including foraminifera, ostracods, coccoliths and dinoflagellate cysts, are also present throughout the Kellaways and Oxford Clay formations. The Lower Oxford Clay of the East Midlands is a well-known source of vertebrate fossils including fish and marine reptiles. Representative faunas of the Oxford Clay are figured by Martill and Hudson (1991).

The boundary of the Kellaways Formation with the underlying Cornbrash occurs only in the subcrop (see Chapter 2). The position of the base of the Oxford Clay is commonly difficult to determine because about 2 m of interbedded coarse siltstone and silty mudstone separate the sandstones and siltstones of the Kellaways Formation from the overlying bituminous mudstones of the Lower Oxford Clay. Following Horton et al. (1974), the base of the latter is taken at the top of the highest sandstone of the Kellaways Formation and any transition beds are included in the Oxford Clay.

The Lower Oxford Clay has been extensively worked for brickmaking (see pp.104–105) near Bletchley (Newton Longville [SP 85 32] and Loughton [SP 851 363]) (Figure 6); the former is a key section for the district although quarrying has recently ceased there. Excavation in the Lower Oxford Clay continues near Marston Moretaine [SP 99 41] and Stewartby [TL 02 42], about 4 km north of the district. The Kellaways Formation has been exposed in drainage trenches in the floors of these pits. Middle and Upper Oxford Clay were once worked in long-obscured pits, for example at Woburn Sands [SP 92 36] and Aspley Guise [SP 94 36], but detailed knowledge of these parts of the Oxford Clay has only come in more recent years from temporary sections (e.g. A5 road diversion [SP 858 358] at Milton Keynes and the General Motors (formerly Vauxhall) proving track [TL 005 390] at Millbrook) and from cored boreholes (e.g. BGS Ampthill Borehole (1970)) (see Details).

Details

BLETCHLEY AND MILTON KEYNES

Newton Longville brickpit

Details of the section in the London Brick Company's pit [SP 85 32] at Newton Longville are recorded in Callomon (1968) and Horton et al. (1974). The Lower Oxford Clay was also described by Duff (1974). Callomon's account incorporates information from the pit [SP 8510 3638] further north at Loughton which, according to Horton et al. (1974), still showed a good section in the working face in 1968. Other pits, e.g. Slad Farm [SP 869 311] and Cow Common [SP 868 324], which had shown similar sections were already flooded or infilled at that time. Although there is general agreement on overall thickness, there is considerable variation between thicknesses recorded for individual beds (sometimes up to 50 per cent), as well as differences of bed demarcation and detail. The following section, which is based on data from all sources, is framed around the marker beds (nos 3b, 5, 7, 9, 11, 13a, 14, 16 and 17 of Callomon (1968)) which appear to have been identified by all recorders of the Newton Longville section; these are printed in bold below. Callomon's bed numbers are used for these markers, and where possible elsewhere, because they already feature in the published literature. Superficial structures distort the upper part of the section and the effects of valley bulging have been well displayed (Horton et al., 1974). The combined Acutistriatum Band (17)—Comptoni Bed (16) forms the main lithological marker although together they show considerable lateral variation (Horton et al., 1974, fig. 13). In the following section, faunal detail is based on Callomon (1968) and Duff (1974).

Thickness
m

MIDDLE OXFORD CLAY

Athleta Zone, Proniae Subzone

[21] Mudstone, medium grey; scattered pyritic
concretions formed around pieces of fossil
wood; *Gryphaea lituola*, *Hibolithes* and
crinoid columnals; pyritised ammonites
including *Choffatia* aff. *lahuseni*, *Kosmoceras
duncani*, *K. proniae*, *K. rowlstonense*,
Longaeviceras sp., *Peltoceras* spp.   seen 1.7+

[20] Limestone, argillaceous, impersistent   0–0.30

[19] Mudstone, medium grey; scattered *G. lituola*   c.1.5

LOWER OXFORD CLAY

Athleta Zone, Phaeinum Subzone

[18] Alternations of medium grey mudstone and
olive-grey, bituminous, fissile mudstone,
sometimes separated by marked
interburrowed horizons; pyritised nuculoid
shell bed with *Kosmoceras* at base   7.3–7.6

17 **Acutistriatum Band:** Limestone, olive-grey,
fine-grained, hard and massive with few
shells, passing laterally into hard,
calcareous or well-laminated, bituminous
shales; bivalves including *Corbulomima*
and *Mesosaccella*; scattered *Binatisphinctes
comptoni*, *Hecticoceras* sp., *Kosmoceras* spp.
including *K. acutistriatum* and *K. phaeinum*,
aptychus   0.18–0.30

Coronatum Zone, Grossouvrei Subzone

16 **Comptoni Bed:** Marl, greenish to olive-grey,
coarse gritty texture, grading in places to
shell bed with abundant nuculoids
(*Mesosaccella* and *Palaeonucula*) together
with *Procerithium*, *Corbulomima* and other
bivalves; ammonites including common
Binatisphinctes comptoni with *Erymnoceras*,
Hecticoceras and *Kosmoceras* including
K. castor and *K. grossouvrei*; belemnites   up to 0.38

[15] Mudstone, greenish grey with abundant
shell debris; *Bositra*, *Corbulomima*,
Meleagrinella, *Mesosaccella* and *Kosmoceras*   0.13–0.15

14 **Nuculoid shell bed:** mudstone, greenish
olive-grey, with abundant nuculoid
bivalves and *Procerithium*; *Corbulomima*,
Entolium, *Meleagrinella*, belemnites, shell
debris; some pyritisation; interburrowed
junction at base   0.10–0.20

[13b–e] Mudstone, olive-grey, greenish grey or
greyish green with some interburrowed
horizons and including some *Meleagrinella*
shell beds with *Procerithium*, *Corbulomima*,
Mesosaccella, *Palaeonucula* and *Kosmoceras*;
these taxa also present elsewhere together
with arcids, *Bositra*, *Discomiltha*, *Entolium*,
gryphaeate oyster, *Parainoceramus*, *Pleuromya*,
Pteroperna, *Thracia*; *Kosmoceras grossouvrei*
and *K. gulielmi*; crustaceans and crocodile
jaw   0.66–0.94

13a **Thin continuous band of pyrite**   0.012

[12] Mudstone, olive-grey, greenish grey or
green, fissile in parts; *Procerithium*, *Bositra*,
Corbulomima, *Entolium*, *Grammatodon*,
Isocyprina, *Meleagrinella*, *Mesosaccella*,
Palaeonucula, *Thracia*; two or three

Thickness
m

layers of crushed, pyritised ammonites
including *Cadoceras*, *Erymnoceras*,
'*Grossouvria*', *Kosmoceras castor*,
K. obductum posterior, *K. pollux* and
Longaeviceras sp.   2.73–3.56

Coronatum Zone, Obductum Subzone

11 **Pyritised nuculoid shell bed:** mudstone
with pyritised fauna predominantly of
nuculoids, *Erymnoceras* and *Kosmoceras*
including *K. gulielmi* and *K. obductum*;
also *Procerithium*, *Discomiltha*,
Meleagrinella, oysters, *Pleuromya*,
Plicatula, *Thracia*, *Cadoceras*,
Hecticoceras, belemnites and lignite;
lenses of calcareous cement   0.13–0.38

[10] Mudstone, greenish to olive-grey; scattered
pyritised ammonites including
Erymnoceras and *Kosmoceras obductum*;
other fauna not differentiated from [8b]
below   2.4–3.5

9 **Layer of ellipsoidal septarian nodules:**
medium grey micritic limestone with vein
calcite infilling joints which may be lined
with pyrite; sparsely fossiliferous;
Kosmoceras obductum   0–0.25

[8] Mudstone, greenish grey, massive to
sub-blocky; ammonites including
Kosmoceras obductum (above) and
K. jason (below); with [10] above, other
fauna includes *Lingula*, *Dicroloma*,
Procerithium, *Bositra*, *Corbulomima*,
Discomiltha, *Meleagrinella* (including
plasters and shell beds), nuculoids
(*Mesosaccella* and *Palaeonucula*),
Oxytoma, *Parainoceramus*, *Pinna*,
Thracia, crustaceans   5.36–6.95

Coronatum Zone, Obductum Subzone—
Jason Zone, Jason Subzone boundary
within [8]

7 **Pyritic shell bed:** silty clay with abundant
oysters, *Kosmoceras*, belemnites and shell
debris, together with bone fragments
and fish teeth   0.03–0.10

Jason Zone, Medea Subzone

[6] Mudstone, olive to greenish grey, massive
but fissile weathering; fauna dominated
by *Procerithium*, *Bositra*, *Corbulomima*,
Kosmoceras including *K. medea* and
shell debris; terebratulids, *Entolium*,
Meleagrinella, *Mesosaccella*, *Palaeonucula*,
Parainoceramus, *Pinna* and *Thracia* also
present   0.35–0.48

[6] *Gryphaea* shell-bed: silt, greenish grey,
lenticular, bioturbated; abundant
Gryphaea and belemnites; also *Procerithium*,
Bositra, *Corbulomima*, *Discomiltha*,
Palaeonucula and *Thracia*   0–0.05

[6] Mudstone, olive-grey, burrowed; fauna
dominated by *Meleagrinella*, oysters and
Kosmoceras; rhynchonellids, *Procerithium*,
Bositra and *Corbulomima* also present   0.03–0.10

5 **Pyritic shell bed:** silt, greenish grey,
lenticular, bioturbated; abundant *Gryphaea*

		Thickness m
	and belemnites; also *Meleagrinella*, nuculoids, *Kosmoceras* and shell debris	0–0.03
[4]	Alternating grey, variably silty mudstone and thin, greenish grey silt; fauna includes *Lingula*, rhynchonellids, *Procerithium*, *Bositra*, *Corbulomima*, *Discomiltha*, *Entolium*, *Grammatodon*, *Meleagrinella*, *Modiolus*, *Nicaniella*, *Palaeonucula*, *Pinna*, *Protocardia*, *Thracia* and ammonites including *Kosmoceras gulielmi*, *K. medea* and *Pseudocadoceras*; some shell beds with oysters or belemnites; lenses of shells and shell debris, and ammonite or oyster plasters in basal part	1.2–1.5

Calloviense Zone, Enodatum Subzone

| 3b | **Silt and sand:** medium to pale grey; argillaceous wispy bedding with well-sorted coarser laminae; bioturbated; lenticular aggregates of shells and shell debris including rhynchonellids, *Gryphaea*, *Oxytoma* and very common *Sigaloceras enodatum* | 0.2–0.51 |
| [3a] | Mudstone, medium olive-grey, silty and bioturbated, with partings of silt; scattered shells including oysters, *Kosmoceras gulielmi anterior*, *Sigaloceras enodatum* and perisphinctids | 0.24–0.46 |

KELLAWAYS FORMATION

Calloviense Zone, Calloviense Subzone and Koenigi Zone

[2]	Sand, medium grey, very fine-grained and argillaceous; bioturbated; calcareous nodules; *Gryphaea*-belemnite layer 0.10 m from top; scattered shells including *Catinula*, *Gryphaea*, *Myophorella* and belemnites; ammonites including *Chamoussetia*, *Proplanulites* and *Sigaloceras calloviense*	0.3
	Mudstone, greenish grey or black, very silty with silt partings; bioturbated with clay-filled burrows at top and pyrite-cemented burrows below.	0.13
	Sand, medium grey, silty and argillaceous with scattered pyritic and phosphatic nodules; bioturbated with paler silty, sand-filled burrows; pockets of hard calcareous cement	seen 0.08

Herveyi Zone, Kamptus Subzone

| [1] | Mudstone, silty, black, with buff phosphatic nodules; *Macrocephalites* cf. *herveyi* and *M. typicus* | ? |

A5 road diversion (1978), Milton Keynes

A section [SP 858 358] through about 10 m of Middle Oxford Clay was recorded and collected by Prof. J H Callomon during construction of a new road cutting for the A5 diversion at Milton Keynes in 1978 (Figure 7). Specimens were also collected on behalf of the Milton Keynes Development Corporation and both collections were donated to the BGS. The following section and fossil determinations are based largely on Callomon's original unpublished notes.

		Thickness m
Drift		

MIDDLE OXFORD CLAY

Athleta Zone, Proniae Subzone

7	Mudstones, weathered, selenitic c poorly fossiliferous; ammonites including significant number of *Hecticoceras* (0.5 m+) b 'Coral Bed' with abundant *Trochocyathus magnevilleanus* (0.2 m) a 'Rhynchonella Bed' with abundant *Rhynchonelloidella socialis*, occasional *Gryphaea* and other oysters, *Kosmoceras* aff. *spinosum*, perisphinctids and rare *Peltoceras* (0.8 m)	c.2.0
6	Limestone or calcareous marl with scattered cementstone concretions (marker bed); almost barren	0.2
5	Mudstone, olive-grey, calcareous, blocky; fossils particularly common in lowest metre with pyritised ammonites including *Kosmoceras proniae* and *K.* aff. *spinosum*, *Chlamys scarburgensis*, *Gryphaea lituola*, nuculoids and *Oxytoma inequivalve*; perisphinctids common in highest metre	3.0
4	Marl or highly calcareous mudstone, locally hardened into soft limestone; *Peltoceras* and *Cylindroteuthis*	c.0.3
3	Mudstone, highly calcareous; pyritised ammonites including *Kosmoceras duncani*, *Longaeviceras* and *Peltoceras* spp. (including large macroconchs); *Gryphaea lituola*	1.0
2	Limestone, soft and marly, or highly calcareous clay, locally hardened into large, round, marly concretions; layer of pyritic concretions (?chondritic burrowfills); *Gryphaea lituola*	0.2–0.4
1	Mudstone, calcareous, blocky; pyritised trails, shell debris, *Genicularia vertebralis* and *Gryphaea lituola*	3.0

Boreholes MK16 and MK24

A large number of boreholes were drilled as part of the geological investigations that were undertaken in connection with the planning and development of Milton Keynes following its designation as the site of a new town in 1965. Within the new town area, the most complete sequences through the Oxford Clay were proved in boreholes MK16 [SP 8908 3545] and MK24 [SP 8658 3133]; the former also cored the complete Kellaways Formation:

	Thickness m	Depth m
KELLAWAYS SAND		
Siltstone, greenish grey, coarse-grained passing to sand. Well cemented in places. Finely disseminated shell debris throughout, with occasional indefinite argillaceous wisps and bands. Scattered *Gryphaea*	0.10	19.66
Mudstone, olive-grey, with coarse silt wisps and large bivalves	0.13	19.79
Siltstone, greenish grey, hard and massive. Becoming finer-grained downwards with		

	Thickness m	Depth m
an increasing proportion of clay. Greenish grey, well cemented from 19.91 m. Very argillaceous below; passing down into	0.61	20.40
Sandstone, pale greenish grey, fine-grained, massive and moderately bedded. Scattered bivalves including *Gryphaea* and oysters, with belemnites and infrequent ammonites. Becoming less massive below with finely disseminated pyrite in the matrix. Indistinct channelling and bioturbation structures throughout. Continuing below in pale greenish grey, bioturbated sandstone with numerous shells. Becoming finer grained in basal 0.15 m. Seen to	2.21	22.61

KELLAWAYS CLAY

Mudstone, medium grey, subshaly with scattered gastropods and bivalves. Slightly silty at top. Increasingly shaly downward, with rare shells and finely disseminated pyrite and some small nodules. Becoming very dark grey below, with much pyrite and abundant thick-shelled bivalves. Irregular base	1.46	24.07

Other borehole logs and details are included in Horton et al. (1974).

WOBURN SANDS AND ASPLEY GUISE

M1 motorway cutting

During construction of the M1 motorway north of Woburn Sands and Aspley Guise, Smart (1960) recorded 0.6 m of Lower Oxford Clay beneath the Drift at the bottom of a foundation hole excavated for the Woburn Sands—Salford road bridge within his Cutting 24 [SP 933 384].

Woburn Sands

Both Middle and Upper Oxford Clay were once worked in brickpits at Woburn Sands; although these were cited by Davies (1916), there is no record of a detailed section. Material in the old collections from both Eastwoods (or Eastmans) brickworks [SP 920 362] and Woburn Sands Station [SP 924 364] includes *Hecticoceras, Kosmoceras, Peltoceras* and a perisphinctid, as well as bivalves (*Chlamys, Gryphaea, Meleagrinella*), belemnites and *Rhynchonelloidella*; these suggest a similar Middle Oxford Clay sequence to that recorded at the A5 diversion, Milton Keynes (see above). Unlocalised material from Woburn Sands but inferred by Davies (1916) to come from the Eastwoods (or Eastmans) brickworks includes ammonites (*Alligaticeras, Choffatia, Kosmoceras, Quenstedtoceras*) in the characteristic preservation of the Lamberti Limestone, together with pyritised cardioceratids and oppeliids from the Upper Oxford Clay. The latter are also present amongst material from the 'Tileworks' (possibly the Avenue Tileworks [SP 926 360], about 460 m south of Woburn Sands Station) together with *Hecticoceras, Properisphinctes, Gryphaea dilatata*, belemnites and serpulids; the ammonite assemblage indicates Upper Oxford Clay of the Mariae Zone, Scarburgense Subzone.

Aspley Guise and Ridgmont

Upper Oxford Clay was almost certainly exposed in brickyards at Aspley Guise from where Woodward (1895) recorded '*Ammonites crenatus*' [= *Creniceras*]. Near Ridgmont [SP 97 36], there are records of bands of limestone and large *Gryphaea* [= *G. dilatata*] together with 'many [unspecified] fossils' (Woodward, 1895). The overlying West Walton Formation was also almost certainly exposed hereabouts (see p.27). Material from 'Aspley Brickyard (Wavendon)', which was probably closer to Aspley Heath than Aspley Guise, includes bivalves (arcids, *Gryphaea, Lopha, Nanogyra nana*, nuculoid, *Pinna*), a belemnite and rhynchonellid brachiopod from 'calcareous bands in clay'; this material was collected in 1886 and ammonite material amongst it has been discarded in the past, presumably because of pyrite decay. Davies (1916) implied that he had seen Upper Oxford Clay in a small excavation above the railway halt.

BGS Birchmoor Farm and Froxfield 1 boreholes

Short runs of Middle Oxford Clay core were recovered from the subcrop in boreholes drilled in 1990 south of Aspley Guise. In the Birchmoor Farm Borehole [SP 9494 3518], 7.3 m of basal Middle Oxford Clay with *Genicularia vertebralis* were recovered from below the Woburn Sands at a depth of 52.36 m. In the BGS Froxfield 1 Borehole [SP 9737 3337], 2.47 m of Middle Oxford Clay including a bed rich in *Trochocyathus magnevillianus* were recovered from below the Woburn Sands at a depth of 81.05 m (Cox, 1991).

AMPTHILL AND MILLBROOK

Sections in the Ampthill railway cutting [TL 020 393 to TL 022 373], which exposed Upper Oxford Clay below West Walton Formation and Ampthill Clay, and excavations at the Ampthill (Flitwick) sewage works [TL 0390 3640], which yielded material from the Upper Oxford Clay and West Walton Formation, are detailed on p.25.

General Motors proving track, Millbrook

In 1968, the south slope of excavations for the proving track at Millbrook provided a temporary section on the north side of Heydon Hill [TL 005 390] through the Middle and Upper Oxford Clay and the overlying West Walton Formation. The section, which is about 500 m north of the Leighton Buzzard Sheet boundary, was described and collected by A Horton and Prof. J H Callomon. Their notes and specimens (including bed numbers and fossil identifications) are available at BGS, and summarised in Wyatt et al. (1988) (Figure 7).

BGS Ampthill Borehole

In the BGS Ampthill Borehole [TL 0244 3804] (Figure 7), 27.43 m of Upper Oxford Clay were cored (from 35.36 m to 62.79 m) beneath the West Walton Formation and the Ampthill Clay (p.25). The following log of the Oxford Clay is based on the original descriptive log of A Horton; the ammonites were examined by Prof. J H Callomon in 1970 and his identifications, with some amendments, are included.

	Thickness m	Depth m
WEST WALTON FORMATION (see p. 26)		35.36

UPPER OXFORD CLAY

Cordatum Zone, Costicardia Subzone
  Mudstone, pale grey, bioturbated with many pyritised trails and some *Chondrites*; shell and plant debris; *Chlamys, Gryphaea, Lopha,*

	Thickness m	Depth m
Nanogyra, Hibolithes, Cardioceras (*C.*) *costicardia*; interburrowed junction at base	0.66	36.02
Mudstone, pale grey with dark carbonaceous burrows; *Procerithium* and bivalves; becoming hard and blocky below; shell-debris-filled and clay burrowfills; darker and increasingly carbonaceous below with scattered shells including *Hibolithes*; interburrowed junction at base	0.28	36.30
Mudstone, pale grey, hard, blocky; becoming increasingly carbonaceous with *Chondrites*; large foraminifera-encrusted *Gryphaea* and interburrowed junction at base	0.28	36.58
Mudstone, dark grey, carbonaceous; *Pinna* in growth position; scattered ammonites including *Cardioceras* (*C.*) *costicardia* and *C.* (*Scarburgiceras*) aff. *harmonicum*; indistinct interburrowing at base	0.30	36.88
Mudstone, pale grey, slightly carbonaceous with pyritised pins etc.; becoming silty, calcareous and blocky below 37.01 m	0.20	37.08
Mudstone, medium to dark grey, carbonaceous with large burrows; *Meleagrinella, Nicaniella, Cardioceras* (*C.*) aff. *costellatum, C.* (*Vertebriceras*) cf. *quadrarium*	0.13	37.21
Mudstone, medium grey, slightly silty, carbonaceous with indistinct burrows and scattered *Cardioceras*; large plant fragments and *Myophorella* with interburrowed junction at base	0.23	37.44
Mudstone, pale grey with large *Gryphaea* at top; *Procerithium*, wood fragments and numerous small ammonites including *Cardioceras* (*V.*) cf. *quadrarium*	0.13	37.57
Mudstone, pale grey, hard and massive with carbonaceous burrows; *Gryphaea, Oxytoma* and scattered ammonites including *Cardioceras* (*V.*) cf. *quadrarium*; less calcareous below 37.80 m with *Chondrites, Gryphaea* and *Hibolithes*	0.53	38.10
Mudstone, medium to pale grey, with carbonaceous burrows; scattered shells including *Nanogyra* fragments, *Cardioceras* (*C.*) aff. *costellatum* and *C.* (*V.*) *quadrarium*	0.13	38.23

Cordatum Zone, Bukowskii Subzone

	Thickness m	Depth m
Siltstone, pale grey, hard, calcareous with scattered ammonite fragments in upper part; harder, more massive and well cemented below	0.17	38.40
Mudstone, pale grey with fine shell debris; blocky and weakly calcareous with rare pyritised trails; ammonites, including *Cardioceras* (*C.*) cf. *costellatum* and *C.* (*V.*) cf. *quadrarium*, scattered throughout; rare bivalves including *Modiolus* and *Myophorella*; increasingly carbonaceous downward with weakly interburrowed junction at base	0.26	38.66
Mudstone, hard, calcareous and blocky with *Chondrites* and rare shells including *Myophorella*; interburrowing at 38.96 m; very hard and massive for 80 mm at 39.04 m; *Cardioceras* (*Scarburgiceras*) *bukowskii* at 39.07 m; increasingly carbonaceous downward		

	Thickness m	Depth m
with interburrowed junction, *Gryphaea* and ammonites, including *Cardioceras* (*C.*) cf. *costicardia*, at base	0.51	39.17
Mudstone, compact, massive and calcareous with scattered plant debris; scattered fauna including rare *Nicaniella*, nuculoids and *Cardioceras* (*C.*) *costicardia*; scattered pyritised pins; very hard and calcareous for 80 mm at 39.57 m; interburrowed junction at base	0.61	39.78
Mudstone, dark grey, carbonaceous; hard, calcareous and blocky in top 0.15 m with scattered bivalves including *Gryphaea, Nicaniella, Palaeonucula?*; *Cardioceras* (*S.*) *bukowskii* at base	0.15	39.93
Siltstone, pale grey, moderately hard and calcareous	0.05	39.98
Mudstone, pale grey with *Chlamys*, small *Gryphaea*, occasional ammonites including *Cardioceras* (*S.*) *bukowskii* and a belemnite; increasingly carbonaceous below 40.08 m; distinct burrowing at 40.16 m; abrupt base	0.33	40.31
Mudstone, dark grey, very carbonaceous with much fine plant debris; fine shell debris throughout with scattered shells including *Chlamys* and *Cardioceras* (*S.*) *bukowskii*; scattered pyritised tubes; belemnite; interburrowed junction at base	0.30	40.61
Mudstone, pale grey; scattered shells; nodular mass of entwining serpulids at 40.69 m with pale fawn, concretionary filling; scattered foraminifera-encrusted serpulids and *Gryphaea*; scattered echinoid spines; pyritised shell-debris-filled burrow at 40.77 m; large serpulid-mass at 40.79 m; bed of serpulid-encrusted *Gryphaea* with ammonites (including *Euaspidoceras*) at 40.82 m; abundant fine shell debris below; abrupt base	0.23	40.84
Mudstone, pale grey with darker burrows infilled with shell debris; scattered ammonite fragments including *Peltoceras* at 41.15 m; *Dicroloma*, arcid, *Gryphaea, Nicaniella*; silt- and debris-filled burrows and -lined tubes in mottled grey mudstone below; large-scale burrows at base	0.61	41.45
Mudstone, pale grey, indistinctly burrowed with fine shell debris and spat; scattered small bivalves; *Cardioceras* (*S.*) *bukowskii* at 41.55 m; increasing proportion of broken shells below with pyritised *Peltoceras* and much plant debris; shell layer with oysters and *Peltoceras arduennense* at 41.76 m; ammonite plaster with *Cardioceras* (*S.*) *bukowskii, Euaspidoceras* sp., *Peltoceras arduennense* and *Gryphaea* at 41.91 m	0.61	42.06
Mudstone, pale grey, fine-grained with ill-defined burrows and ammonites including *Cardioceras* (*S.*) *bukowskii*; belemnite, several *Pinna* and oysters; shell-bed with *Gryphaea dilatata, Nicaniella, Cardioceras* (*Scarburgiceras*) *praecordatum, Hecticoceras svevum* and *Properisphinctes bernensis* at base	0.56	42.42

Mariae Zone, Praecordatum Subzone

Mudstone, pale grey, fine-grained with

	Thickness m	Depth m
subblocky fracture; pyritised trails and indistinct burrows; distinct *Chondrites* where more carbonaceous; *Dicroloma, Gryphaea, Myophorella, Oxytoma, Pinna* fragments, rare small bivalves and crustacean plates; distinct *Chondrites* to base	2.36	44.78
Siltstone, pale grey, weakly calcareous	0.03	44.81
Mudstone, pale grey, fine-grained, hard, calcareous; indistinct mottling, *Chondrites* and scattered pyritised trails and tubes; foraminifera-encrusted *Gryphaea* at 45.21 m; belemnite at 45.26 m, scattered *Pinna* (some in growth position) below; *Gryphaea, Modiolus,* ammonites including *Cardioceras* sp., *Goliathiceras* sp. and *?Quenstedtoceras (Q.) mariae*, crustacean fragments; nests of *Dicroloma* at 46.56 m; barren, hard and calcareous below	2.66	47.47
Siltstone, pale grey, weakly calcareous	0.05	47.52
Mudstone, pale grey becoming increasingly dark with depth and with scattered fine shell debris; pyritised trails, shell-debris-lined burrows and *Chondrites*; *Gryphaea, Nicaniella* and *Pinna*; *Cardioceras (S.) praecordatum* and *Scaphitodites scaphitoides*; *Dicroloma* and weakly interburrowed junction at base	0.77	48.29
Mudstone, pale grey with shell debris and numerous pyritised trails; *Chondrites* below 48.46 m; pyritised masses and tubes below 48.72 m; occasional crustacean fragments below 48.77 m; extremely carbonaceous below 49.07 m; *Camptonectes, Dacryomya, Nicaniella* and *Thracia?*; distinct burrowing and coarse *Chondrites* in basal 0.01 m; abrupt base	0.88	49.17
Mudstone, pale grey, fine-grained, blocky and calcareous; indefinite *Chondrites* and rare pyritised trails; rare shells including *Dacryomya, Gryphaea, Opis, Pinna* and *Hibolithes*	0.13	49.30

Mariae Zone, Scarburgense Subzone

	Thickness m	Depth m
Siltstone, pale greenish grey, hard, massive and calcareous; pyritised trails and indistinct *Chondrites* throughout; rare shells including belemnite fragment	0.15	49.45
Mudstone, pale grey with pyritised trails; increasing proportion of fine shell debris downwards; foraminifera-encrusted oyster fragments below 50.02 m; increasingly carbonaceous below with pale grey *Chondrites*; scattered *Dicroloma*; ammonites including *Cardioceras (S.) praecordatum* and *Quenstedtoceras (Q.) woodhamense*; abundant fine shell debris below 50.14 m; distinct interburrowing at base with coarse *Chondrites*	0.84	50.29
Mudstone, pale grey, fine grained with scattered pyritised trails; scattered wisps of immature shells and foraminifera below 50.34 m; increasingly fossiliferous below with large *Gryphaea* and many small bivalves including *Dacryomya* and *Protocardia*, together with *Dicroloma*; scattered pyritised pins and shell-filled burrows; increasingly carbonaceous		

	Thickness m	Depth m
below 50.83 m with distinct *Chondrites; Camptonectes, Nicaniella, Pseudolimea*; dark grey with burrow-mottling in basal 0.10 m	0.92	51.21
Mudstone, pale grey, finely carbonaceous with occasional pyritised pins etc.; scattered bivalves including *Entolium*, foraminifera-encrusted *Gryphaea, Oxytoma, Pinna* and shell debris; *Dicroloma* in nests; large wood fragment; increasingly fossiliferous below 51.71 m with burrow-mottling; extremely carbonaceous in basal 30 mm with oyster fragments; interburrowed junction at base	0.94	52.15
Mudstone, pale grey; pyritised trails and *Chondrites*; scattered ammonites including *Cardioceras* sp. and *Quenstedtoceras woodhamense*, with *Dicroloma, Oxytoma, Parallelodon* and *Pinna*; increasing fine shell debris with larger pale grey burrows near base; interburrowed junction	1.42	53.57
Mudstone, pale grey, compact and blocky with scattered pyritised trails; becoming increasingly carbonaceous with paler burrows; extremely carbonaceous at base with *Dicroloma, Oxytoma* and *Pinna*; interburrowed junction	0.10	53.67
Mudstone, pale grey with scattered pyritised trails etc. and indefinite *Chondrites*; becoming harder and more blocky below; plant-rich burrows at 54.56 m and increasingly carbonaceous below; scattered *Dicroloma* and wisps of fine shell debris; *Cardioceras (S.) scarburgense*	1.09	54.76
Siltstone, pale greenish grey, hard, calcareous with scattered pyritised trails	0.10	54.86
Mudstone, pale grey, slightly carbonaceous with *Chondrites* and pyritised trails; increasingly shelly below with *Pinna* common at base; interburrowed junction	0.69	55.55
Mudstone, pale grey with *Chondrites*; increasingly carbonaceous below; nests and burrowfill clusters of *Dicroloma*; *Gryphaea, Pinna, Trigonia* (in shell layer at top); ammonites including *Cardioceras* sp. and *Hecticoceras svevum*	1.12	56.67
Limestone, pale grey, fine-grained, silty with pyritised trails	0.12	56.79
Mudstone, pale grey, silty with scattered pyritised trails etc; distinct *Chondrites*; increasingly carbonaceous below and with more shell debris; very carbonaceous below 58.06 m; nests of profuse *Dicroloma; Entolium, Nicaniella, Pinna; Cardioceras (S.)* cf. *praecordatum, C. (S.)* cf. *scarburgense, Goliathiceras?*; *Hibolithes*; interburrowed junction at base	1.43	58.22
Mudstone, pale grey with pyritised trails etc.; becoming increasingly carbonaceous and with increasing shell debris below 59.26 m; burrows in carbonaceous mudstone at 59.39 m; *Dicroloma, Pinna, Cardioceras (S.) praecordatum, C. (S.)* cf. *scarburgense, Goliathiceras?, Hibolithes*; interburrowed junction at base	1.29	59.51
Mudstone, pale grey with pyritised trails and indefinite *Chondrites*; increasingly carbonaceous below 59.61 m; weakly interburrowed junction at base	0.23	59.74
Mudstone, pale grey with pyritised trails; slightly carbonaceous; indefinite *Chondrites*		

	Thickness	Depth
	m	m

and some interburrowed horizons; scattered
  shell debris; plant debris below 60.27 m; pale
  fawn, ferruginous impregnation at 62.15 m but
  generally uniform and poorly fossiliferous;
  Dicroloma, Procerithium, Dacryomya, Grammatodon,
  Gryphaea, Pinna, Thracia?, Cardioceras (S.)
  scarburgense, Quenstedtoceras mariae, Q.
  woodhamense, crustacean fragments; seen to   3.05   62.79

LEIGHTON BUZZARD

In the subcrop north of Leighton Buzzard, 3.01 m of upper-most Middle Oxford Clay were cored beneath the Woburn Sands at a depth of 92.64 m in the BGS Potsgrove 1 Borehole [SP 9406 3066]. Pale grey, calcareous mudstones with a siltstone were recovered. These beds yielded several *Gryphaea lituola, Oxytoma* and pyritised *Kosmoceras* ex gr. *spinosum*; this association is indicative of a level close below the Lamberti Limestone.

An exposure [SP 9071 2768] in the bank of the River Ouzel west of Nares Gladley Farm yielded pyritised cardioceratid ammonite nuclei and inner whorls including *C.(C.)* cf. *ashtonense, C.(C.)* cf. *cordatum, C. (Vertebriceras)* cf. *quadrarium* and *Goliathiceras?, Gryphaea dilatata* (some encrusted with serpulids and heavily bored), *Lopha* sp., *Nanogyra nana* and *Hibolithes*. This assemblage indicates the highest part of the Upper Oxford Clay belonging to the Cordatum Zone, Costicardia Subzone. A similar level was almost certainly formerly exposed in the nearby brickyard near Rushmere Pond, Nares Gladley. The faunal list published in Woodward (1895) clearly includes serpulids, *Gryphaea dilatata, Lopha* (rather common), *Cardioceras, Euaspidoceras* or *Peltoceras*, perisphinctids and *Hibolithes*.

Excavations [SP 906 290] at a dam near Upper Kiln Farm, south of Great Brickhill yielded material from up to 3 m of clay beneath the contact with the Woburn Sands; a 0.1 m-thick cementstone or silty bed was recorded about 1 m above the base of the clay. Specimens include large valves of *Gryphaea dilatata*, some heavily encrusted with serpulids, bryozoa and foraminifera, and some heavily bored, a siltstone with *G. dilatata* and *Lopha*, and pieces of siltstone and cementstone, some pale grey and nodular with chondritic mottling and larger burrowfills (cf. *Gastrochaenolites*). This assemblage could be from the Upper Oxford Clay or overlying West Walton Formation. However, comparison with the Millbrook section suggests that the closest match there for the cementstone band is Callomon's Bed 27 or 29 in the Upper Oxford Clay (Figure 7).

WEST WALTON AND AMPTHILL CLAY FORMATIONS

For many years, following Blake and Hudleston (1877), the term Corallian or Corallian Beds has been used in all areas of the English outcrop and subcrop for the strata between the Oxford Clay (below) and the Kimmeridge Clay (above). In areas from Dorset to Oxfordshire and in Yorkshire, coral reef and associated limestone and sandstone deposits apparently dominate this interval but north-eastwards from Oxford, and throughout the East Midlands, the sequence is predominantly of mudstone. Since Seeley (1869), the upper and greater part of this mudstone has been called the Ampthill Clay (Formation). Following Gallois and Cox (1977), a lower unit of more variable silty and calcareous lithology, which in the

past acquired a variety of local names, is referred to the West Walton Beds (or Formation). Although in this district both these formations can be recognised in borehole cores and exposed sections, it has not proved possible to differentiate the two at outcrop and they have been mapped together (Figure 8). A feature-forming cementstone nodule band at or near the base of the West Walton Formation (see p.27) has been mapped in the country between Stoke Hammond [SP 88 29] and Soulbury (Figure 8). Its outcrop demonstrates the presence of a shallow synclinal fold in the Jurassic rocks below the Cretaceous unconformity; the fold axis trends northwest—south-east through Stoke Hammond (Figure 31). Between Great Brickhill and beyond Ridgmont, the West Walton Formation and Ampthill Clay appear to be absent below the base of the Woburn Sands because of the pre-Aptian folding referred to above. However, about 4 m of these strata were noted in the M1 cutting near Ridgmont, although it was not possible to map them in the contiguous ground because of drift cover (see Details; Wyatt et al., 1988) (Figure 8).

Much of the outcrop is masked by drift deposits and sandy wash from the Woburn Sands above, and there is only minimal exposure. However, a few temporary exposures and a cored borehole [TL 0244 3804] at Ampthill provide some important stratigraphic information, in particular about the Ampthill Clay in its type area (see Details). There is also sufficient information from the Thame (Sheet 237) district, which adjoins to the south-west, to indicate that the latter formation, at least, is comparable with the sequence there (Horton et al., in press).

In its type area in the Fenland of Norfolk, the West Walton Formation consists of alternating interburrowed calcareous mudstone and silty mudstone with cementstone or siltstone doggers at many levels (Gallois and Cox, 1977; Cox and Gallois, 1979). Although other limestone facies, such as coralline and algal-rich deposits, occur locally at this stratigraphic level on the southern edge of the Fenland and elsewhere, the argillaceous facies is the more widespread. In the eastern part of the district, the lower and middle parts of the formation are much reduced or absent due to condensed sequences and minor nonsequences. As well as the typical silty mudstone, the upper part of the formation contains a unit of thin cementstones and oyster lumachelles with abundant *Nanogyra nana* for which, in the past, the name Oakley Clay (Buckman, 1927) or Oakley Beds (Arkell, 1933) has been used. This facies persists, possibly intermittently, from its type locality in the Thame district. Overall, there are clearly facies and thickness changes between the eastern part of the Leighton Buzzard district and the Thame district, but there is insufficient data from the western part of the former district to establish the details of the local sequence and its relationship with that of adjoining areas.

The overlying Ampthill Clay consists largely of dark grey, shelly mudstone, slightly silty mudstone (which occurs particularly in the lower part, forming a transition with the West Walton Formation) and pale grey calcareous mudstone (which occurs particularly in the upper part); there are doggers and thin beds of cementstone at several levels, associated in particular with the more cal-

Figure 8 Leighton Buzzard and adjoining district showing West Walton and Ampthill Clay formations outcrop, and localities referred to in text.

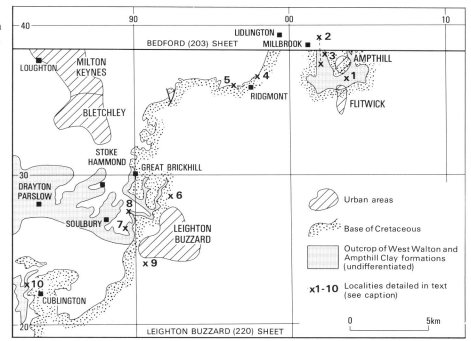

careous mudstone. Thin beds of organic (kerogen-rich) mudstone occur at one level at least. In the upper part of the formation, there are several minor erosion surfaces marked by phosphatic pebbles and oysters.

The BGS Ampthill Borehole proved a thickness of 11.92 m for the West Walton Formation and 12.62 m for the Ampthill Clay; only the lower part of the latter formation is preserved beneath the unconformity at the base of the Woburn Sands (Figure 9). In the Leighton Buzzard area, the Woburn Sands also cut out the upper part of the Ampthill Clay but higher beds are known in the nearby subcrop from a borehole at Ascott Farm Sandpit [SP 9078 2408]. The total thickness of the combined West Walton and Ampthill Clay formations in this area is estimated at about 30 m which is similar to the estimate for the combined West Walton Formation and Ampthill Clay in eastern parts of the Thame district (Horton et al., in preparation).

Both West Walton and Ampthill Clay formations have a macrofauna dominated by bivalves and ammonites; the latter are used as the basis of the standard zonation (Figure 9). At outcrop, the most likely fossils to be found are the oysters because their robust calcitic shells make them more resistant to weathering. *Gryphaea dilatata* is common throughout much of the sequence but is replaced in the upper part of the Ampthill Clay by *Deltoideum delta*; specimens are often encrusted, particularly with serpulids, and show drill-holes made by boring organisms. Belemnites are also sufficiently robust to occur commonly in the soil at outcrop. Other molluscan groups and rarer brachiopods, echinoderms and crustaceans also occur, together with marine microfauna and microflora including foraminifera, ostracods, coccoliths and dinoflagellate cysts. In the West Walton Formation, the mudstone is often plant-speckled and contains wood fragments.

By combining the macrofaunal and lithological characters within the framework of the ammonite zonation, the West Walton and Ampthill Clay formations can be subdivided into a number of smaller units (Figure 9). Although originally established in cored borehole sequences in eastern England, these units or standard beds (WWF1—WWF16 and AmC1—AmC42) can be recognised further afield in southern Britain (Gallois and Cox, 1977; Cox and Gallois, 1979). They have been used to elucidate the stratigraphy in the present district, although there remain some problems with the detailed classification of the West Walton Formation as it passes south-westwards to the more varied facies of the Oxford area. In addition to the BGS Ampthill Borehole, the BGS Hartwell Borehole [SP 7926 1223], in the adjoining Thame district, is an important reference section for the Ampthill Clay (Figures 8 and 9).

In the Ampthill area, the base of the West Walton Formation is taken at the base of a thin (about 0.30 m) very dark grey, pyritic, highly fossiliferous mudstone which rests with interburrowing on pale grey, poorly fossiliferous mudstone (Upper Oxford Clay). Less than half a metre above the base, there is an ammonitiferous septarian limestone. A similar limestone forms a feature in the western part of the district near Leighton Buzzard and has been used as a guide to mapping the base of the formation in that area (see Details).

Unlike the Oxford Clay and the Kimmeridge Clay, there are no lithological records of old brickpits in the clays of the West Walton and Ampthill Clay formations. The cutting made during the construction of the Bedford & Luton railway near Ampthill, provided the 'type' section for the Ampthill Clay (Seeley, 1869), but this is now completely overgrown. Not until major civil engineering projects in the area, nearly 100 years later, did

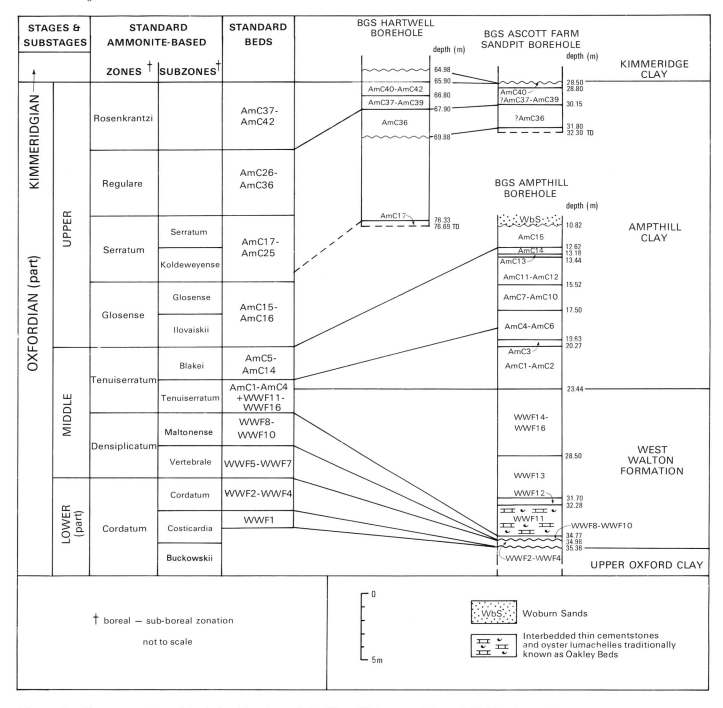

Figure 9 Chronostratigraphical classification of the West Walton and Ampthill Clay formations and reference sections for the Leighton Buzzard district.

knowledge of the local sequences advance; these include excavations made during the construction of the M1 motorway near Ridgmont [SP 97 36] (1958), the vehicle proving track at Millbrook (1968) and a sewage works near Ampthill (1970). Data about the sequence beneath the Woburn Sands to the west of Leighton Buzzard is available from the BGS Ascott Farm Sandpit Borehole and an exposure at Bakers Wood pit (see Details).

Details

AMPTHILL–FLITWICK

Ampthill (Flitwick) sewage works

Material collected from spoil heaps (and therefore without stratigraphic control) during excavations for a new sewage works [TL 0390 3640] at Ampthill in 1970 indicate the presence of both the West Walton Formation and the underlying

Upper Oxford Clay (see p.19). Many of the ammonites (identified and in part collected by Prof. J H Callomon) are heavily bored, worn and encrusted; they include *Euaspidoceras akantheen*, *E.* cf. *catena*, *E.* cf. *crebricostis*, *E. paucituberculatum*, *Goliathiceras* cf. *titan*, *G.* (*Pachycardioceras*) sp., *Perisphinctes* (*Arisphinctes*) cf. *cotovui*, *P.* (*A.*) *helenae*, *P.* (*A.*) *ingens* and *P.* (*A.*) cf. *kingstonensis*. Also present is a rich *Cardioceras* fauna including *C.* cf. *costicardia*, *C.* cf. *harmonicum*, *C.* cf. *reesidei*, *C. sequanicum* and *Goliathiceras falcatum*, together with *Peltoceras* sp. Belemnites (*Hibolithes hastatus* and *Pachyteuthis* sp.), *Dicroloma*, serpulids, *Rhynchonella*, and bored and encrusted *Gryphaea* are also present. Comparison with the Millbrook section (see p.19) indicates that the *Euaspidoceras* and *Perisphinctes* fauna comes from a bed just above the base of the West Walton Formation (Bed 32 of Millbrook; Wyatt et al., 1988). The *Cardioceras* fauna comes from the Upper Oxford Clay, but no lower than Bed 26 of Millbrook (Figure 7). Records of more recent excavations at this site, together with specimens, are held in Bedford Museum (written communication, Dr K N Page, March 1990).

Ampthill railway cutting

According to Woodward (1895, p.136), the section in the railway cutting [TL 020 393 to TL 022 373] at Ampthill exposed about 21 m of Jurassic clays. Although it was not measured or collected in detail, the section apparently showed a southerly dipping sequence of Upper Oxford Clay overlain by the West Walton Formation and the Ampthill Clay. Specimens alleged to have come from 'impure limestone bands in clay' at the northern end of the tunnel include serpulids, rhynchonellid brachiopods, *Pleurotomaria*, bivalves (arcids, *Gryphaea*, *Lopha*, *Modiolus*, *Oxytoma*, *Nanogyra nana*, nuculoids, pectinids, *Pholadomya*, *Pinna*, and *Plicatula*), cardioceratid ammonites including *C.* (*S.*) *praecordatum*, *Hibolithes*, a crinoid and cidarids. *Dicroloma*, arcids, serpulid-encrusted oysters, *Thracia*, cardioceratid ammonites, *Decipia decipiens* and belemnites including *Pachyteuthis* are recorded from the southern end of the tunnel. Additional taxa from amongst unlocalised material include *Gryphaea dilatata*, encrusted with *Plicatula*, and *Cardioceras* (*Cawtoniceras*) spp. Nearly all the specimens were collected in the 1880s and 1890s. A more recent trial excavation in the cutting reported by Wright (1980, p.70) showed 'Of the Ampthill Clay proper at most 10 m … preserved below the Lower Greensand' with ammonites indicating the Glosense Zone, Ilovaiskii Subzone. This is compatible with the nearby BGS Ampthill Borehole (see below) where the youngest Ampthill Clay belongs to AmC15 of the standard sequence (Figure 9).

BGS Ampthill Borehole

The BGS Ampthill Borehole [TL 0244 3804] (Figure 9) penetrated the Ampthill Clay, West Walton Formation and part of the Upper Oxford Clay beneath about 10 m of Lower Cretaceous Woburn Sands. The original descriptive log was prepared by A Horton and forms the basis of that given below; ammonites were examined by Prof. J H Callomon in 1970 and his identifications, with some amendments, are included. Sited close to Seeley's (1869) original, but now obscured, Ampthill Clay section in the railway cutting (see above), the borehole provides a permanent and important reference section.

	Thickness m	Depth to base m
WOBURN SANDS		
Sand, soft, friable, pale brown	10.16	10.16
Sand, pale green, coarse; scattered ?phosphatic pebbles; abrupt		

	Thickness m	Depth to base m
erosional base	0.66	10.82
AMPTHILL CLAY		
Upper Oxfordian, Glosense Zone		
AmC15		
Mudstone, pale grey; scattered shells including *Dicroloma* in clusters, *Procerithium*, *Entolium*, *Grammatodon*, *Myophorella*, oysters, *Pinna*, *Thracia* and other bivalves, partially pyritised and iridescent *Amoeboceras* and perisphinctids including *Decipia* nuclei; pyritised trails, chondritic mottling.	1.80	12.62
Middle Oxfordian, Tenuiserratum Zone		
AmC14		
Mudstone, pale grey with calcareous nodules and pale brown impregnations; shell debris increasing downward; *Dicroloma*, *Chlamys* and partially pyritised perisphinctid nuclei; serpulids and oysters near base; interburrowed junction at base.	0.56	13.18
AmC13		
Mudstone, pale grey becoming darker grey and bioturbated below; *Dicroloma* and scattered small bivalves including pectinid; *Gryphaea* shell bed at base.	0.26	13.44
AmC11–AmC12		
Mudstone, medium grey, becoming silty with depth and with increasing shell debris; scattered shells including *Lingula*, *Dicroloma*, *Entolium*, *Grammatodon*, *Modiolus*, *Myophorella*, *Neocrassina*, nuculoids, foraminifera-encrusted oysters, *Thracia*, and cardioceratid and perisphinctid ammonites; pyritised pins and trails; shell-lined and indistinct burrows above weakly interburrowed junction at base.	2.08	15.52
AmC7–AmC10		
Mudstone, medium grey, becoming pale grey, hard and calcareous with depth; silty, calcareous nodules at 16.38 m, blocky and calcareous below; variably shelly with serpulids, *Lingula*, *Dicroloma*, arcid, *Gryphaea*, *Myophorella*, *Oxytoma*, *Thracia*, *Cardioceras*, *Perisphinctes* and shell debris; pyritised pins and trails; passing down into	1.98	17.50
AmC4–AmC6		
Mudstone, medium grey, calcareous, with indefinite darker burrows at top; weak, ferruginous impregnation with chondritic mottling in lower part; plant debris increasing with depth; scattered shells including *Dicroloma*, *Chlamys*, *Grammatodon*, *Gryphaea*, *Myophorella*, *Oxytoma*, *Pinna*, *Cardioceras*, including *C. kokeni* and		

	Thickness m	Depth to base m
C. maltonense?, and Perisphinctes; belemnites near interburrowed junction at base.	2.13	19.63

AmC3
Mudstone, dark grey, carbonaceous, with some pale grey burrows; abundant shell debris; scattered shells including *Grammatodon*, *Cardioceras* spp. including *C. tenuiserratum*, and *Hibolithes*; pale grey and blocky above interburrowed junction at base. — 0.64 — 20.27

AmC1–AmC2
Mudstone, medium grey, slightly calcareous, sparsely shelly with occasional pyritised trails; becoming shelly and carbonaceous below 20.68 m with *Lingula*, *Dicroloma*, bivalves including *Grammatodon* and *Thracia*, and *Cardioceras* spp. including *C. maltonense* and *C. tenuiserratum*; increasingly dark and carbonaceous in lowest 0.20 m with abundant shell debris and gastropods, bivalves and ammonites including *C. tenuiserratum*; interburrowed junction at base. — 3.17 — 23.44

WEST WALTON FORMATION
WWF14–WWF16
Mudstone, pale grey, blocky, sparsely shelly with occasional *Nanogyra*, *Perisphinctes* and scattered *Cardioceras tenuiserratum*; pyritised burrows common near base. — 1.81 — 25.25

Limestone, pale grey, argillaceous, hard and massive; *Lingula* — 0.18 — 25.43

Mudstone, pale grey, calcareous with some ill-defined and pyritised burrows, and scattered shell debris, *Myophorella* and *Pinna*; becoming medium grey and carbonaceous below 26.59 m with *Myophorella*, *Nanogyra*, *Cardioceras tenuiserratum* and *Perisphinctes*; indefinite chondritic mottling; interburrowed junction at base. — 3.07 — 28.50

WWF13
Mudstone, medium grey becoming paler below, calcareous; pyritised trails and burrow-mottling including *Chondrites*; poorly fossiliferous with *Pinna* and *Perisphinctes*; passing down with burrow-mottling into — 2.18 — 30.68

Limestone, pale grey, very silty and argillaceous; *Cardioceras tenuiserratum* — 0.18 — 30.86

Mudstone, medium grey with chondritic and other burrow-mottling; pectinid bivalves, *Cardioceras* cf. *schellwieni*, *C. tenuiserratum*, *Perisphinctes*, pentacrinoid columnals, cidarid spines, shell debris; large *Gryphaea* fragments at base; passing down into — 0.84 — 31.70

WWF12
Mudstone, medium grey, extremely silty with much fine plant and shell debris; chondritic and other burrow-mottling; scattered *Lopha* and *Nanogyra*, some serpulid-encrusted, pectinid bivalves and cidarid spine — 0.58 — 32.28

WWF11
Mudstone and limestone, thinly interbedded (generally less than 0.15 m), pale grey and silty, including lumachelles of *Nanogyra nana*, often serpulid and foraminifera encrusted and serpulids; chondritic mottling; other bivalves including arcid, *Chlamys*, *Lopha*, 'myids' in growth position and *Oxytoma*; rare *Cardioceras* cf. *tenuiserratum* and *Perisphinctes*; crinoids and cidarid spines; wood fragments and plant debris — 2.49 — 34.77

Middle Oxfordian
Densiplicatum Zone, Maltonense Subzone
WWF8–WWF10
Mudstone, pale to medium grey, extremely silty; concretionary limestone in top 0.05 m; concretion, possibly phosphatic, at 34.90 m; burrow-mottling including *Chondrites*; bivalves including *Camptonectes*, *Chlamys*, serpulid-encrusted *Gryphaea*, foraminifera-encrusted *Nanogyra*, *Pinna* (some in growth position); pyritised ammonite fragments; cidarid spines; bored *Gryphaea* relict at 34.93 m; heavily mottled at base with *Gryphaea*, large *Pinna* and pyritised *Cardioceras* — 0.21 — 34.98

[WWF5–WWF7 absent]

Lower Oxfordian
Cordatum Zone, Cordatum Subzone
WWF2–WWF4
Mudstone, pale and dark grey, heavily bioturbated with chondritic mottling; serpulids, *Gryphaea* including bored relict, *Lopha*, *Modiolus*, foraminifera-encrusted *Nanogyra*, *Cardioceras* (*C.*) ex gr. *cordatum*, *Hibolithes*; becoming very dark and pyritic downward with *Chlamys*, *Lopha*, *Myophorella*, *Nicaniella*, *Pinna* (in growth position), cardioceratid ammonites and shell debris; basal layer with serpulids, *Gryphaea* and *Lopha*; interburrowed junction at base — 0.38 — 35.36
[WWF1 absent]

UPPER OXFORD CLAY
Mudstone, pale grey, bioturbated with many pyritised trails see p.19

RIDGMONT

A section [SP 980 366] through about 4 m of 'Corallian' strata was logged and collected by Survey officers during construction of the M1 motorway near Ridgmont in 1958. The section is part of Cutting 21 of Smart (1960, p.35) and exposed the West Walton Formation and Ampthill Clay. It has not been possible to map the formations at this locality because of an extensive cover of head.

	Thickness m
WOBURN SANDS (basal pebble bed)	1.1
AMPTHILL CLAY (Tenuiserratum Zone)	
Mudstone, medium and pale grey, silty with pyritised trails, plant-speckling and shell debris (?in burrowfill clusters); *Dicroloma*, *Chlamys*, *Grammatodon*, oyster fragments, *Pinna*, *Thracia*; common *Cardioceras tenuiserratum* with pinkish white shell preservation, also *C. maltonense*, *C. cawtonense* and *Perisphinctes*	1.5
WEST WALTON FORMATION	
Limestone, sandy with *Perisphinctes*	0.15–0.3
Mudstone, 'blue-grey'	0.6
Limestone, 'sandy'	0.15
Mudstone, grey	0.6
Mudstone, 'sandy' with *Gryphaea dilatata*, mostly lightly encrusted with serpulids and, less commonly, *Lopha*	1.2

Micropalaeontological data from samples taken at a depth of about 2 m below the surface at a site [SP 966 358] on the Woburn Experimental Farm, south-west of Ridgmont, suggest that this is the lower part of the Ampthill Clay (Whatley *in* Catt, King and Weir, 1974).

LEIGHTON BUZZARD

During the recent survey, about 3 m of Ampthill Clay (representing AmC13–AmC17) were poorly exposed beneath the Woburn Sands at the Bakers Wood Sand Pit [SP 9230 2860], Heath and Reach. The sequence is interpreted on the basis of specimens collected from spoil. Large *Gryphaea dilatata*, some heavily encrusted with serpulids, *Nanogyra nana*, *Plicatula* and foraminifera, and some enclosing pale calcareous concretions, typify AmC13. Perisphinctid ammonite body chambers (*Decipia?*) preserved in cream-coloured phosphate, cream-coloured phosphatic nodules and a cluster of *Nanogyra nana* and serpulids with a pale phosphatic matrix typify AmC14. Medium and pale grey, shelly mudstones with *Dicroloma*, *Chlamys* (*Radulopecten*), *Grammatodon*, *Nicaniella*, small oysters, *Thracia*, iridescent and pyritised perisphinctid nucleus and fragments, and a small buff-coloured phosphatic nodule are tentatively assigned to AmC15; silty grey mudstone with incipient nodules of cream-coloured phosphate, pyritised pins and trails, and a fauna of *Grammatodon*, *Pinna*, *Protocardia*, *Thracia*, pyritised nuclei and inner whorls of nontuberculate *Amoeboceras* and *Perisphinctes* is tentatively assigned to AmC17.

Some 3 km to the south-west, specimens of a septarian cementstone horizon with large *Perisphinctes* were collected from field brash at Liscombe Park [SP 8926 2632]; this horizon forms a mappable feature for short distances and has been used to map out the local base of the West Walton Formation (see p.22). Further north, a similar septarian cementstone was collected from a ploughed field [SP 8960 2770] and has been taken to represent the same bed.

The topmost beds of the Ampthill Clay were cored in the BGS Ascott Farm Sandpit Borehole [SP 9078 2408] on the south-west side of Leighton Buzzard (see p.30 for details).

CUBLINGTON

Two adherent valves of *Deltoideum delta* with a ?lithophagid boring were collected from field brash [SP 8316 2252] west of Cublington. These almost certainly indicate the outcrop of the upper part of the Ampthill Clay.

KIMMERIDGE CLAY FORMATION

The outcrop of the Kimmeridge Clay is restricted to the south-west corner of the district (Figure 10); elsewhere, the formation is overstepped by Woburn Sands or Gault (Lower Cretaceous). Much of the outcrop is masked by drift deposits and exposure is poor. However, the succession is probably comparable with that on the eastern edge of the Thame district, which adjoins to the south-west (Horton et al., in press).

The Kimmeridge Clay is a sequence of marine mudstones which may be calcareous, kerogen rich (bituminous mudstone and oil shale) or, less commonly, silty or sandy; there are associated thin cementstones, siltstones and sandstones, which occur as tabular beds or doggers. Throughout southern Britain, these lithologies occur in a complex sequence of small-scale rhythms, many of which can be correlated over tens of kilometres. For descriptive purposes, it is convenient to retain the long-standing two-fold division of the formation into Lower Kimmeridge Clay and Upper Kimmeridge Clay although, under modern rules of stratigraphic nomenclature, these 'subformations' have no formal lithostratigraphical status; they can be readily distinguished on the basis of ammonite genera (see below). In the lower part of the Lower Kimmeridge Clay, an idealised rhythm consists of siltstone or silty mudstone overlain by dark grey mudstone and then pale grey calcareous mudstone; in the upper part of the Lower Kimmeridge Clay and the greater part of the Upper Kimmeridge Clay, brownish grey bituminous mudstone or oil shale takes the place of the basal silty lithology.

To the south-west of this district, the Upper Kimmeridge Clay contains beds of sand and silt which are not present at the type locality on the Dorset coast, nor in eastern England where the formation is well known from boreholes. These sands and silts reflect proximity to the London Platform and its fringing reefs in the Late Kimmeridgian; they have been variously known as the Hartwell Clay (Buckman, 1922), Shotover Grit Sands (Buckman, 1922), Shotover Fine Sands (Buckman, 1922), Wheatley Sands (Buckman, 1922), Thame Sands (Buckman, 1926), Elmhurst Silt (Oates, 1991) and Hartwell Silt (Oates, 1991) (see also Arkell, 1947 and Cope, 1978) (Figure 11). There is limited evidence to indicate that these lithologies also occur in the present district but it is uncertain how much of the Upper Kimmeridge Clay is preserved beneath the erosive base of the overlying Portland Formation. The total thickness of

Figure 10 Leighton Buzzard and adjoining district showing Kimmeridge Clay outcrop and localities referred to in text.

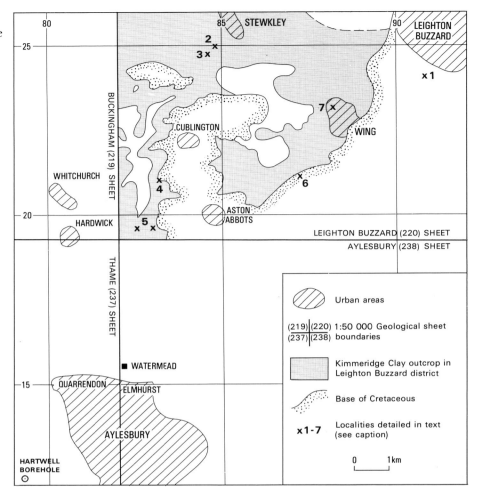

the Kimmeridge Clay is estimated at about 30 m. This is much thinner than the sequence seen in eastern England, where it is over 100 m thick, or in the type sequence in Dorset, where it is over 500 m thick.

The Kimmeridge Clay is highly fossiliferous and at most levels contains abundant ammonites (used as the basis of the standard zonation; Figure 11) and bivalves. Other molluscan groups, echinoderms, brachiopods, serpulids and crustaceans are also present amongst the invertebrate fossils, and there are abundant microfauna and microflora including foraminifera, ostracods, coccoliths and dinoflagellate cysts. Marine vertebrates are also present; records suggest that these were relatively common in the Kimmeridgian seas adjacent to the London Platform. By combining the faunal markers and the rhythmic variation in lithology within the framework of the ammonite zonation, the formation is subdivided into a number of small units (Figure 11). These units or standard beds (KC1– KC49) were originally established in cored borehole sequences in eastern England, and can be recognised widely throughout southern Britain (Gallois and Cox, 1976; Cox and Gallois, 1979, 1981). They have been used to elucidate the stratigraphy in this district, although there remain some problems with the detailed classification of the Upper Kimmeridge Clay sequence, and its correlation with the standard Upper Kimmeridgian ammonite zonation of Cope (1967; 1978). The nearest reference sections for the district are, the Aylesbury sections described by Oates (1991) for the Upper Kimmeridge Clay, and the BGS Hartwell Borehole [SP 7926 1223] for the Lower Kimmeridge Clay (Figures 10 and 11).

The base of the Kimmeridge Clay is taken at a phosphatic nodule bed containing black phosphatic chips and pebbles in a matrix of medium and dark grey shelly mudstone. It rests on pale grey mudstone and cementstone of the Ampthill Clay and there is a striking colour contrast and interburrowing at the contact. The phosphatic nodule bed marks the base of the Lower Kimmeridgian Cymodoce Zone and probably represents a combination of the phosphatic nodule beds of KC5 and KC8; the boundary was proved in the BGS Ascott Farm Sand Pit Borehole [SP 9078 2408] (see Details).

The Kimmeridge Clay was once worked for brickmaking at Stewkley; it was formerly exposed at the bottom of the brickpit at Littleworth, Wing but these sections are no longer visible (see Details). Without fortuitous excavations, the most likely horizons to be detected at outcrop in this drift-covered terrain are the relatively hard cementstones which occur within the Lower Kimmeridge

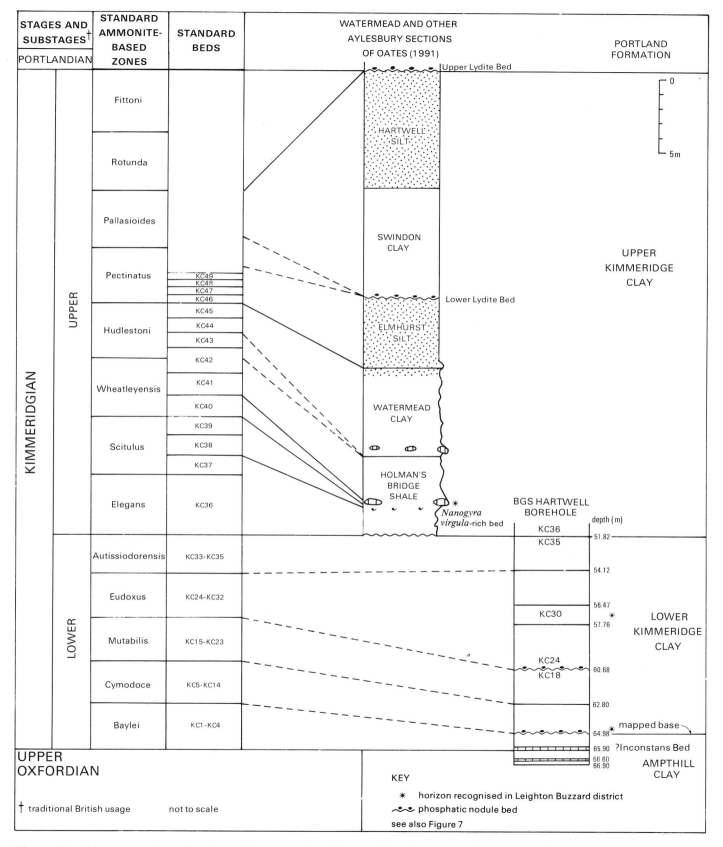

Figure 11 Chronostratigraphical classification of the Kimmeridge Clay, and reference sections for the Leighton Buzzard district.

Clay and lower part of the Upper Kimmeridge Clay. These are often developed as variably silty, shelly, septarian doggers. At least two such horizons have been recognised near Aston Abbotts, Cublington and Wing (Figure 10; see Details). North-west of Quarrendon [SP 80 15], to the south-west of the district, the stratigraphical position of the lower of these two horizons is well established in KC30 of the Eudoxus Zone by its fauna. KC30 is one of the most readily identifiable units of the Lower Kimmeridge Clay. As well as cementstone doggers, its pale calcareous mudstones contain abundant specimens of the small striate oyster *Nanogyra virgula*, which may occur in cemented masses (= Virgula Limestone), and the Crussoliceras Band (a widespread ammonite marker bed), together with a characteristic Eudoxus Zone ammonite fauna of *Aspidoceras, Aulacostephanus, Laevaptychus* and *Sutneria*. Comparison with a section at Watermead [SP 822 157] on the northern outskirts of Aylesbury (Oates, 1991) and the BGS Hartwell Borehole suggests that the higher cementstone horizon recognised in this district represents KC40 of the Upper Kimmeridgian Wheatleyensis Zone (Figure 11; see Details).

Details

BGS Ascott Farm Sand Pit Borehole, Leighton Buzzard

The boundary of the Kimmeridge Clay and Ampthill Clay was proved in mudstone recovered from beneath the Woburn Sands in a BGS borehole at Ascott Farm Sandpit [SP 9078 2408]. The following sequence was recorded in U4 undisturbed percussion samples between 26.75 m and the final depth of 32.30 m:

	Thickness m	Depth to base m
LOWER GREENSAND		26.75
KIMMERIDGE CLAY		
Mudstone, medium and pale grey, sparsely shelly with *Lingula*, scattered iridescent raseniid ammonite fragments, partially pyritised turriform gastropods and rare small bivalves	1.25	28.00
Mudstone, pale to medium grey with iridescent shell fragments including ammonites; becoming darker below 28.20 m with chondritic mottling, shell-debris-rich and silty burrowfills, scattered black phosphatic pebbles, oysters, *Thracia*; very shelly to base with marked interburrowing	0.50	28.50
AMPTHILL CLAY		
Mudstone and cementstone, pale and very pale grey, sparsely shelly with scattered serpulids and shell fragments including oysters	0.30	28.80
Mudstone, medium and pale grey, intensely burrow-mottled in upper part; moderately shelly with partially pyritised, iridescent perisphinctid ammonite inner whorls and nuclei, serpulids, *Dicroloma*, arcid, nuculoid and pectinid bivalves, *Oxytoma, Thracia*, oysters including *Deltoideum delta* with		

	Thickness m	Depth to base m
plaster at 30.15 m; pyritised trails; cream-coloured phosphatic patches at 30.65 m, black phosphatic pebble and chip at 31.15 m and 31.25 m	2.90	31.70
Mudstone, medium grey with cream-coloured phosphatic pebbles and burrowfills at 31.75 m and 31.80 m; partially phosphatised macroconch *Amoeboceras* at 32.00 m, oysters and *Thracia*	0.60	32.30

The ammonite fauna of the Kimmeridge Clay consists of fragmentary raseniids indicative of the Cymodoce Zone (probably KC9–KC14); the phosphatic nodule bed at its base (28.50 m) probably represents a combined KC5 and KC8. The Inconstans Bed, which is traditionally taken as the basal Kimmeridge Clay and Kimmeridgian Stage marker, and which has been recognised at various localities to the west, is cut out beneath this nodule bed.

Stewkley

The Kimmeridge Clay was worked in three pits at Stewkley [SP 846 248, SP 848 250 and SP 856 249] (Buckinghamshire County Museum, 1980); records and collected material from the first two provide the best direct information on the Kimmeridge Clay of the district.

Hedge's pit [SP 848 250] exposed highly fossiliferous 'shaley clay' (possibly oil shale) with a thin seam of sand. The locality has been recorded by a number of authors (Fitton, 1836, p.292; Woodward, 1895, p.169; Davies, 1901, pp.139–140, 1915, p.91) and there is a small amount of fossil material in the BGS collections. The faunal list includes *Lingula*, '*Discinisca*' [= the limpet-type gastropod *Pseudorhytidopilus*; Wignall, 1990], '*Liostrea*', *Modiolus*, *Nanogyra virgula* (fairly common), *Protocardia*, *Laevaptychus*, *Amoeboceras* (*Nannocardioceras*), *Aulacostephanus* ex gr. *eudoxus*, fish scales and reptile bones. The combination of lithology and fauna indicates Lower Kimmeridge Clay belonging to the upper part of the Eudoxus Zone or the lower part of the Autissiodorensis Zone (KC31–KC34, but most probably KC31–KC32). The Kimmeridge Clay at this pit was affected by folding, believed to be of glacial origin (Davies, 1914, p.151, pl. IVB).

A younger sequence, exposed at Bliss' pit [SP 846 248] (Plate 2), was better known for the large septaria that it yielded than its fossils. These septarian doggers were apparently up to 1 m in diameter and displayed fine 'cone-in-cone' structures on their surfaces and beautiful nail-head spar calcite in their septae. The only published fossil record is '*Discinisca*' (see above) although there were clearly others which were 'too much crushed for satisfactory identification' or easy collecting (Davies, 1901, p.140; 1915, p.91). There are manuscript records by Pringle in BGS archives (dated 1922) of *Nanogyra virgula*, *Protocardia* and large 'perisphinctid' ammonites 'probably referable to *Gravesia*' (Oates, 1991). The size of the doggers and the faunal records suggest that the doggers most likely correlate with the lower dogger horizon recorded by Oates (1991) in the Upper Kimmeridge Clay of Watermead. This horizon is known to occur throughout the Thame district and its persistence is indicated by the fact that the doggers are regularly penetrated in small diameter cored boreholes. At Watermead, they contain an ammonite fauna of the Wheatleyensis Zone; they are believed to represent KC40 (see also Cublington, Aston Abbotts and Wing below).

Plate 2 Septarian nodule in Kimmeridge Clay, Bliss's Pit, Stewkley [SP 846 248] in 1914. The large septarian nodule may represent the widespread dogger horizon, which forms a persistent marker bed low in the Upper Kimmeridge Clay (Wheatleyensis Zone; KC40) of Oxfordshire and Buckinghamshire. (British Association photograph 8150, T W Reader; now deposited in BGS archives).

CUBLINGTON

Specimens from two cementstone horizons were recovered from a ditch section [SP 8312 2105 to SP 8324 2105] south-west of Cublington. The western end of the ditch (at SP 8312 2105 and 8315 2105) yielded assorted loose valves and a few complete specimens of *Nanogyra virgula*. Pieces of grey, silty, shelly cementstone collected at SP 8317 2105 contained common shell fragments (mainly indeterminate bivalves but including *N. virgula*, *Protocardia?* and a serpulid); these have been tentatively assigned to KC30 in the Lower Kimmeridge Clay. To the east (at SP 8324 2105), pieces of a similar but weakly septarian cementstone yielded common small shell fragments (mainly indeterminate bivalves), together with *Corbulomima?*, a large lucinid (*Discomiltha?*), a moderately large pectinid (*Entolium?*), *Pleuromya*, *Protocardia?* and impressions of pectinatitid ammonite fragments; these have been assigned to KC40 in the Upper Kimmeridge Clay.

ASTON ABBOTTS

Small pieces of cementstone collected from field brash to the west of Aston Abbotts also probably represent KC30 and KC40, as at Cublington (see above). A piece of silty cementstone with shell fragments, including a 'perisphinctid' ammonite and a serpulid, collected at [SP 8256 1961] is tentatively assigned to KC30; small pieces of septarian cementstone with tiny shell fragments, including *Protocardia?*, collected at [SP 8296 1959] are tentatively assigned to KC40.

WING

Pieces of shelly cementstone were collected from the bed of a stream [SP 872 211], south-west of Wing by C R Bristow. The specimens compare well with those from the eastern end of the ditch section near Cublington (see above) and, like them, they are assigned to KC40 in the Upper Kimmeridge Clay. As well as abundant but mainly indeterminate shell fragments, the cementstone yielded *Pectinatites*, *Corbulomima* and a large lucinid (*Discomiltha?*). Cementstones and septarian nodules, up to 0.6 m diameter, in a nearby stream [SP 875 217 to 885 215] (Bristow, 1963), are probably from the same horizon.

This horizon is also believed to have been exposed at the bottom of the brickpit at Littleworth, Wing [SP 881 232] where, according to Green (in Woodward, 1895, p.169; in Jukes-Browne, 1900, p.278), 1.8 m of stiff, bluish-black clay with large septaria and lignite were seen below the Gault. Fossils recorded include *Myophorella*, 'perisphinctid' ammonites, a belemnite but 'chiefly reptilian bones' (Davies, 1901, p.140). The glacial clays of this pit also yielded quite an extensive derived Jurassic fauna (Bristow, 1963); the belemnite listed above may, in fact, be from these clays rather than the Kimmeridge Clay. The Gault exposure at this pit is discussed later.

The highest beds of the Kimmeridge Clay preserved beneath the Upper Lydite Bed at the base of the overlying Portland Formation were augered [SP 8676 2258] to the west of Old Park Farm (Wyatt et al., 1988). They were described as silty, slightly sandy, olive-grey clay (0.4 m) on medium grey clay (0.35 m). Bristow (1963) assigned similar silty clays, which he recovered by augering beneath the Upper Lydite Bed nearby, to the Hartwell Clay (Pallasioides Zone) but the possibility that they represent a lower unit of silty and sandy clays in the Pectinatus Zone cannot be ruled out.

PORTLAND AND PURBECK FORMATIONS (INCLUDING WHITCHURCH SAND)

The outcrop of the Portland Formation is mainly restricted to a plateau area of about 4 km² to the west of Wing [SP 88 23], and is largely shrouded by drift deposits; small outcrops occur in the adjacent valley slopes. The eastern extremity of another outcrop, north of Dunton [SP 82 24], encroaches on to the western margin of the district at Newlands Farm [SP 821 247]. These areas are the most northerly occurrences of the Portland Formation in Britain (Arkell, 1933). The outcrop of the overlying Purbeck Formation is even more restricted; it is confined to a small area around Warren Farm [SP 851 243] in the north-western corner of the main Portland outcrop.

Due to the drift cover and limited outcrop, it has not been possible to establish the full succession within the Portland Formation nor to confirm the sequence described by Bristow (1968). However, it is clear that the sequence is similar to that in the Thame district and the classification adopted there (Horton et al., in preparation) is also applied to sections in this district. There are two members; the lower, Portland Sand, member comprises the Upper Lydite Bed and Glauconitic Beds. The upper, Portland Stone, member comprises the Aylesbury (or Rubbly) Limestone, Crendon Sand and Creamy Limestones. The overlying Purbeck Formation is poorly exposed and was observed in situ at only one locality during the recent survey (see Details). The lower part, the Purbeck Limestone, consists of bedded limestones with interbedded clay and marl; the upper part, the Whitchurch Sand, consists of fine-grained sands with a few dark clay beds. In the adjoining Thame district where exposure is better, the Whitchurch Sand has been mapped as a separate formation, and a full discussion of this unit and its age (Jurassic or Cretaceous) is given in the memoir for that district (Horton et al., in preparation). The thickness of the Portland Formation is about 12 m; the overlying Purbeck Formation (including Whitchurch Sand) is 2 to 3 m.

The base of the Portland Formation is marked by the Upper Lydite Bed which consists of rounded black chert pebbles ('lydites'), phosphatic nodules and worn fossils derived from the underlying Kimmeridge Clay, set in a matrix of glauconitic silt and sandy clay which locally passes into limestone. In this district, the bed is thought to be about 0.4 m thick. The base of the Purbeck Formation is marked by a distinctive, 0.25 m-thick, fissile, ostracod-rich limestone known as the 'Pendle'.

The most common fossils found in the Portland Formation are characteristically large bivalves such as *Camptonectes lamellosus*, *Isognomon bouchardi*, *Protocardia dissimilis* and trigoniids including *Myophorella incurva* and *Laevitrigonia gibbosa*, and whorl fragments of large ammonites. Ammonites are used as the basis of the standard zonation but their large size and weight, and the logistical problems of recovery and identification that this creates, means that, in practice, they provide limited stratigraphical control compared with the underlying clay formations. As elsewhere in Oxfordshire and Buckinghamshire, the Portland Formation of this district is believed to span three ammonite-based zones: Glaucolithus Zone (Upper Lydite Bed and part of the Glauconitic Beds), Okusensis Zone (parts of the Glauconitic Beds and overlying Aylesbury, or Rubbly, Limestone) and Kerberus Zone (part of the Aylesbury, or Rubbly, Limestone, the Crendon Sand and Creamy Limestones) (Wimbledon and Cope, 1978; Wimbledon, 1980). The boundary between the Portland and Purbeck formations is believed to fall within the Kerberus Zone. The latter formation does not have an ammonite fauna because its sediments are not fully marine, but brackish and freshwater gastropods and bivalves are present. However, for biostratigraphical purposes, the most important fossil group is the ostracods.

Information on the Portland and Purbeck formations of the district comes almost exclusively from the quarry at Warren Farm, Stewkley which was first described by Fitton (1836) and later by Woodward (1895), Davies (1915), Barker (1966), Bristow (1968) and Radley (1980). There is also a limited amount of other data from auger-holes, old wells and various small pits. The exposure of fossiliferous Glauconitic Beds in a stream bed at Wing Sewage Farm [ST 855 220], reported by Bristow (1963; 1968), is now believed to be an ex-situ occurrence.

Details

WARREN FARM QUARRY, STEWKLEY

Working ceased at the Warren Farm quarry (Plate 3) many years ago and only about 3 m of Portland Stone (Creamy Limestones overlying Crendon Sand) and up to about 2 m of Purbeck Formation (Whitchurch Sand on Purbeck Limestone) were seen during the recent survey (Wyatt et al., 1988). A composite section through the Portland and Purbeck formations at this locality, based on all records, is given below. Bed numbers given in square brackets relate to Bristow (1968) for the Purbeck Formation, and Davies (1915) for the Portland Formation.

	Thickness m
PURBECK FORMATION	
Whitchurch Sand	
Disturbed block of carstone with marine bivalves (Bristow, 1963)	0–0.15
[14] Sand, red and yellow, buff and ochreous, fine-grained, silty; sharp planar base	0.46
[13] Clay, brown and grey, carbonaceous, shelly	0.03–0.05
Purbeck Limestone	
[12] Marl, buff and pale grey	0.18
[11] Limestone, marly	0.10
[10] Limestone	0.10
[9] Shell bed with ostracods	0.01
[8] Limestone, marly	0.25–0.30
[7] Clay, grey	0.30
[6] Marl, shelly with ostracods	0.03–0.05
[5] Marl, clayey, dark grey	0.13
[4] Marl, clayey, pale grey	0.15
[3] Limestone, fissile [= Pendle]	0.25
PORTLAND FORMATION, PORTLAND STONE MEMBER	
Creamy Limestones	
[11] Shell marl, greyish brown; bivalves including mytilids, oysters, trigoniids	0.08
[10] Limestone, marly, chalky white; *Laevitrigonia*	0.38
[9] Clay, shaly, grey	0.15
[8] Marl, shaly, white and yellow, very shelly; oyster fragments and small gastropods	0.25
[7] Limestone, pale grey, hard, fine-grained, massive, shell-detrital; casts of trigoniid bivalves	0.08–0.15
[6] Marl, pale grey, laminated, shelly	0.15
[5] Limestone, white, very irregularly jointed; fossils including trigoniid bivalves	1.12
[4] Limestone, hard, grey	0.23

(*Camptonectes lamellosus*, *Isognomon bouchardi*, *Protocardia dissimilis*, other bivalves and gastropods,

Plate 3   Purbeck and Portland formations exposed at Warren Farm Quarry, Stewkley in 1914. The figure stands on top of the Crendon Sand of the Portland Formation, which is overlain by the Creamy Limestones (about 3 m thick), with the Purbeck Formation above. (British Association photography 7633; T W Reader; now deposited in BGS archives).

and unspecified large ammonites also recorded from within beds [4] to [11])

Crendon Sand

[3]	Sandstone, calcareous with fossil casts and rare lydites	0.23
[2]	Sand, fine-grained, slightly glauconitic	2.74

Aylesbury (or Rubbly) Limestone

[1]	Limestone with large ammonites ['*Olcostephanus triplicatus*' ? = *Galbanites* (*Kerberites*)] and probably *Isognomon bouchardi*	seen 0.6

OLD PARK FARM, WING

Limestone from the basal part of the Portland Formation was reputedly dug from two small pits [SP 8695 2273 and 8698 2267] near Old Park Farm, Wing (Wyatt et al., 1988). By augering and with the aid of soil brash and deep ploughing, Bristow (1963) established a sequence in the Portland Formation and, tentatively, in the overlying Purbeck Formation but the recent survey suggests that the latter is unlikely to be preserved beneath the Till except in the area immediately south-east of Warren Farm quarry (see above). The sequence hereabouts, based on all records, is:

	Thickness m
PORTLAND FORMATION, PORTLAND STONE MEMBER	
Creamy Limestones	
Limestone, pale grey, very fossiliferous	2.7
Crendon Sand	
Sand, mustard-yellow, fine-grained, silty	1.8
PORTLAND FORMATION, PORTLAND SAND MEMBER	
Limestone, very glauconitic with bands of glauconitic marly clay and sand	2.7

	Thickness m
Sand, red and green mottled or ochreous, fine-grained, silty with chert pebbles up to 3 mm in diameter near base (Upper Lydite Bed)	0.6–0.9

KIMMERIDGE CLAY (?Hartwell Silt) below

WELLS AND OTHER AUGER-HOLES

Wells at North Cottesloe [SP 860 233] and Red House Farm [SP 858 235] proved the Portland Formation beneath Till and Gault (Woodward, 1895; Bristow, 1963). At North Cottesloe, Portland Stone was proved at a depth of about 6 m. At both localities, records suggest Creamy Limestones on Crendon Sand on Aylesbury (or Rubbly) Limestone.

An auger-hole [SP 8515 2241] sited close to the base of the Crendon Sand near Lockharts proved:

	Thickness m
HEAD	1.2
PORTLAND FORMATION, PORTLAND SAND MEMBER	
Aylesbury (or Rubbly) Limestone	
Clay, dark grey, laminated with silt partings; locally silty at base	0.3
Marl, pale grey	0.3
Limestone	

The limestone encountered in this auger-hole was formerly dug nearby [SP 8538 2218], and solifluction debris from this bed was noted in a ditch cut to the east [SP 8546 2211] (Wyatt et al., 1988).

FOUR
Cretaceous: Woburn Sands

Named after the Woburn area within the district, the Woburn Sands crop out eastwards from Leighton Buzzard across the district to Clophill, and form a prominent north-east-trending escarpment rising above the subdued topography of the Upper Jurassic plain to the north (Figure 12). A deep embayment in the escarpment is present in the Ampthill area. Where the sands are overlain by till the escarpment feature is less well defined. West of Leighton Buzzard the formation thins abruptly beneath the overlying Gault, and is absent to the west of Wing. This westerly termination appears to coincide with a major north-south-trending basement lineament (Figure 30). The formation is of late Aptian and early Albian age and is approximately equivalent to the Sandgate Beds and Folkestone Beds of the Lower Greensand of the Weald. The Woburn Sands rest with marked unconformity on gently folded Upper Jurassic strata, the Oxford Clay, West Walton, Ampthill Clay and Kimmeridge Clay formations. Thus, there is a considerable sedimentary hiatus representing much of the Early Cretaceous period. Structural contours on the base of the formation show an irregular, deeply eroded base.

The sediments which make up the Woburn Sands are generally quartzose sands of variable grain size and tend to be ferruginous and glauconitic; they are usually oxidised to ochreous colours in the weathered zone. The sands are dug for building and industrial purposes; to the north and south of Leighton Buzzard there are several large working pits (Figure 13), and also some pits around Clophill. The sections in these pits and those in the fuller's earth workings at Woburn and Clophill provide the main source of stratigraphical data for the formation, which is otherwise only poorly exposed. Lenticular seams of fuller's earth (calcium smectite) of commercial importance occur within the sands near Woburn and Clophill. Historically, phosphatic nodules associated with a conglomeratic basal bed have been dug locally as a source of fertiliser. The nodules indicate periods of minimal deposition and persistent winnowing of the sea floor; some contain derived Upper Jurassic fossils.

The sands were laid down in a shallow shelf sea, subjected to considerable tidal influences. This sea covered much of southern England in late Early Cretaceous times, when a southern sea in the Wealden area flooded the south Midlands to join with the Boreal Ocean (Casey, 1963).

LITHOSTRATIGRAPHY

Several distinct lithological units are recognised within the working sand pits near Leighton Buzzard (Figure 14)

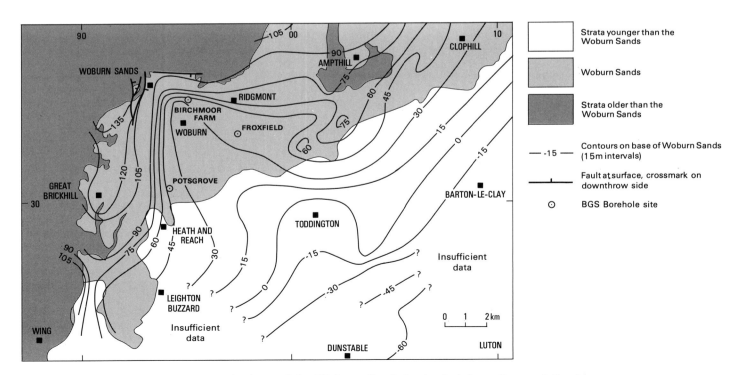

Figure 12 Structural contours on the base of the Woburn Sands in the Leighton Buzzard district.

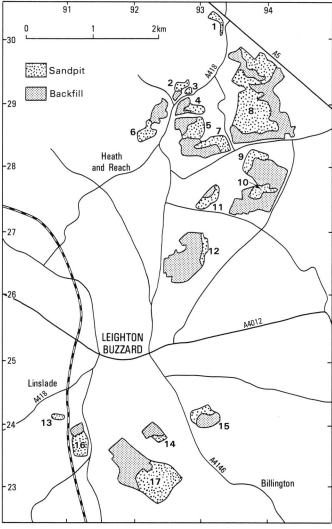

1 A5 Pit
2 Hall's Fox Corner Pit
3 Buckland's Fox Corner Pit
4 Stone Lane Pit
5 Bryants Lane Pit
6 Baker's Wood Pit
7 Reach Lane Pit
8 Double Arches Pit
9 Mundays Hill Pit

10 Nine Acres Pit
11 New Trees Pit
12 Chamberlains Barn Pit
13 Ascott Farm Pit
14 Brickyard Pit
15 Pratt's Pit
16 Tiddenfoot New Pit
17 Grovebury Pit

Figure 13 Location of the principal pits in the Woburn Sands around Leighton Buzzard.

(Bristow, 1963; Shephard-Thorn et al., 1986; Wyatt et al., 1988). However, they cannot be mapped at the surface, but are used here as informal descriptive terms. From base to top these are: 'Brown Sands', 'Silver Sands', 'Silty Beds' and 'Red Sands'. Eyers (1991) proposed a two-fold division into a Lower Woburn Sands Formation, equivalent to the 'Brown Sands', and an Upper Woburn Sands Formation, equivalent to the 'Silver Sands', 'Silty Beds', and 'Red Sands', but these formations do not form map-

pable units and have not been adopted here. Indeed, the lateral lithological variation within the Woburn Sands is such that it is unlikely that any subdivision within the sands could be traced for more than a few kilometres.

The 'Brown Sands', exposed in pits to the north of Leighton Buzzard, comprise up to 45 m of ferruginous, fine- to medium-grained, cross-bedded quartz sands with glauconite and other dark grains. The brown colour is due to an abundance of hydrated iron oxide associated with clay partings and trace fossil burrows. Irregular sheets of 'iron pan' and burrows in ferruginous preservation are conspicuous on weathered quarry faces. A bed of sandy, pebbly (quartz and chert), ferruginous clay separates the 'Brown sands' from the overlying 'Silver Sands' and forms a prominent marker bed in several of the sand pits. The clay bed represents a nonsequence, and was followed by a transgressive episode.

The 'Silver Sands', from 6 m to 15 m, thick consist of white, pebbly, well-sorted and well-rounded, medium- to coarse-grained, almost pure quartz sands with little fine-grained material (Plate 4). The pebbles include chert, 'lydite' and quartz and are up to 7 mm in diameter. In places, 'carstone reefs' occur within the 'Silver Sands' (Plate 1). These are sandstones with a ferruginous cement and form linear features; they may be 10 to 25 m in width and 2 to 3 m in height. Abundant fossil wood fragments occur within the sands; strong planar cross-bedding, commonly showing reversal of direction, is indicative of deposition in tidal conditions.

The 'Silty Beds', up to 4.5 m thick, are present locally. These comprise mottled silt, silty sand and subordinate clay; all are characterised by carbonaceous and ferruginous streaks and bands, and sporadic coarse pebbly (mainly quartz) lenses. They are overlain abruptly by the 'Red Sands' except around Shenley Hill, north of Leighton Buzzard, where the Shenley Limestone and associated ironstone, within the basal Gault (Chapter 5), overlie the 'Silty Beds'.

In the north, the 'Red Sands' (Plates 5 and 6), up to 5 m thick, occupy channels cut through the 'Silty Beds' into the underlying 'Silver Sands'. Elsewhere they overlie the 'Silver Sands', and progressively replace them southwards towards Leighton Buzzard. South of the town, the 'Red Sands' are up to 11 m thick and rest directly on the 'Brown Sands'. In this area the 'Brown Sands' are fine-grained, laminated and contain thin interbeds of black silty clay; they are known locally as 'Compo'. The 'Red Sands' are medium- to coarse-grained, limonitic sands, usually slightly silty, and commonly pebbly, containing well-rounded quartz, quartzite and chert pebbles (Kirkaldy, 1947) up to about 5 mm in diameter. Concentrations of dark coffee-coloured, highly polished and well-rounded goethite grains diversify the sands with dark streaks and bands picking out cross-bedding structures. Impersistent bands of ferruginous nodules and boxstone concretions are also common. Rarely, thin seams of pipeclay or partings of clay are present. Many beds are strongly bioturbated, giving the sands a mottled appearance. Additionally, discrete burrow traces, up to 5 cm in diameter, stand out boldly on weathered sur-

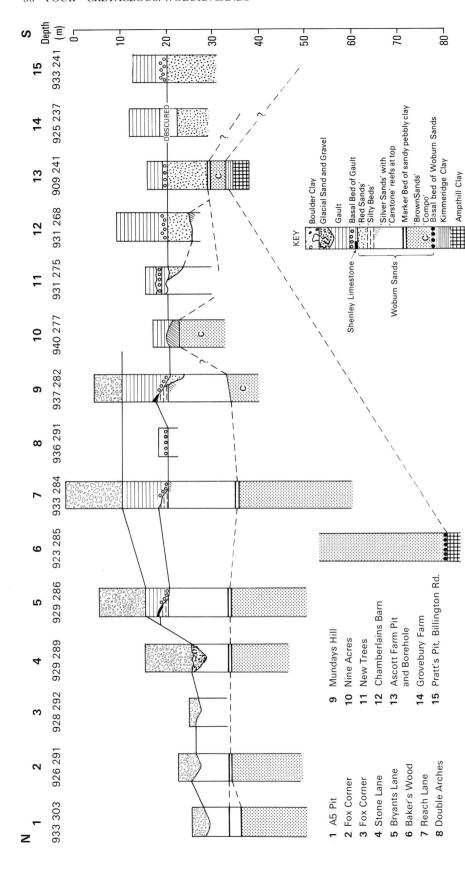

Figure 14 Lithostratigraphical correlation of pits in the Woburn Sands around Leighton Buzzard.

Plate 4   Large-scale cross-bedding in 'Silver Sands' division of the Woburn Sands, New Trees Quarry, Shenley Hill [SP 931 275] (Joseph Arnold & Sons Ltd). Gault clay overburden has been removed to allow the extraction of medium- to coarse-grained, slightly pebbly sands (A14474).

faces. Much larger, vertical columns with U-shaped distortions of the bedding are locally numerous; these may represent crustacean burrows (*Diplocraterion* type). Although typically reddish brown, the 'Red Sands' are predominantly yellow, pale buff and orange in sand pits to the south of Leighton Buzzard.

In the northern and eastern part of the district, the Woburn Sands appear to be broadly comparable with the 'Brown Sands' of the Leighton Buzzard area, except that the overall grain size is finer (Hallsworth, 1986), and some of the pebbles are several centimetres in diameter. The pebbles are mostly of quartz and quartzite, but black, smooth, very shiny pebbles, known as 'lydites', are locally abundant, for example, in Woburn Park [SP 9630 3505]. A thin section of one of the 'lydites' showed a quartz-schorlite hornfels similar to those found within the aureoles of the south-west of England granite intrusions (Catt et al., 1974).

A basal conglomerate to the formation has been recorded in the Brickhill, Ridgmont and Ampthill areas,

and also noted in several borehole logs throughout the district. The conglomerate, which is both phosphatic and fossiliferous, is described more fully below (p.45). Conglomeratic horizons have also been recorded at higher levels within the Woburn Sands, for example in the BGS Froxfield Borehole [SP 9737 3337] to the east of Woburn, and in the Potton area several kilometres east of the present district.

FULLER'S EARTH

Fuller's earth (calcium smectite) occurs as impersistent, lenticular seams at several horizons within the Woburn Sands, and has been worked commercially to the south of Woburn Sands village and to the east of Clophill. In the Woburn area the fuller's earth is yellowish green, but in the Clophill area it is typically dark bluish grey. The variation in colour is almost certainly due to greater oxidation of the fuller's earth in the Woburn area, which

Plate 5 Cross-bedded 'Red Sands' of the Woburn Sands, Pratt's Pit, Leighton Buzzard [SP 931 240] (Joseph Arnold & Sons Ltd). The bedding is accentuated by the concentration of dark clay and goethite ooliths on certain foresets in the medium- to coarse-grained sands (A14485).

stands above the level of the local water table; whereas around Clophill, the fuller's earth occurs below it.

The presence of unworn crystals of zircon, sphene, biotite, and feldspar in the fuller's earth clays is evidence of their volcanic derivation (Cowperthwaite et al., 1972; Jeans et al., 1977). The thinner beds, a few tens of centimetres thick, may result from primary ash falls, but the thicker beds of commercial earth commonly show planar bedding and low-angle cross-bedding, produced by the reworking and concentration of ash in shallow lagoons, perhaps as a result of rapid erosion from an adjoining landmass. The volcanic vents from which the ash was derived have not been positively identified; Cowperthwaite et al. (1972) suggested the Wolf Rock in the Western Approaches as a possible source, but more recent work (Dixon et al., 1981) on North Sea sediments, favours an easterly derivation.

In the area to the south of Woburn Sands village, the outcrop of the worked seam, here referred to as the Main Seam, extends from Aspley Heath [SP 927 352],

across the northern end of Old Wavendon Heath, through Aspley Wood, to north of Birchmoor Green [SP 943 340] (Figure 15). To the south, the fuller's earth lies beneath a thick sheet of till. The Main Seam has been extensively quarried and most of the former workings are backfilled with sand, and replanted with conifers. The Main Seam attains a maximum thickness of about 3.75 m, dipping to the south-west. It is currently worked by Steetley Minerals Ltd, west of the A5130 [SP 932 345], beneath an overburden of between 25 and 42 m of sand (Plates 12 and 13).

A section through the Aspley Heath area (Cowperthwaite et al., 1972, fig. 6), shows that the south-westerly dipping Main Seam is truncated to the west against the east-north-easterly dipping upper surface of the underlying Oxford Clay.

Within the present workings an upper seam of fuller's earth, less than 1 m thick, and some 24 m above the Main Seam was visible in 1985. It thinned and died out eastwards within the confines of the quarry. The seam,

Plate 6   Working face in 'Red Sands' division of the Woburn Sands, Pratt's Pit, Leighton Buzzard [SP 931 240] (Joseph Arnold & Sons Ltd). Up to 8 m of medium- to coarse-grained, slightly pebbly sands are extracted below Gault overburden. Concentrations of dark clay and goethite ooliths on the foresets pick out cross-bedding typical of sand waves in shallow tidal seas (A14484).

which was less pure than the Main Seam, contained an appreciable quantity of sand grains, and was removed as waste with the overburden.

In 1986 two boreholes were drilled by BGS to investigate the stratigraphy of the lower part of the Woburn Sands in the Woburn Sands area (Moorlock and Wyatt, 1986). The BGS Woburn Sands A Borehole [SP 9308 3438] (Figure 16) was drilled in the bottom of the working quarry, and proved seams of fuller's earth at 13.43–13.56 m and at 21.75–21.77 m depth, 9.2 m and 17.5 m below the base of the Main Seam respectively.

The BGS Woburn Sands B Borehole [SP 9323 3526], drilled to the east of the A5130 road, proved 4 seams of fuller's earth below the main seam (Figure 16). Two thin seams, each 5 cm thick, occur at 13.95 and 15.90 m depth. The upper seam has a mica–smectite assemblage with the Ca-smectite showing some random interstratification with mica (Hallsworth, 1986). Quartz and zeolite

are also present. The lower seam consists predominantly of quartz, tridymite and mica, with only a trace of smectite. The presence of tridymite and zeolite probably indicate alteration of original volcanic components, although the presence of quartz and the mixed-layer clays is indicative of a significant detrital component. A third seam, 1.25 m thick, proved at 19.73 m depth, consists essentially of pure Ca-smectite with traces of zeolite and quartz. A further seam of pure fuller's earth, 0.38 m thick, was encounterd at 31.61 m depth. Both boreholes were terminated within the Woburn Sands due to drilling difficulties.

Seams of fuller's earth, generally less than 1 m thick and lying stratigraphically below the Main Seam, have also been recorded in the logs of several water wells (SP93NW 50, SP93NW 56, SP93NW 58) beneath the villages of Woburn Sands and Aspley Guise (Figure 15). One of these seams, about 10 m above the local base of

Figure 15 Extent of the main fuller's earth bed, near Woburn.

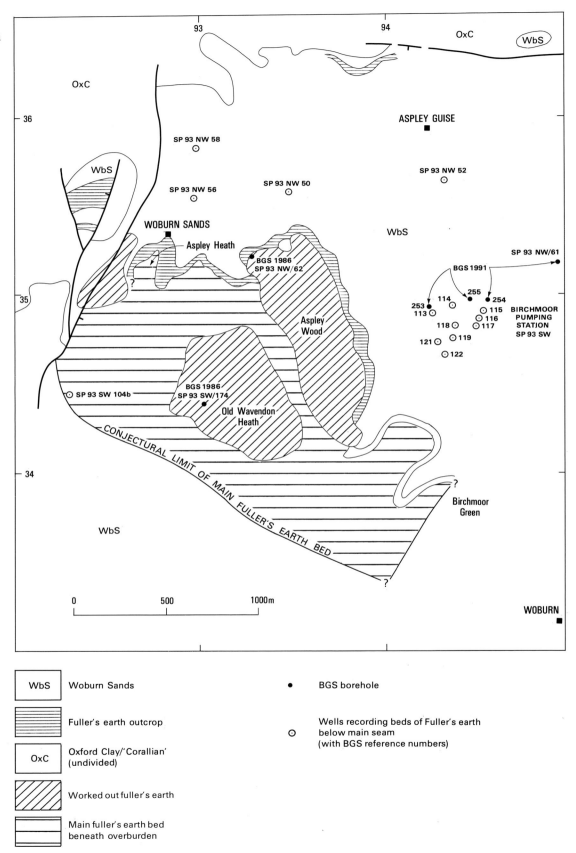

WbS	Woburn Sands
	Fuller's earth outcrop
OxC	Oxford Clay/'Corallian' (undivided)
	Worked out fuller's earth
	Main fuller's earth bed beneath overburden

● BGS borehole

⊙ Wells recording beds of Fuller's earth below main seam (with BGS reference numbers)

Figure 16 Correlation of fuller's earth beds in the Woburn Sands, near Woburn.

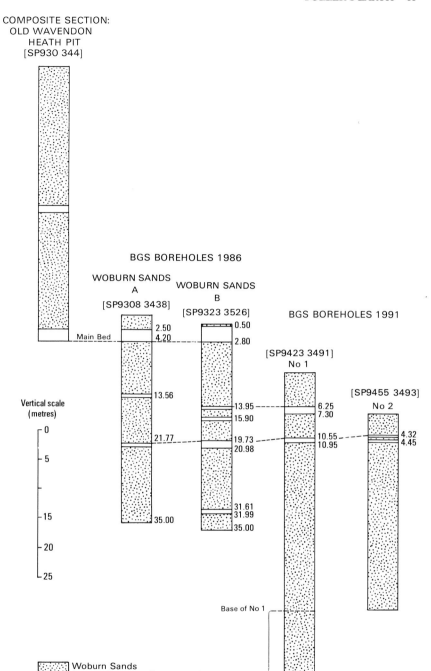

the Woburn Sands, crops out at Aspley Guise, and was formerly exposed in a sand pit [SP 9406 3632]. The seam appears to be very variable in thickness, ranging from 0.15 to 1.83 m (Cameron, 1892; Rastall, 1919).

Some exceptionally thick seams of fuller's earth were recorded in the drillers logs of wells at the Birchmoor Pumping Station [SP 944 348] (see Wyatt et al., 1988, fig. 18), but recent boreholes (SP93NW 161, SP93SW 253, 254, 255) drilled by BGS (Moorlock and Highley, 1991) adjacent to the pumping station failed to detect the thick seams, although a number of minor seams were encountered, and it must be concluded that the earlier logs are inaccurate. A tentative correlation of the seams of fuller's earth in the Woburn area is given in Figure 16. Abridged logs of all recent BGS boreholes in the Woburn Sands formation appear in Appendix 2.

Two seams of fuller's earth, bounded by faults to the east and west, crop out within a small outlier of Woburn Sands to the west of Woburn Sands village, but the relationship of these seams to the Main Seam is not clear.

At Clophill, the worked seam has a maximum thickness of about 3.1 m and lies some 17 m above the base of the Woburn Sands. In the northern part of the quarry a second seam, irregular, and with a maximum thickness of just over one metre, is present about 2.5 m above the worked seam. The higher seam is of low grade and is removed as waste with the sand overburden. Traced southwards within the pit, the upper seam is truncated by an erosion surface characterised by pebbles that include phosphatic nodules, and rolled ammonite fragments of Upper Jurassic derivation (Figure 17).

The BGS Speedsdairy Farm No. 1 Borehole [TL 1146 3901] drilled to the east of the Clophill fuller's earth pit, at Beadlow, proved a 0.4 m-thick seam of fuller's earth at 21 m depth. The BGS Speedsdairy Farm No. 2 Borehole [TL 1108 3877] was sited some 450 m west-south-west of No. 1 borehole towards the working pit, but this failed to prove any fuller's earth (Appendix 2).

Only a few very minor occurrences of fuller's earth have been recorded between Woburn and Clophill, mainly from exploratory drilling (Moorlock and Highley, 1991).

A minor occurrence of low-grade fuller's earth was noted in the basal layers of the Woburn Sands in the Bakers Wood Sand Pit [SP 921 286] (p.47) in 1988.

THICKNESS VARIATIONS OF THE WOBURN SANDS

The Woburn Sands is very variable in thickness (Wyatt et al., 1988; Eyers, 1991; Ruffell and Wignall, 1990). The greatest proved thickness of 88.65 m was recorded in the BGS Potsgrove Borehole [SP 9411 3069] to the southwest of Woburn (Appendix 2); however, drilling commenced below the top of the formation and the total thickness, hereabouts, is estimated to be at least 120 m. A well [SP 9411 3069] near Woburn proved 85 m, but likewise commenced below the top of the formation. Just east of Leighton Buzzard there are about 60 m of sands, but the thickness decreases rapidly westwards and they wedge out abruptly about 2 km west of the town; they

are absent to the west of Wing. To the east of Woburn, the maximum recorded thickness of Woburn Sands is 81.05 m in the BGS Froxfield Borehole [SP 9737 3337], which started within the formation (Appendix 2). Although evidence is meagre, the sands appear to thin to the east, and to the south of Ampthill only 20 to 30 m of strata are present. Farther east the formation thickens again, and in the Clophill–Shefford area it is some 60 m thick. At Potton, just east of the present district, a BGS borehole [TL 2318 4904] which commenced within the Woburn Sands, penetrated 76.37 m of sands before entering Oxford Clay, proving a further thickening towards the east. The Woburn Sands have also been penetrated in several deep wells in the Dunstable–Luton area, where thicknesses between about 30 and 60 m are recorded.

SEDIMENTARY STRUCTURES

Well-developed cross-bedding is characteristic of much of the Woburn Sands. Planar bedding and low-angle cross-bedded tabular sets, from 0.5 m to 3.0 m thick, are common. Planar cross-bedded sands with depositional dips up to 25° are common and some trough cross-bedded sediments are also present. Both tabular and trough cross-beds display sand-flow cross-strata, formed by avalanching of sand down slip faces (Buck, 1985).

Analyses of cross-bedding by various authors have produced conflicting results regarding current directions and provenance of sediment. Cross-bedding in sands directly above the worked fuller's earth seam at Aspley Heath indicates derivation from the south (Cowperthwaite et al., 1972). These authors also described continuous and bifurcating sand waves below the fuller's earth that indicate a similar direction of sediment transport. Their findings, however, differ from those of Narayan (1963) and Bridges (1982) who demonstrated that the overall direction of transport was from the north and north-west. Johnson and Levell (1980) found evidence for bidirectional palaeocurrents indicating a dominant north-easterly flood direction.

The sedimentological characteristics of the 'Silver Sands' suggest that they were subjected to an extended period of movement and winnowing on the sea floor, in shallow waters within the zone of wave activity, possibly as a belt of continuously shifting shoals. Johnson and Levell (1980) suggest that the tabular cross-bedded sets which overlie concave erosion surfaces indicate inner estuarine channel/shoal deposits.

AGE OF THE WOBURN SANDS

The Woburn Sands is for the most part unfossiliferous, but lenses of calcareous sandstone in the lowest 6 m to 10 m near Brickhill have yielded an abundant indigenous brachiopod fauna and plant fragments (Keeping, 1875, 1883; Horton et al., 1974) associated with phosphatic nodules. Elsewhere, for example at Ridgmont, phosphatic nodules are concentrated in a single bed at

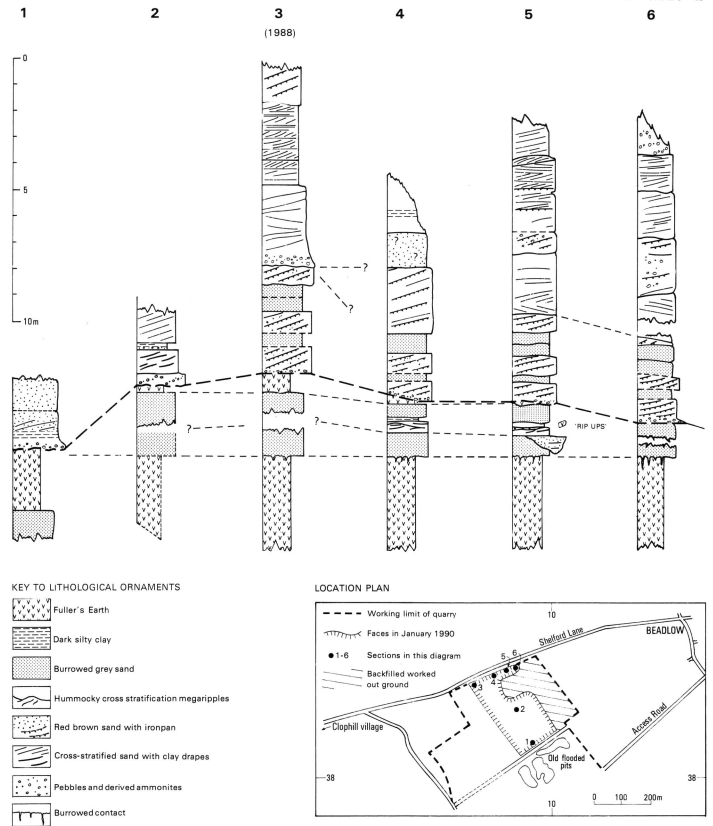

Figure 17 Sections in the Woburn Sands exposed in Clophill Quarry, 1988–89 (based on a drawing by A H Ruffell).

the base of the formation (Casey, 1961; Middlemiss, 1962). The faunas are indicative of the *nutfieldiensis* Zone, *Tropaeum subarcticum* Subzone of the Late Aptian. Ammonites collected by quarry workmen at Clophill, and reputed to be from just above the main worked fuller's earth seam, have been identified by R Casey (in Cox, 1990) as *Parahoplites nutfieldiensis* and *P.* cf. *maximus,* also indicative of the *subarcticum* Subzone, thus providing a direct age link between the fuller's earths of Bedfordshire and those of Surrey. A specimen of *Lytoceras* sp. of no zonal significance has also been collected from the same quarry. There is no firm dating of the upper part of the formation within the district, but at Potton, to the east, evidence of the overlying *cunningtoni* Subzone is provided by in-situ faunas contained in the Potton Nodule Bed towards the top of the Woburn Sands. In the Leighton Buzzard area, the 'Junction Beds' that directly overlie the Woburn Sands belong to the *Leymeriella tardefurcata* Zone (*regularis* Subzone) of the Lower Albian. Thus the unfossiliferous upper sands span the interval occupied by the *Hypacanthoplites jacobi* Zone and the lower part of the *L. tardefurcata* Zone.

DETAILS

CLOPHILL

Sand was formerly dug from a large pit [TL 0800 3800] on the north-west outskirts of Clophill. The sand is dark orange-brown, cross-bedded, stained by goethite, and locally cemented into sandstone. Sand is dug by London Brick (Hanson Trust) in a pit [TL 082 372] to the south-west of Clophill and stockpiled for use in the manufacture of sand-faced bricks. Cross-bedded, yellow to orange-brown, fine- to coarse-grained sand and sandstone have been dug from two small pits [TL 0891 3853 and 0895 3837] east of Great Lane, Clophill.

The fuller's earth quarry, east of Clophill village [TL 099 382], was developed after completion of the recent geological survey, but has since been visited by BGS staff and academic colleagues on several occasions from 1988 to 1991. In late 1989 the working faces were jointly recorded by R W O'B Knox, B S P Moorlock, and E R Shephard-Thorn of BGS and A H Ruffell (then of Imperial College, London) as part of a national study of fuller's earth resources, jointly commissioned by the Department of the Environment and the Department of Trade and Industry (Moorlock and Highley, 1991). Dr Ruffell subsequently drew up the sections illustrated in Figure 17. A total vertical succession of about 18 m of strata were exposed at that time.

The main worked seam is exposed, for about 3.1 m, at the bottom of the workings, though its base was only clearly exposed in Section 1 (Figure 17) where a reduced thickness of 2.4 m, resting on friable bioturbated grey sand, was noted. The reduction in thickness is due to erosion of the top of the bed below the surface indicated in Figure 17, which will be discussed further below. The main seam comprises typical, massive, waxy fuller's earth with a blocky fracture which rapidly disaggregates when wet. In the exposed workings the fuller's earth is a bright greenish grey colour, in contrast to the bluish grey colour reported from borehole samples. It is probable that the colour has changed due to exposure to the atmosphere and the effects of the dewatering process carried out by the company prior to extraction.

In Sections 2 to 5 inclusive, up to 2.5 m of grey, burrow-mottled, medium- to coarse-grained clayey sand overlies the worked seam. A log of fossil driftwood 0.6 m long and 0.1 m in diameter was noted near the top of these sands. The ammonites indicative of the *nutfieldiensis* Zone, *subarcticum* Subzone (see this page and Cox, 1990) collected by the quarry workmen probably also came from these sands, although they have not yet been recorded in situ. The zonal age is also supported by the microfaunas. The fine pyrite cement of the internal casts of the ammonites has probably escaped destruction by oxidation because it remained below the local water table until the quarry was opened and dewatered. In Sections 4 and 5 cross-bedded sands with hummocky cross-stratification overlie the seam. 'Rip-ups' of reworked fuller's earth occur at the base; the sands are overlain by a thin bed of dark silty clay, within the 2.5 m-thick bioturbated clayey sand.

In Sections 2,3,4 and 5 remnants of a lesser fuller's earth seam, up to about a metre thick, are preserved below the erosion surface referred to above. The higher fuller's earth seam resembles the main seam in appearance, but is of lower grade.

As shown in Figure 17 the erosion surface cuts out 3 m or more of strata. Above it a basal pebble/grit lag includes dark 'lydite' and quartz pebbles and phosphatised ammonite fragments of Upper Jurassic provenance. The latter invite comparison with the similar fauna of derived ammonites in the basal layers of the Bargate Beds of the Hogs' Back area of Surrey (Arkell, 1939; Lake and Shephard-Thorn, 1985). The same erosional event may be represented at these two localities on opposite flanks of the London Platform and may thus equate with a sequence boundary of some significance (Ruffell and Wach, 1991, fig. 4). Locally, the erosional event may correlate with the Potton Nodule Bed (Casey, 1961), which includes derived *cunningtoni* Subzone fossils within it, and the 'marker bed' separating the 'Silver Sands' and 'Brown Sands' units in quarries around Leighton Buzzard (Shephard-Thorn et al., 1986). The transgressive event linked with the erosion surface may have occurred during the *nolani* Subzone.

The upper part of the sections above the erosion surface comprise up to 11 m of coarse planar cross-bedded sands with some interbeds of grey bioturbated sands. The upper sands are mostly friable and uncemented, but some ferruginous cement is present in association with clay drapes on cross-bedded surfaces, giving a fretted appearance to the sands on weathered faces. The upper few metres of the sands are weathered to ochreous tints.

In the vicinity of the quarry, boreholes show the worked seam to lie about 17 m above the base of the Woburn Sands, giving a local total of about 35 m of strata. The full formational thickness is up to about 60 m in the wider Clophill area.

AMPTHILL, MILLBROOK AND STEPPINGLEY

North of Green End, medium-grained sands are cemented with limonite and, because of their relative hardness, they form topographic plateaux. Sandstone, commonly cross-bedded, is exposed along several sunken lanes and tracks [TL 0684 3811, 0667 3773, and 0725 3849]. Variably cemented sand and sandstone are exposed in places in the deep cutting of the A6 to the north of Ampthill, and steeply dipping, planar cross-bedded, orange-brown sandstone is exposed alongside a track [TL 0756 3813] leading from the A6.

Buff phosphatic nodules and pebbly, limonite-cemented sandstone fragments from the basal beds of the Woburn Sands are locally abundant in the soil to the south of Millbrook, both east [TL 0175 3743 to 0175 3682] and west [TL 0168 3652] of the Fordfield Road. The nodules, up to about 5 cm in diameter, are commonly composed of the broken whorls of ammonites.

South and east of Steppingley, strong topographic features are produced by hard layers of 'carstone', blocks of which are commonly ploughed up in the soil.

In a mostly overgrown and degraded sand and 'carstone' pit [SP 9965 3404] 850 m north-east of Water End Farm, Eversholt, only the uppermost 2 to 3 m of beds are now visible; these dip at up to 25°. The exposure shows yellow, buff, orange and rusty brown, planar cross-bedded, medium- to coarse-grained sand and sandstone. The latter range from weakly iron cemented and friable to well-cemented and hard. They include bands of hard, gritty, pebbly 'carstone'. The uppermost 2 m at the north-west corner of the pit are orange and buff sands with irregular patchy iron cementation and contain vertical and highly inclined burrow traces about 0.01 m in diameter.

WOBURN AND BRICKHILL

A composite section in the fuller's earth pit at Old Wavendon Heath [SP 932 345] was measured over several faces in September 1985. As the pit is active and constantly changing, the section is intended to identify only the broad units within the sequence.

	Thickness m
Sand, fine-grained, containing many dark grains; strongly bioturbated and with many burrow traces; planar cross-bedded with sets ranging from 0.1 to 0.3 m in thickness; reversals of cross-bedding are common; large hollow ferruginous 'boxstone' concretions and iron-staining along bedding planes; possibly equivalent to the 'Compo' of the Leighton Buzzard area	c.8
Sand, medium- to coarse-grained, containing dark, possibly, limonite and glauconite grains; more heavily iron-stained than above with much 'carstone'; sharp top; cross-bedded with sets up to 1 m thick and forsets dipping at up to 15°; small pebbles on foresets; some clay partings; little bioturbation and few burrows; 0.2 m thick bed of laminated clay at base	c.8
Sand, fine- to medium-grained, with some 'carstone' (2 m); about 1 m unexposed; sand below is planar bedded with 0.2 to 1.0 m thick beds; some small-scale cross-bedding	c.5.4
Fuller's earth clay, locally with greenish sandy partings	c.0.6
Sand, fine- to medium-grained, irregularly iron-stained and containing 'carstone' fragments, with thin clay seams at the top; similar but bioturbated sand below with abundant dark grains	c.4
Sand, fine- to coarse-grained, planar cross-bedded, with cross-bedded sets 0.1 to 1.0 m thick; many dark grains including large chips of glauconite concentrated into bands; bioturbated with small vertical tubules; clayey partings and iron-staining, with a few impersistent 'carstone' horizons; large 'carstone' fragments up to 0.3 m thick occur 2–3 m above the underlying fuller's earth; wet clayey sand in basal 1 m	c.16
Fuller's earth; dark olive-green mudstone	c.3 seen

Two boreholes were drilled in the Old Wavendon Heath–Aspley Wood area during the Spring of 1986 to further investigate the stratigraphy of the lower part of the Woburn Sands (Moorlock and Wyatt, 1986). The boreholes were 35 m in depth and commenced just above the main worked fuller's earth seam. One [SP 9308 3438] was sited in the bottom of the deep workings west of the A5130 road, the other [SP 9323 3526] east of the road (see Appendix 2). Both penetrated a sequence of mainly fine- to medium-grained sands, and proved a thin seam of fuller's earth about 17 m below the main seam. Limitations of the drilling equipment led to both boreholes being terminated whilst still in the Woburn Sands.

Six boreholes were drilled in the Potsgrove–Woburn–Froxfield area by BGS during 1990–91 as part of an appraisal of fuller's earth resources in England and Wales. Abbreviated logs of these boreholes are given in Appendix 2. Three of the boreholes were drilled adjacent to the Birchmoor Pumping Station in an attempt to confirm the logs of several water wells that recorded thick seams of fuller's earth. Although some thin seams of fuller's earth were encountered in these boreholes, they cannot be correlated with the seams recorded in the well logs. No thick seams were proved in the BGS boreholes, and it is concluded that the original well logs are inaccurate. The BGS Birchmoor Farm Borehole [SP 9494 3518], situated less than half a kilometre to the east of the pumping station, proved the lowermost 52.36 m of the Woburn Sands without encountering any seams of fuller's earth. Likewise the BGS Potsgrove Borehole [SP 9406 3066] sited several kilometres to the south proved the lower 88.64 m of the Woburn Sands without proving any fuller's earth. The BGS Froxfield Borehole [SP 9737 3337], to the east of Woburn, penetrated the lowermost 81.05 m of the Woburn Sands and likewise did not encounter any fuller's earth. Within the latter borehole a phosphatic conglomerate of similar appearance to the Potton Nodule Bed occurred at a depth of 24.11 m below the surface.

Phosphatic nodules were formerly dug for fertiliser from the basal beds of the Woburn Sands between Little Brickhill and Great Brickhill. Casts and moulds of bivalves and ammonites occur in *remanié* debris which litter the fields north of Philip's Clump. At Philip's Clump, a degraded section [SP 8987 3148] (Horton et al., 1974) shows the following sequence:

	Thickness m
Hillwash, sandy, orange-brown, silty, containing angular fragments of flint, derived from the Chalky Boulder Clay, and rolled phosphatic nodules	1.0
Sandstone, calcareous, pale brownish yellow, gritty, containing well-preserved bivalves and brachiopods	0.045
Clay and clayey silt, buff; Upper Jurassic	proved to 1.3 by hand auger

The fauna of the calcareous sandstone has been examined by Mr A A Morter. Brachiopods are the dominant element, and include: *Vectella morrisii*, *Praelongithyris* sp., '*Rhynchonella*' *upwarensis*, *Cyclothyris antidichotoma*, *Terebratulina* sp. and *Terebratella* sp. [juv.]. Bivalves are next in importance and include *Acesta longa* and species of *Exogyra* and '*Ostrea*', particularly *Gryphaeostrea canaliculata*. Bryozoans and cirripedes are also represented. The sandstone preserves an abundant foraminiferal fauna, and also includes phosphatic casts of pavloviid ammonites derived from the Kimmeridge Clay.

The above locality is believed to be near a 10 m-high section recorded by Teall (1875) from which Keeping (1875, 1883) obtained a rich brachiopod fauna. Keeping (1875) described the deposit as rather coarse sand, composed of grains of quartz, 'lydian stone' and comminuted shells, in places hardened by iron oxide or calcium carbonate. Phosphatic nodules were recorded not concentrated into a seam as at other localities but scattered throughout the entire thickness of the section. Keeping (1875) recorded the following fauna which he considered to be in situ rather than derived from the reworking of older strata: *Cyrtothyris seeleyi*, *Oblongarcula oblonga*, '*Ornithella*' *pseudojurensis*, '*Ornithella*' *wanklyni*, *Praelongithyris praelongiformis*, *Rectithyris depressa*, *Rhombothyris extensa*, *Rhombothyris microtrema*, *Sellithyris tornacensis*, '*Terebratula*' *moutoniana*, *Terebratulina striata*, *Cyclothyris antidichotoma*, *Cyclothyris depressa*, *Cyclothyris latissima*, '*Rhynchonella*' *cantabridgiensis*, '*Rhynchonella*' *upwarensis*, '*Ostrea*' *macroptera*, '*Lima*' *farringdonensis*, *Limatula dupiniana*, '*Cidaris*' *farringdonensis*.

Many of these species also occur at Farringdon and Upware to the west and east of the district, which led Keeping (1883) to suggest a link between the deposits of the three areas.

At Rectory Farm a temporary exposure [SP 8975 3048] at the base of the Woburn Sands revealed (Horton et al., 1974) 1.6 m of orange-brown, iron-stained, pebbly sand with fragments of broken sandstone (hillwash) resting on grey, medium-grained sand, 70 to 100 mm thick, containing scattered sand-impregnated black phosphatic nodules and some well-preserved whorl fragments of pavloviid ammonites. The sand rests on weathered Upper Jurassic clay.

LEIGHTON BUZZARD AREA

Between the A5 road and the town of Leighton Buzzard, sand has been and is still quarried extensively for a variety of constructional and industrial purposes. The working quarries have been examined and recorded in some detail during the present study. General sections for each quarry are illustrated in Figure 13 with a suggested correlation between them. In the following text the composite general sections, as recorded in 1985 for these quarries, are presented in simplified form for the sake of brevity. To avoid repetition brief details are also included of the basal beds of the overlying Gault.

The most northerly quarry examined is the A5 Pit of P Bennie Ltd [SP 933 303], which is worked for building sand only. The following section in the Woburn Sands was recorded, beneath a till overburden up to 3.5 m thick:

	Thickness m
'**Silver Sands**'	
Sand, fine- to coarse-grained, white, showing variable planar and trough cross-bedding, with some pebbles and ferruginous 'carstone'	up to 4.9
'**Marker Bed**'	
Sand, clayey and silty, fine-grained, interbanded with grey silty clay	up to 2.5
'**Brown Sands**'	
Sand, fine- to medium-grained, glauconitic, planar cross-bedded, with much bioturbation and ferruginous staining. Hard band of dark brown ferruginous 'carstone' (0.3 m) about 4 m below top	up to 15.0

It is estimated that 5 to 6 m of the 'Silver Sands' are absent due to erosion. The clay band separating the 'Silver Sands' and 'Brown Sands' gives rise to a perched water table in the former.

There are two pits at Fox Corner. The larger [SP 926 291], operated by Hall Aggregates (Eastern Counties) Ltd, has been worked for building sand, but is now nearly exhausted and is in the process of restoration by the tipping of approved waste. At the northern end of the workings, till overburden, up to 6 m thick, is present and infills channels cut into the sand. The following section in the Woburn Sands was recorded, probably starting a few metres below the top of the formation:

	Thickness m
'**Silver Sands**'	
Sand, medium- to coarse-grained, cross-bedded, white, locally with ferruginous cementation at the top and ochreous staining near the base, where a thin hard nodular ferruginous layer is present	up to 8.0
'**Brown Sands**'	
Sand, fine- to medium-grained, brownish, glauconitic, with planar cross-bedding and many trace fossils. The latter are prominent on weathered faces due to secondary iron cementation and staining which affects all the unit	up to 15.0

The adjacent, smaller pit [SP 928 292] is operated by Buckland Sand and Silica Co. Ltd on an intermittent basis to supply material to their main quarry at Reach Lane. Till infills a small channel up to 2 m deep cut into the 'Silver Sands'. Up to 6 m of the 'Silver Sands' are exposed and comprise medium-grained, white, cross-bedded sands which are locally iron cemented to 'carstone' near the top. The lower 2 to 3 m of the sands are vividly coloured in shades of brick red and ochreous yellow, which may be related to the presence of the glacial channel mentioned above. Traces of lignitic material occur in the sands.

Nearby, to the south, is the Stone Lane Quarry [SP 929 289] of Joseph Arnold and Sons which has been worked for many years. Initially, the 'Silver Sands' were hand dug for industrial use, but latterly the pit has been deepened and extended to exploit the 'Brown Sands' for building purposes.

The overburden here comprises till and glacial sand and gravel totalling 16 m in thickness. An infilled glacial channel is currently exposed in the eastern face (Plate 11). The following section has been recorded:

	Thickness m
GAULT	
Blue-grey clay, poorly exposed	c.2.0
WOBURN SANDS	
'**Silver Sands**'	
Sand, medium-grained, white, planar cross-bedded, with pinkish and ochreous iron-staining and some 'boxstone' nodules. A few thin clay partings between cross-bedded sets. Local calcareous cementation. Fragments of fossil wood	up to c.6.0
'**Marker band**'	
Sand, coarse-grained, pebbly, clayey, greenish, with ferruginous cementation. Grey and white silty clay near base	0.3
'**Brown Sands**'	
Sand, fine- to medium-grained with limonite and glauconite grains, planar cross-bedded, containing many burrows in ferruginous preservation. Heavily iron-stained. Stained crimson for several metres below glacial channel	up to 12.0

The marker bed between the 'Silver' and 'Brown Sands' is virtually planar as seen in the quarry and gives an indication of the true dip locally, which is 3° to the south-east. It marks a major change in sedimentary style between the two sand groups.

The Bryants Lane Quarry [SP 929 286] of L B Silica Sand Ltd is immediately adjacent to the Stone Lane Quarry on the south, the two being separated only by a narrow lane. This quarry is chiefly concerned with the production of sand for building purposes. The overburden comprises up to 10 m of till with interbedded gravel and up to 4 m of Gault. The section is as follows:

	Thickness m
GAULT	
Clay, blue grey and green with belemnites and layers of phosphatic nodules, including a thin band of brick red clay ('Cirripede Bed') at base	c.4.0
Shenley Limestone	
Limestone, buff and brown, phosphatic, with many dark grains. Well-preserved brachiopods common. Occurs in isolated patch on 'mound' of 'Silty Beds'	up to 0.1
WOBURN SANDS	
'Silty Beds'	
Sand, very fine- to fine-grained, silty, ochreous, bioturbated, with glauconite; rippled dark grey partings and beds of dark coarser clayey sand	0 to 3.0
'Silver Sands'	
Sand, medium- to coarse-grained, with pebbles up to 7 mm across in top 3 m, finer below. Prominent planar cross-bedding and variable ferruginous staining. Local ferruginous 'carstone' reefs at top of sequence. Some 'boxstone' concretions and clay galls	up to 13.0
'Marker Bed'	
Sand, pebbly, ferruginous	c.0.5
'Brown Sands'	
Sand, coarse-grained, pebbly, ferruginous with many burrows	up to 4.0
Sand, fine- to medium-grained, bioturbated, with ferruginous staining and ribbing	c.10.0
Sandstone, hard, ferruginous	0.5
Sand, fine-grained, silty, grey-green, glauconitic, planar cross-bedded	seen to 2.0

To the west of the main road through Heath and Reach, L B Silica Sand Co. operate a pit in Bakers Wood [SP 923 285] where up to 27 m of the 'Brown Sands', forming the lower part of the Woburn Sands, have been exploited for building purposes. In the floor of the pit a basal nodule bed, up to 0.15 m thick, rests on the Ampthill Clay. The nodule bed comprises 'coprolites' and phosphatic casts of perisphinctid ammonites and bivalves (derived from Upper Jurassic rocks) in a sandy ferruginous matrix. The approximate level of the base of the formation here is 93.5 m above OD. Worked out pits to the north have been restored after use as landfill sites.

In 1988, workings in the lowest 2 to 3 m of the Woburn Sands in the north western area of Bakers Wood Pit [SP 921 286] revealed the unexpected presence of thin fuller's earth deposits. In the cleaned section two layers of yellowish green fuller's earth up to 0.1 m thick were draped on planar cross-bedding sets dipping at a low angle in an apparent north-easterly direction. Elsewhere a layer 0.6 m thick had been dug and sampled. This site is of some interest as the only known occurrence of fuller's earth south of the Woburn workings, but the fuller's earth does not occur in a seam of workable thickness. Mr S Kemp reports that X-ray diffraction and surface area studies of the fuller's earth showed a smectite content of only 61 per cent, with minor kaolinite, feldspar, goethite and cristobalite; it thus constitutes a low-grade fuller's earth.

The Reach Lane Quarry of the Buckland Sand and Silica Co. [SP 933 284] is immediately south of and partly contiguous with the Bryants Lane Quarry described above. It produces foundry sands from the 'Silver Sands' and building sand from the underlying 'Brown Sands'. Some 20 m of overburden are currently being removed, comprising up to 12 m of till with pockets of gravel and about 8 m of Gault. The section is as follows:

	Thickness m
GAULT	
Mudstone, blue-grey and grey-green, with layers of phosphatic nodules	c.8.0
'Conglomerate' of ferruginous 'boxstone' nodules and glauconite in sandy clay matrix	0.4
WOBURN SANDS	
'Silty Beds'	
Sand, fine- to coarse-grained, grey-brown, silty, with dark clay partings	up to 2.0
'Silver Sands'	
Sand, fine- to medium-grained, white, with scattered dark grains. Planar cross-bedded with partings of grey silty clay between sets	up to 15.0
'Marker Bed'	
Clay, ferruginous, with silty micaceous laminae	0.3
'Brown Sands'	
Sand, fine- to medium-grained, with ferruginous preservation; hard 'carstone' band (0.3 m thick) c.5 m above base	seen to 25.0

On the eastern side of the till-capped ridge, into which the preceding quarries are dug, there is an extensively worked area of about 1 km, operated in part by Joseph Arnold and Sons Ltd as their Double Arches Quarry (now exhausted) and also by George Garside (Sand) Ltd as the Churchways Quarry, from which small amounts of sand are still extracted. Few large sections are now visible; those seen in the early 1960s were described by Bristow (1963).

Garsides also operate a quarry at Mundays Hill [SP 937 282] where the coarse-grained development of the 'Silver Sands' is a valuable source of industrial sand. Up to 16 m of overburden, comprising 6 m of till and up to 10 m of Gault, is removed to expose the 'Silver Sands'. The sequence is variable in detail and the units described below are not necessarily present everywhere in the quarry.

	Thickness m
GAULT	
Mudstone, colour-banded bluish, greenish and black, with bands of phosphatic nodules and common fossils. Brick-red mudstone ('Cirripede Bed'), up to 0.3 m, noted locally near base	up to 10.0
Shenley Limestone	
Limestone, phosphatic, pale-brown, with limonite and glauconite grains; many brachiopods locally	up to 0.1
WOBURN SANDS	
'Red Sands'	
Sand, medium- to coarse-grained, cross-bedded, with goethite grains concentrated in thin	

Thickness
m

bands giving a striped aspect. These sands
overlie the 'Silty Beds' and 'Silver Sands' with
marked erosion at the contact   up to 4.0

'Silty Beds'
Sand, very fine-grained, silty, clayey. Wavy
partings of dark grey silty clay. Sporadic pockets
of coarse grit and 'boxstone' nodules   up to 4.5

'Silver Sands'
Sand, medium- to coarse-grained, white, with
small pebbles of quartz and chert (up to 5 mm
across). Well-developed planar cross-bedding
and abundant lignitic fossil wood. Ochreous
staining, associated with 'carstone reefs', of
ferruginous cemented sandstone at top.
Irregular, undulating base with layer of
'boxstone' nodules in clay   4.0–10.0

'Compo'
Sand, very fine-grained, silty, grey-white,
speckled with glauconite. Cross-bedded, with
many wavy partings of grey silty clay. Trace
fossils and 'boxstone' nodules   seen to 5.0

The occurrence of 'carstone reefs' at the top of the 'Silver
Sands' at Mundays Hill (Plate 1), and as formerly seen at
Double Arches, have been discussed by Bristow (1963). The
reefs are linear features formed of iron-cemented 'Silver Sands';
in cross section they may be 10 to 25 m in width and 2 to 3 m in
height. They are apparently laterally continuous over distances
of a kilometre or more and seem to be related to the margins of
remnant banks of the 'Silty Beds' (Bristow, 1963, fig. 16, p.280).
Beneath the remnants of 'Silty Beds', the 'Silver Sands' are
white and relatively free of iron but, where the 'Silty Beds' have
been removed and 'Red Sands' directly overlie the 'Silver
Sands', the latter show an ochreous stain to a greater or less degree. The change from clean to iron-stained 'Silver Sands' is
quite abrupt and coincides with the position of the 'carstone
reefs'. This relationship is important in quarrying as the iron-
stained 'Silver Sands' are of much less value for industrial use.

Contiguous with Mundays Hill Quarry on the south is the
Nine Acres Pit [SP 940 277] of Joseph Arnold and Sons Ltd,
where an overburden of up to 3 m of slipped Gault obscures its
junction with the Woburn Sands. Traces of Shenley Limestone
have been noted in an abandoned part of this pit adjacent to
Munday's Hill Quarry. The highest division of the Woburn
Sands currently exposed, the 'Silver Sands', is here seen chiefly
in ferruginous preservation as a 'carstone reef', 1.5 m high and
25 m in width. The 'reef' comprises red-brown, medium- to
coarse-grained, pebbly sandstone, with clay galls and fossil
wood included. Some small patches of clean sand remain near
the base, which is marked by a conglomerate of 'boxstone'
nodules resting on an erosion surface. Beneath this, very fine-
grained micaceous silty sands, equivalent to the 'Compo' at the
base of the Mundays Hill section, are exposed for up to 10 m.
They are planar cross-bedded with common silty clay partings
and much bioturbation, and contain abundant fossil wood and
sporadic 'boxstone' nodules. Sand from this pit is taken to
Arnold's plant at Double Arches for processing with other
sands for a variety of uses.

Shenley Hill, capped by till, lies south-west of Nine Acres and
has some worked-out and restored ground on its eastern flank.
On the west of the hill lies Arnold's New Trees Quarry [SP 931
275], where Woburn Sands are exploited beneath about 4 m of
Gault overburden (Plate 4). The following sequence has been
recorded:

Thickness
m

GAULT
Mudstone, blue-grey, calcareous, with phosphatic
nodules   up to 3.0
'Carstone Conglomerate' comprising 'boxstone'
nodules and fragments of 'carstone' in a
greenish ochreous sandy clay matrix   up to 0.45
Sand, clayey, glauconitic, grey-green, bioturbated,
with fossil wood; irregular erosional base   seen 0.20
                                                 to 0.40

WOBURN SANDS

'Silver Sands'
Sand, fine- to coarse-grained, white, planar cross-
bedded, bioturbated, with scattered dark grains
and some fossil wood   up to 6.0
Sand, fine- to coarse-grained, grey and brown,
pebbly in part; some dark grains, local
ferruginous cementation and 'boxstone' nodules   up to 3.0

To the south-west of Shenley Hill lies Arnold's Chamberlains
Barn Quarry [SP 931 268], which has been worked for many
years and has been extensively backfilled with Gault overburden material. The Gault overburden in the current workings
on the east is up to 11 m thick. The section in the working part
of the quarry in 1985 was as follows:

Thickness
m

GAULT
Mudstone, bluish and greenish grey, with layers
of phosphatic nodules; trace of glauconite near
base   up to 10.50
'Carstone Conglomerate' comprising fragments
of ferruginous sandstone in a sandy clay matrix,
with a layer of 'carstone' nodules at base   0.22
Clay, sandy, green and ochreous, much
bioturbated, with pebbles up to 7 mm across;
sharp base   0.25

WOBURN SANDS

'Red Sands'
Sand, medium- to coarse-grained, pebbly, grey-
brown, strongly cross-bedded and bioturbated.
Abundant limonite and glauconite grains give
an overall dark colour   1.0–2.5
Sand, medium- to coarse-grained, heavily
bioturbated, with a white and ochreous
striped effect due to concentration of
goethite grains in bands on cross-bedding.
A few pebbles near the top and a thin basal
layer of 'boxstone' nodules in a clayey matrix.
Wavy irregular base   up to 2.4

'Silver Sands'
Sand, fine- to medium-grained, white, brown
and ochreous, bioturbated, with some clay
partings. Ferruginous cementation on 'highs'
at top   seen to 2.0

This section clearly demonstrated the overlapping relationship of the 'Red Sands' on the 'Silver Sands'. The output of
this quarry goes almost entirely to the adjacent concrete tile
works.

Away from the quarries, exposures in the Woburn Sands are
rare and the outcrop area is generally mantled with a sandy
wash, which locally becomes thick enough to map as head. A

few metres of ochreous cross-bedded sandstone are exposed near the north [SP 911 262] and south [SP 911 259] portals of the Linslade Railway Tunnel.

The Woburn Sands die out abruptly to the west of Great Brickhill (approximately at easting 895) and between Leighton Buzzard and Wing. In the latter area the evidence of their presence is apparently given by a well log situated about 1.5 km north-east of Wing [SP 8935 2420] which revealed the following sequence:

	Thickness m
Till	9.1
Glacial sand and gravel (gravels)	10.4
?Woburn Sands (sands)	8.5
Upper Jurassic clays	63.4

The sands could be glacial deposits, but are more likely to represent the feather edge of the Woburn Sands.

Sand has been worked in a number of pits to the south of Leighton Buzzard. The working face of Ascott Farm Sand Pit of Hall Aggregates Ltd [SP 9090 2405], just south of Linslade, affords a good exposure of the 'Red Sands'. Up to 11 m of beds are present, comprising mainly yellow and fawn, medium- and coarse-grained, commonly pebbly sand, which occurs as planar beds or gently cross-bedded tabular sets from 1.5 to 2.5 m thick. Dark streaks and layers contain tiny, polished goethite grains. Bioturbation is common and, at certain levels, there are subvertical burrow traces up to 1 cm in diameter. Larger *Diplocraterion*-type burrow traces are also common. Sporadic iron cementation produces irregular 'boxstones' and doggers. The top surface of the sand beneath the Gault is sharp and planar. A few large blocks of white, very hard, calcite-cemented, gritty, pebbly sandstone lying loose in the pit are, presumably, doggers excavated from the sand. This lithology is similar to that of the gritty nodules in the overlying 'Junction Beds' of the Gault which have, however, been phosphatised.

In the floor of this pit, at [SP 9094 2406], a trial excavation proved 1 m of very dark grey, thinly bedded clay with pale silt partings and pyritic nodules. This clay is comparable to the one exposed in Tiddenfoot New Pit (see below) on the other side of the railway line. BGS Ascott Farm Sand Pit Borehole, 150 m to the west [SP 9078 2408], proved 1.05 m of the same clay below 7.75 m of 'Red Sands'. Underlying the clay there are 2.95 m of pale to mid grey, slightly glauconitic, well-sorted sand with sporadic thin bands of black laminated silty clay. The sand is thought to correspond to the 'Brown Sands/Compo' of the sand pits north of Leighton Buzzard; they rest on Kimmeridge Clay.

At the north-east corner of Tiddenfoot New Pit [SP 9120 2396], also worked by Hall Aggregates Ltd, the following section was recorded beneath 1.2 m of river terrace deposits:

	Thickness m
'Red Sands'	
Sand, gold-brown, coarse-grained, slightly glauconitic, gently cross-bedded in part and slightly bioturbated at some levels; scattered small quartz pebbles near base; almost planar base	max 3.0
'Brown Sands'	
Sand, yellow, pale grey and fawn, in three ill-defined units, each c.0.6 m thick; top unit medium-grained, well-sorted and slightly glauconitic; middle unit gently cross-bedded	

and slightly bioturbated, containing impersistent stringers of small clay flakes and thin lenses of brown silty clay up to 0.01 m thick; lowest unit similar to top unit but fine-grained. Impersistent strings of small ferruginous 'boxstone' concretions occur throughout ... max 1.8

At the base of the pit face, about 100 m to the west-south-west, there is a lenticular body of very dark grey clay which wedges out between the 'Brown Sands' and 'Red Sands' described above. The section in the clay is:

	Thickness m
Clay, very dark grey, silty, beds about 0.01 m thick, with grey silt partings	1.0
Clay, very dark grey, silty, poorly bedded, with impersistent sandy partings and scattered tabular pyrite nodules	max 0.6 seen

The clay appears to be barren of macrofossils. Formerly, it extended over the greater part of the worked out area of the sand pit, with a maximum proved thickness of about 2.5 m.

Trial boreholes about 150 m ENE of Grove Hospital [SP 9139 2338] proved up to 14.3 m of yellow-brown, medium- to coarse-grained sand ('Red Sands') beneath the Ouzel valley alluvium, overlying from 3.6 to 4.3 m of interbedded pale grey, fine-grained, laminated sand and very dark grey silty clay ('Brown Sands').

The section in the small working Brickyard Pit (George Garside Ltd), adjacent to Grovebury Farm [SP 9245 2373], excludes the topmost c.2 m of the Woburn Sands which have been stripped off:

	Thickness m
'Red Sands'	
Sand, yellow, medium- to coarse-grained, slightly pebbly, gently cross-bedded, with some very coarse, very pebbly streaks and lenses; also dark brown streaks containing dark polished goethite grains; sporadic ferruginous iron-staining	max 1.0
Sand, yellow and fawn mottled, medium-grained, slightly pebbly, heavily bioturbated, cross-bedded in part	0.6–1.5
Sand, pale yellow and fawn, medium- to very coarse-grained, thinly banded (bands 0.02–0.12 m thick), trough cross-bedded, with many dark brown streaks and layers; some very pebbly bands; bioturbated in upper part, with common *Diplocraterion*-type burrow-traces	0.8–1.9
Sand, brown, medium-grained, very pebbly	0.6–1.2
Sand, pale yellow, gold-brown and fawn, medium grained, thinly bedded, bioturbated, slightly pebbly, with some dark brown streaks; sporadic *Diplocraterion*-type burrow-traces	max 1.8 seen

The only readily accessible face in Arnold's Pratt's Pit (Billington Road) at the time of survey was at the north-eastern end [SP 9326 2408] (Plates 5 and 6):

Thickness
m

'Red Sands'

Sand, wedge-bedded, comprising interbedded
sets up to 1.5 m thick of: a) fawn, medium- and
coarse-grained, slightly pebbly, bioturbated sand,
and b) brown, very pebbly, gritty, fine- to coarse-
grained gritty sand, with impersistent stringers of
small pebbles and abundant polished goethite
grains — c.4

Sand, varicoloured (yellow, fawn, very dark brown,
orange, rusty-brown), medium- and coarse-grained,
with pebbly beds up to 0.15 m thick; many
heavily bioturbated bands; slightly glauconitic
in part; a few impersistent weakly iron-cemented
layers; some large *Diplocraterion*-type burrow-traces
and vertical narrow burrow-traces (mostly 2–3 mm
in diameter, some c.10 mm in diameter); all with
planar cross-bedding in sets 0.5–1.0 m thick,
except for the basal 3.0 m, which is a single set,
dip averages 20° to 25° — 6–7

The other working faces showed up to 8 m of strongly cross-bedded striped sands with numerous thin, dark layers of goethite grains (Plates 5 and 6).

The lengthy working face of Garside's flooded Grovebury Pit [SP 925 237] is inaccessible because the 'Red Sands' are dredged from below water level. The exposed face, 10–12 m high, consists dominantly of cross-bedded sands which appear to be similar to those recorded in nearby pits. Up to 5 m of sands are worked from below the water line. Beyond the work-ing face the overlying Gault and drift deposits have been stripped off to reveal a bench cut in orange, buff, yellow and rusty brown, medium- and coarse-grained, slightly pebbly sands.

In the south eastern part of the district, a number of deep wells have been sunk to tap the Woburn Sands aquifer beneath Chalk and Gault cover, for brewing and industrial purposes. Total recorded thickness of the Woburn Sands ranges from 31 to 71 m; the top of the Woburn Sands generally occurs at depths between 10 m above and below Ordnance Datum. In all cases the lithological descriptions of the formation given in the drillers logs is inadequate and forbids any attempt at correlation between the well sections or indeed with the exposed sections around Leighton Buzzard and Woburn. For example, the record of a well [TL 0644 2170] at a pumping station near Chaul End, Luton, proving the maximum thickness of 71.2 m of Woburn Sands, has only the single word description 'green-sand'.

The logs give a general impression of a dominantly sandy formation of medium to coarse grain size, variably cemented to sandstone and grey, greyish green or green in colour; the green colours suggest the presence of glauconite. Thin beds of bluish grey clay are recorded in a few cases, as is the somewhat enigmatic 'gault'.

The thickness of the formation around Totternhoe, Dunstable and Luton seems to be variable about a mean of 60 m. The underlying strata, penetrated only for a few metres in two boreholes, are described as grey mudstone with thin limestone beds. No specimens of these rocks have been available for stratigraphical study; they are presumed to be of Upper Jurassic age on regional grounds.

FIVE
Cretaceous: Gault and Upper Greensand

Gault and Upper Greensand strata, of Middle to Upper Albian age, crop out in a broad diagonal belt extending from the south-west to the north-east across the district, but large tracts are concealed by drift deposits (Figure 2). The Upper Greensand formation is essentially a sandy-silty facies of the highest Gault, and the two formations are treated together in this chapter for convenience. The 'Junction Beds' between the Woburn Sands and the Gault and the local development of the Shenley Limestone are also discussed here, though some authors would include them with the Woburn Sands on biostratigraphical grounds (Casey, 1961). In some cases details of these beds have been given in the descriptions of sand quarries at the end of the previous chapter.

The Gault comprises up to 75 m of pale to medium grey, variably calcareous mudstone, with a number of persistent layers of in-situ or reworked phosphatic nodules (usually marking nonsequences) and several glauconitic layers. Macrofossils are generally abundant and include ammonites, bivalves, belemnites, gastropods and echinoids. Microfossils occur throughout the sequence and trace fossils are also common. Owen (1972) has recognised the presence of lower and upper divisions of the Gault, around Leighton Buzzard, separated by a considerable sedimentary hiatus. The Lower Gault is variable in thickness up to a maximum of about 10 m.

The Upper Greensand, up to 10 m thick, is present only in the south central part of the district, having been removed elsewhere by pre-Cenomanian erosion. Thickness variations in the Gault and Upper Greensand sequence of the district are, in part, due to this period of erosion. The dominant lithologies of the Upper Greensand are grey micaceous muddy siltstone and silty mudstone with variable amounts of glauconite and some phosphatic nodules. These rocks are significantly less calcareous than the Chalk Marl or the Gault in the Sundon Borehole section (p.65).

Exposures are generally rare, except in the sand pits around Leighton Buzzard where the Gault is removed as overburden (Owen, 1972). Several former brickpits exploited the Gault and faunal collections and records of some are available in BGS archives. The BGS Sundon Borehole [TL 0405 2724] (p.56) penetrated 3.4 m of glauconitic siltstone and mudstone representing the Upper Greensand and about 6 m of the Upper Gault. Further information has come from temporary exposures associated with recent roadworks.

The full thickness of the formations has been penetrated in several deep wells that tap the Woburn Sands aquifer beneath the Totternhoe, Dunstable and Luton areas. However, the descriptive logs of these wells are inadequate and no detailed section is available for the district. In most cases the presence or absence of the Upper

Greensand is not confirmed nor is the Lower Chalk base fixed accurately, so that thickness values for the Albian formations must be regarded as unreliable in this area.

In drift-free terrain the Gault gives rise to heavy, poorly drained soils which become sticky when wet and brick-hard in dry summers. Small, whitish calcareous concretions known as 'race' are common in the top few metres of the subsoil, and occur in sufficient numbers to cause possible confusion with chalky till when augered. Locally the clay soils of the Gault are modified by mixing with sandy hill wash.

STRATIGRAPHY

The detailed stratigraphy of the Gault was first studied in the coastal exposures near Folkestone, Kent (De Rance, 1868; Price, 1874, 1877), and a sequence of 13 numbered beds was recognised. Spath (1923–43) monographed the ammonites of the Gault and established a zonal system, which has been subsequently modified and refined by Casey (in Smart, Bisson and Worssam, 1966), Wright and Wright (1947) and Owen (1971, 1976). Owen (1972) has also written on the Gault sections in the sand pits around Leighton Buzzard. The Gault of East Anglia has been reassessed by Gallois and Morter (1982), mainly from borehole sequences. They recognised up to 19 rhythmic units or 'beds' within the Gault. Each 'ideal' rhythm commences with a burrowed erosion surface overlain by a lag of phosphatic pebbles and shell debris in a silty mudstone matrix; passing upwards, the mudstone becomes paler grey, more calcareous and less silty to the top of the rhythm. Since these rhythmic units are bounded by erosion surfaces the ammonite zones and subzones can be correlated with them fairly readily (Gallois and Morter, 1982, fig. 3, p.355). Owen (1988) has subsequently reassessed the *Douvilleiceras mammillatum* Zone in Europe, in the light of sections in Russia. Reference herein is to his (1972) classification of the Leighton Buzzard sections. Benthonic foraminifera provide the basis of a complementary microfaunal zonation (Carter and Hart, 1977) and ostracods have also proved to be useful stratigraphical indicators (Wilkinson and Morter, 1981, Wilkinson, 1990b). Table 2 (based on Owen, 1972) outlines the ammonite zonation of the Gault and indicates the zones known to be present in the district.

Calcareous nannofossils are also useful in interpreting Albian stratigraphy. The nannoflora of the Gault sequence exposed at Mundays Hill quarry [SP 937 282] has recently been described by Crux (1991), whose results are in accord with Owen's (1972) ammonite zonation of the same section. Crux recognises high latitude

Table 2 Ammonite zones and subzones of the Albian (based on Owen, 1972).

	Zone	Subzone
Upper Albian	*Stoliczkaia dispar*	**Mortoniceras (Durnovarites) perinflatum** **Mortoniceras (Mortoniceras) rostratum**
	Mortoniceras (Mortoniceras) inflatum	**Callihoplites auritus** **Hysteroceras varicosum** **Hysteroceras orbignyi** **Dipoloceras cristatum**
Middle Albian	*Euhoplites lautus*	*Anahoplites daviesi* *Euhoplites nitidus*
	Euhoplites loricatus	*Euhoplites meandrinus* *Mojsisovicsia subdelaruei* **Dimorphoplites niobe** **Anahoplites intermedius**
	Hoplites (Hoplites) dentatus	*Hoplites (Hoplites) spathi* *Lyelliceras lyelli* *Hoplites (Isohoplites) eodentatus*
Lower Albian	*Douvilleiceras mammillatum*	Protohoplites (Hemisonneratia) puzosianus **Otohoplites raulinianus** **Cleoniceras (Cleoniceras) floridum** Sonneratia kitchini
	Leymeriella (Leymeriella) tardefurcata	**Leymeriella (Leymeriella) regularis** *Hypacanthoplites milletoides* *Farnhamia farnhamensis*

Subzones recognised in the Leighton Buzzard district are shown in **bold** type. The Lower Albian is represented by the highest beds of the Woburn Sands formation and the basal 'Junction Beds' of the Gault.

* Owen (1988) recognised *Isohoplites eodentatus* as a junior synonym of *Pseudosonneratia (Isohoplites) steinmanni*, which takes precedence. He proposes that the base of the Middle Albian should now be taken at the base of the *L. lyelli* Subzone.

elements in the nannoflora which suggest relatively cold waters during the deposition of the earliest Lower Gault beds and those of the earliest Upper Gault, both deposited during periods of marine transgression. It is inferred that continuous marine connection existed between this area and low-latitude areas throughout the period of Albian time represented by the exposed Gault strata.

Certain bivalves are also valuable stratigraphical indicators, for example the inoceramid genus *Birostrina*. It is represented by the species *concentrica* (with concentric ribbing) in the Middle Albian. This evolves into the radially ribbed form *B. sulcata* at the base of the *cristatum* Subzone. *B. sulcata* continues as the common form through the *cristatum* and *orbignyi* subzones, but reverts to the *concentrica* morphotype at the end of the latter subzone. The genus *Aucellina* shows evolution of the left valve shell ornament from the *auritus* subzone of the Upper Albian into the Lower Cenomanian (Morter and Wood, 1983), which is of stratigraphical significance.

Detailed stratigraphical studies of the Gault in the district (Wright and Wright, 1947; Owen, 1972) have confirmed the presence of the lower and upper subdivisions of the formation recognised in south-east England. The Gault has been shown to overstep the Woburn Sands from south-east to north-west to rest uncomformably on the Portland and Kimmeridge Clay formations. In all exposures, the Lower Gault is present above the basal 'Junction Beds'. The boundary between Lower and Upper Gault (corresponding to the Middle and Upper Albian) is marked by a nonsequence and a complex phosphatic nodule/pebble bed. In a full sequence the break occurs between the *lautus* and *inflatum* Zones (beds 10 and 11 of

Gallois and Morter (1982). In the Leighton Buzzard exposures, however, a considerable hiatus is present between Lower and Upper Gault, with the *subdelaruei, meandrinus, nitidus* and *daviesi* subzones (beds 7 to 10 inclusive of Gallois and Morter) apparently missing.

Differential erosion seems to have occurred between the deposition of the highest Albian and the lowest Cenomanian. In the south-central part of the district, as exemplified in the Sundon Borehole, very little, if any break is present between the Upper Greensand and the Lower Chalk. North-eastwards towards Barton-le-Clay increasing amounts of the highest Albian have been removed below the base of the Lower Chalk. With the total removal of the Upper Greensand north-west of Dunstable, the weakly developed Glauconitic Marl, at the base of the Lower Chalk is replaced by the Cambridge Greensand which contains many derived phosphatised high Albian fossils.

Junction Beds

After the deposition of the Woburn Sands a break in sedimentation occurred prior to the deposition of the Lower Gault; this break was possibly associated with a regression of the sea in mid-*tardefurcata* Zone times (Morter in Shephard Thorn et al., 1986). Renewed sedimentation accompanied a widespread Lower Albian transgression, during which much erosion and reworking of the pre-existing sediments took place. These events are recorded in the 'Junction Beds' at the base of the Gault in the district (Wright and Wright, 1947; Bristow, 1963; Owen, 1972). The 'Junction Beds' show considerable variation.

In the quarried areas around Shenley Hill, north-north-east of Leighton Buzzard, eroded remnants of the 'Silty Beds' of the Woburn Sands seem to have formed low mounds on the contemporary sea floor. Capping these mounds in some cases are developments of gritty ironstone associated with thin lenticular beds of the Shenley Limestone. The latter is a pale fawnish brown phosphatic limestone with scattered polished goethite ooliths; it is noted for its rich and varied fauna of rhynchonellid and terebratulid brachiopods (Lamplugh and Walker, 1903; Lamplugh, 1922; Casey, 1961), and more restricted belemnite, bivalve, gastropod and echinoid faunas; rare ammonites of the genus *Leymeriella* indicative of the *tardefurcata* Zone also occur. The Shenley Limestone is restricted geographically to the Shenley Hill area, with one or two possible occurrences where the limestone has been reworked, south of Leighton Buzzard urban area. It passes rapidly into glauconitic sandy marls with phosphatic nodules and ironstone ('carstone') fragments away from the mounds. Above the limestone, a distinctive bed of fissile red mudstone, up to 1.2 m thick, is sometimes present; it is regarded by some previous workers as the basal bed of the Gault. It has been referred to as the Red Clay or the 'Cirripede Bed'; the latter name is based on the occurrence of valves of *Cretiscalpellum unguis* and *Pycnolepas rigida* (Toombs, 1935).

Another kind of 'Junction Beds' assemblage is of wider distribution south of Leighton Buzzard. Here scattered fragments of ferruginous 'carstone' (hard gritty ironstone) or 'boxstone' (siderite nodules), rare Shenley Limestone, and quartz and quartzite pebbles in a gritty matrix, rest on the eroded surface of the Woburn Sands. Locally the pebbles are sufficiently abundant to form a basal conglomerate. Brownish, sandy, gritty fossiliferous clays and clayey sands with glauconite and bands of phosphatic nodules overlie the basal bed. Lenticles of Shenley Limestone have been recorded at the base of similar clayey sands in a former sand pit at Southcott Mill [9045 2453] (Lamplugh, 1922; Owen, 1971) and in the Gault basement bed at Littleworth [881 233], in Wing (Owen, 1971).

The 'Junction Beds' are a condensed Lower Albian sequence, in which depositional breaks are marked by the bands of phosphatic nodules; locally these bands may coalesce, with consequent mixing of faunal elements. Broadly the 'Junction Beds' represent the upper part of the *tardefurcata* Zone and the lower part of the *mammillatum* Zone with the top of latter missing (Table 2); they are approximately equivalent in age to the upper part of the Folkestone Beds of the Weald.

Lower Gault

Detailed research (Wright and Wright, 1947; Owen, 1972) on the Gault sections around Leighton Buzzard has confirmed the presence of up to 10 m of Lower Gault above the 'Junction Beds'. The mudstone and associated phosphatic nodule beds are richly fossiliferous so the ammonite zonation is well established. The *dentatus* and *loricatus* Zones of the Lower Gault are represented in the district by their *eodentatus* and *spathi* subzones and *intermedius* and *niobe* subzones respectively (Table 2). Owen (1972, figs. 2 and 3) illustrates the considerable variations in subzonal thickness that occur, notably in the *spathi* and *intermedius* subzones. He suggests that contemporary tectonic movements could have resulted in the establishment of slightly deeper 'basins' locally.

The higher subzones of the Lower Gault are missing in the district, below the base of the Upper Gault.

Upper Gault and Upper Greensand

The quarry sections around Leighton Buzzard include representatives of the *cristatum*, *orbignyi* and *varicosum* subzones of the *inflatum* Zone (Owen, 1972), totalling up to 10 m in thickness. These subzones correspond to beds 11 to 14 inclusive of Gallois and Morter (1982). It appears that only the upper part of the *cristatum* Subzone is present, above the basal nodule bed of the Upper Gault. The base of the *orbignyi* Subzone is marked by an horizon with *Euhoplites inornatus*, above which the Subzonal index *Hysteroceras orbignyi* and *Birostrina sulcata* are common. The base of the *varicosum* Subzone is marked by a band of *remanié* phosphatic nodules, in which *B. sulcata* is absent, indicating that no admixture of *orbignyi* Subzone sediments has occurred locally.

Elsewhere in the district the *auritus* and *dispar* Zones are represented in poorly exposed mudstones and silty mudstones, and in the Upper Greensand, corresponding to beds 15 to 19 inclusive of Gallois and Morter. There is little biostratigraphical information for this interval but it would appear that beds 15 to 19 are markedly thicker here than in East Anglia (Gallois and Morter, 1982). Micropalaeontological studies of the Sundon Borehole suggest the presence of the *perinflatum* Subzone in the highest Albian, which is slightly younger than Bed 19. The total thickness of the Upper Gault and Upper Greensand combined is about 60 m. Selected details of sites and boreholes within the district are given below; other sites, visible around 1960, have been described by Bristow (1963).

Details

CUBLINGTON, ASTON ABBOTTS AND WING

In the south western corner of the district, the Gault oversteps the Woburn Sands and Portland formations to rest on an eroded surface of Kimmeridge Clay. To the south-south-west of Cublington the base of the Gault drops 15 m over a distance of 700 m, giving some impression of the degree of overstep. At its lowest elevation the base of the Gault rests on the Kimmeridge Clay at a level approximately 7 m above Bed KC40 (see p.31).

East of the Hardwick Stream between Littlecote, Cublington and Aston Abbotts, the Gault crops out above the Kimmeridge Clay, high on the valley side, and below a capping of glacial deposits. There are no surface exposures, but auger-holes show that the Gault consists of grey to olive-grey, more or less silty, clays which generally weather to brownish tints, and are locally creamy white. It contrasts strongly with the darker grey Kimmeridge Clay.

In the above localities, layers of fossiliferous phosphatic nodules crop out on the valley side giving rise to slight positive features and abundant soil brash. At the base of the Lower Gault, where it rests on Kimmeridge Clay, there is a persistent bed of small white patinated nodules with some hoplitid ammonites. The field evidence suggests that the maximum thickness of Lower Gault hereabouts does not exceed 5 m. Slightly higher up the valley sides a stronger feature is associated with a nodule bed marking the base of the Upper Gault. Amongst the phosphatised ammonites collected at a locality south of Cublington [SP 8356 2190], *Euhoplites* aff. *vulgaris*, indicative of the *inflatum* Zone has been identified. In some instances soil creep and hill wash have apparently transported Upper Gault ammonites downslope below the feature marking the base.

A former marl pit [SP 8381 2393] c.1.7 km north of Cublington, now ploughed over, yielded an abundant and relatively diverse ammonite fauna, dominated by specimens of *Euhoplites*, including *E.* aff *trapezoidalis*, *E.* aff. *vulgaris*, *E.* aff. *ochetonotus*, *E. solenotus?* and *E. alphalautus*, as well as indeterminate specimens of *Euhoplites*. Other ammonites include *?Anahoplites* sp., *?Lepthoplites* sp., *?Callihoplites* sp., *Hysteroceras orbignyi*, *H.* aff. *carinatum*, *Mortoniceras (Deiradoceras?)* sp., *M. (Deiradoceras)* sp., and *M.(D.)* aff. *devonense*. All of the material is fragmentary and preserved mostly in dark heavily abraded and bored phosphate. An encrusting oyster fauna was noted on several nodules, including *Pycnodonte* and *Atreta*, with associated *Birostrina sulcata*. This fauna as a whole is quite characteristic of the Upper Gault *inflatum* Zone; it suggests an origin from several distinct horizons within the Upper Gault, but could include a composite phosphatic horizon as suggested for the Ford–Aston Clinton area of the Thame district (Wood, 1990).

Around Wing, the Gault rests on Kimmeridge Clay, but the outcrops are largely concealed by drift deposits. In the last century a brick pit [SP 881 233] at Littleworth, north of Wing, reputedly exposed Lower Gault overlying Kimmeridge Clay beneath a thick sequence of glacial drift; the thick drift is possibly the infill of a 'buried' channel. Jukes-Browne (1900, p.278) quotes the following section recorded by A H Green around 1860:

		Thickness m
Drift	Sand and pebbly sand	4.27
Gault	Pale blue laminated clay with whity brown phosphatic nodules	4.57
	Yellow earthy concretionary limestone with much ochre, pyrites, some carbonate of copper and brown phosphatic nodules	0.46–0.61
Kimmeridge	Stiff bluish black clay with large septaria	1.83

A similar section was recorded by Davies (1915), who noted a fuller drift sequence totalling 15.4 m (see p.93).

The basement bed contains fragments resembling the Shenley Limestone of Shenley Hill. Lower Gault fossils recorded include the ammonites *?Euhoplites truncatus* and *Hoplites dentatus* with the belemnite *Neohibolites minimus*, but the collecting horizon is not stated.

The geometry of the Gault overstep on the Kimmeridge Clay in this area is not known in any detail. However, the reported level of the base of the Gault here is below that interpreted south of Wing, so the possibility of structural disturbance has to be considered. It seems most probable that the Gault sequence at Littleworth is part of a faulted outlier downthrown in a general northerly direction.

SOUTH OF LEIGHTON BUZZARD

To the south of Linslade the following section was recorded in the north face of Ascott Farm Sand Pit [SP 9090 2409]:

	Thickness m
Brown clayey soil	0.4
LOWER GAULT	
Clay, pale, olive-brown, weathered, passing down into grey clay with brown mottling	1.1
Clay, grey, stiff, with a few scattered white-patinated, dark brown phosphatic nodules; a concentration of similar nodules at the base, some containing ammonites; sharp base	1.5
'JUNCTION BEDS'	
Clay, bluish grey becoming khaki, very sandy, pebbly, gritty, containing much medium to coarse-grained sand; some wisps and lenses of clayey sand; pebbles up to a maximum of 0.01 m in diameter are well-rounded and mainly of quartz	0.25
Sand, clayey, rusty brown, medium to coarse-grained, containing much medium to coarse-grained, containing pebbles as above; some discrete pods and lenses of khaki sandy clay	0.22
'Nodule Bed', containing many irregularly shaped whitish-weathering, bright red-mottled, phosphatic, gritty, pebbly, coarse-grained sandstone nodules in a matrix similar to that of the overlying bed	0.10
Sand, rusty brown, slightly clayey, coarse-grained, gritty, pebbly, with intercalations of grey and khaki sandy clay; pebbles increase downwards with scattered 'boxstone' concretions at base; sharp junction with underlying Woburn Sands	0.50

A similar sequence was penetrated in the nearby Ascott Farm Sand Pit Borehole [SP 9078 2408] (see Appendix 2 p.117).

Gault is exposed in the south-west corner [SP 9110 2340] of the worked-out Tiddenfoot New Pit but is inaccessible because of flooding. An estimated 6 m of Gault, including the 'Junction Beds' overlies about 8 m of cross-bedded Woburn Sands, above the water line. Owen (1972) recorded a section in this pit [SP 9114 2355] of which the following is an abridged version:

	Thickness m
?UPPER GAULT	
Clay, pale grey with scattered phosphatic nodules: phosphatic nodule band at base	0.76
LOWER GAULT	
Clay, pale grey and fawn grey; scattered phosphatic nodules in upper part	2.19
Clay, dark grey with scattered phosphatic nodules; phosphatic nodule bed at base	2.96
'JUNCTION BEDS'	
Sand, brown, with clay wisps; phosphatic nodule bands at and near base	0.48
Grit, ferruginous, with phosphatic nodules	0.12
Sand, brown, gritty, pebbly; sporadic blocks of Shenley Limestone	0.68

The basal beds of the Gault are poorly exposed in a small working sand pit adjacent to Grovebury Farm [SP 9245 2368]. About 6 m of grey clays of the Lower Gault, containing sporadic phosphatic nodules are exposed on a degraded slope above the working sand face. The 'Junction Beds' are obscured by talus.

The same beds were exposed in Pratt's Pit (SP 9322 2400]. In the section given below the nodule beds I and II are as described by Wright and Wright (1947).

	Thickness m
LOWER GAULT	
Clay, darkish grey, weathered pale brown and brown-mottled in top 2.5 m; some white-patinated phosphatic nodules	c.6
'JUNCTION BEDS'	
Clay, dark grey, sandy, containing rusty brown, slightly pebbly sand intercalations; passing down into	0.30
Sand, dark brown, clayey, fine-grained, slightly pebbly, with dark grey sandy clay intercalations; becoming rusty brown and less clayey towards base; some scattered phosphatic nodules and a few carbonaceous plant fragments	0.28
Clay, sandy, pale khaki and dark greenish grey with many small intercalations of rusty brown sand; a few scattered pebbles, mainly quartz but including 'carstone'; sporadic phosphatic nodules at base (Nodule Bed II)	0.18
Sand, clayey, rusty brown, fine- to medium-grained with scattered small quartz pebbles (0.01 m diameter); irregular intercalations of sandy clay; phosphatic nodules at or close to base (Nodule Bed I)	0.40
Sand, rusty brown, fine- to medium-grained, slightly clayey, slightly pebbly, with a few small clay lenses; pebbles increase downwards; sporadic 'boxstone' concretions at base; sharp junction with underlying Woburn Sands	0.25

Sections of the Gault and lists of its fauna in this pit have been published at various dates (e.g. Lamplugh, 1915; Wright and Wright, 1947; Hancock, 1958; Casey, 1961; Middlemiss, 1962; Owen, 1972). Wright and Wright distinguished four ill-defined layers of phosphatic nodules in the 'Junction Beds', the bottom three corresponding with those at Chamberlains Barn Pit [SP 931 268].

At the large Grovebury Sand Pit, a clear section of the Gault was recorded in the south-east corner [SP 9275 2305]:

	Thickness m
ALLUVIUM	
Clayey soil on brown clay; gravelly at base	0.9
LOWER GAULT	
Clay, stiff, grey, with scattered calcareous 'race' nodules	1.2
'JUNCTION BEDS'	
Clay, darker grey, sandy, with rusty brown sand lenticles and sporadic phosphatic nodules; sharp base at calcreted top of Woburn Sands	0.7

A fuller section elsewhere in this pit [SP 9230 2288], recorded by Owen (1972, p.291), is given here in abridged form:

	Thickness m
UPPER GAULT	
Clay, weathered, pale grey; phosphatic nodule 0.60 m below top; scattered nodules in basal 0.83 m	2.08
LOWER GAULT	
Clay, grey and fawn, with scattered phosphatic nodules	6.39
Clay, dark grey, shelly, with phosphatic nodules in basal 1.37 m	1.97
Clay, dark grey, gritty, with phosphatic nodules	0.60
'JUNCTION BEDS'	
Clay, grey, sandy, pebbly, with phosphatic nodules; gritty, pebbly loam at base	0.77
Grit, brown, with large pebbly phosphatic nodules	up to 0.10
Sand, brown, with phosphatic nodules in top 0.12 m; a few Shenley Limestone fragments	0.35

NORTH OF LEIGHTON BUZZARD

Around Heath and Reach, just north of Leighton Buzzard, Gault is exposed as overburden in the following quarries, which exploit the Woburn Sands: Bryants Lane [SP 929 286], Reach Lane [SP 933 284], Mundays Hill [SP 937 282]. Chamberlains Barn [SP 931 268] and New Trees [SP 931 275]. Brief accounts of the Gault sections have been included with descriptions of the Woburn Sands (Chapter Four).

STANBRIDGE, TILSWORTH AND SUNDON

Around Stanbridge and Tilsworth, pale grey, slightly micaceous, silty clay of the Upper Gault is separated from the very pale brownish grey marl of the Lower Chalk by two units of slightly micaceous clayey siltstone, which together vary in thickness from about 2 m to 8 m. The lower siltstone unit (up to 6 m thick) is pale grey, with a trace of glauconite but no phosphatic nodules, while the upper (up to 5 m thick) is greenish grey and conspicuously glauconitic, and contains locally numerous phosphatic nodules similar to those in the Gault. Contacts between these units are generally fairly well defined.

Microfaunal studies of these beds, sampled by hand-augering from between [SP 9852 2472] and [SP 9942 2386], showed that the highest Gault clay is of Zone 5 and low to middle Zone 6 age, and the siltstone belongs to upper Zone 6 and Zone 6A. They can therefore be assigned to the topmost Albian (*inflatum* and *dispar* Zones), and the siltstone is taken to be the local development of the Upper Greensand. The overlying pale marl, on the other hand, yielded a basal Lower Cenomanian microfauna of Zone 8 (Aldiss, 1990; Wilkinson, 1990a).

Subsequently, excavations made during 1990 for the Leighton Linslade Southern Bypass provided sections in the Gault, the Upper Greensand and the basal Lower Chalk [SP 9740 2285 to SP 9750 2287]. The lower part of the Upper Greensand is faulted out of the section, so that at the western end of this section the greenish grey glauconitic siltstone rests directly against pale grey Gault clay. This siltstone, which includes *Aucellina* sp., but no inoceramids, is overlain on a burrowed surface by a bed (1.5 m thick) of pale grey calcareous clayey siltstone with fairly common dark brown phosphatic nodules but only sparse glauconite. This bed, which is itself overlain on an apparently sharp contact by chalky marls, contains terebratulid brachiopods and both *Aucellina* sp. and fragmentary inoceramids, indicating that it was deposited during Lower Cenomanian times and is therefore the lowest bed of the Chalk at this locality. Microfaunal analysis of this bed also indicated a Cenomanian rather than an Albian age (Wilkinson, 1991). No lithotype corresponding to the Glauconitic Marl is present at this locality.

The Sundon Borehole [TL 0405 2724] was drilled to investigate the Lower Chalk sequence below the Totternhoe Stone and its relationship with the underlying Upper Greensand and Gault strata. The base of the Lower Chalk is marked by a weakly developed Glauconitic Marl, above a depth of 46.20 m in the borehole. The Upper Greensand was proved to 49.61 m, and Upper Gault thence to the end of the borehole at 55.65 m. The Lower Chalk sequence is described in the following chapter. An abbreviated log of the Upper Greensand and Gault is given below.

	Thickness m	Depth m
LOWER CHALK	46.20	46.20
UPPER GREENSAND		
Siltstone, muddy calcareous, medium to dark greenish grey, with traces of coarse silt grade glauconite and shell debris in large burrow-fills, *Chondrites* mottling, minute cubes of pyrite and phosphatic nodules, scattered fossils	1.05	47.25
Siltstone, slightly muddier and darker than above, calcareous, micaceous, traces of glauconite and scattered small phosphatic nodules, heavily bioturbated, several fossils	0.85	48.10
Siltstone, paler grey, micaceous and glauconitic with fish debris	0.10	48.20
Core lost	0.06	48.26
Siltstone, darker and more marly than above, intensely bioturbated	0.11	48.37
Siltstone, pale grey with darker burrow-fills, bivalves	0.10	48.47
Siltstone, darker grey, homogenous with fine burrows	0.40	48.87
Siltstone, somewhat paler grey, muddy, micaceous, calcareous, speckled with a fine glauconite; passing down in to:	0.74	49.61
UPPER GAULT		
Mudstone, silty, micaceous, calcareous, medium to dark grey with scattered dark glauconite grains; silty material in burrow-fills and in wisps. Microfaulting. Fawn phosphatic nodule at 50.25 m and band of nodules at 50.51 m.	0.90	50.51
Mudstone, as above, slightly darker, possible erosion surface at 51.18 m with large burrows filled with pale silty glauconitic mudstone below. Fawn phosphatic nodule at 51.32 m.	0.86	51.37
Mudstone, silty, calcareous, medium grey with *Thalassinoides* and *Chondrites* burrows, a few phosphatic nodules, some associated with burrows, traces of silt, mica and glauconite in burrow fills. Shelly ?erosion surface at base.	0.71	52.08
Mudstone, silty with burrow-fills rich in shell debris, fawn phosphatic nodules and clasts of glauconitic mudstone, pyritised plant debris at 52.18 m. Oyster encrusting phosphatic nodules at 52.25 m another at 52.30 m. Erosion surface at base.	0.55	52.63
Siltstone, muddy, micaceous, calcareous, pale grey: intensely burrowed to 52.78 m.		

	Thickness m	Depth m
Small buff phosphatic nodule below and another at 52.90 m less burrowed below.	0.38	53.01
Mudstone, silty, medium to dark grey, with *Chondrites* and *Thalassinoides* burrows, microfaulting, brown phosphatic nodules at 53.20 m, 53.34 m, 53.37 m and 53.45 Coarse shell debris in burrow-fills from 53.53 to 53.59 m associated with fawn phosphatic nodules at 54.08 m. Erosion surface at base.	1.09	54.10
Mudstone, paler, burrowed, with phosphatic nodule at 54.16 m, 54.26 m, 54.36 m and 54.53 m, microfaulting below. Further nodules at 54.83 m, from 54.90 to 54.93 m, 55.30 m and 55.37 m less silty below.	1.55	55.65

The calcimetry curve and natural gamma log of the Sundon Borehole, reproduced in Figure 21, confirm the lithostratigraphical identity of the Upper Greensand. Biostratigraphical studies have been carried out on the borehole core material. Microfaunal investigations of the foraminifera (Fletcher, 1989) and ostracods (Wilkinson, 1989) broadly confirm the late Albian age of the Upper Gault and Upper Greensand strata, ranging from Zone 5 to Zone 6 of Carter and Hart (1977), i.e., the *varicosum* to *perinflatum* subzones of the ammonite zonal system. The presence of Zone 6a (of certain highest Albian to basal Cenomanian age) has not been confirmed in the borehole, although it has been recorded from surface exposures near Mead Farm [SP 9528 2314] (Aldiss, 1990). Diagnostic ammonite species are not represented in the macrofaunal collections, but an interesting sequence of *Aucellina* demonstrating changes in left valve ornament as detailed by Morter and Wood (1983) has been collected, lending support to the microfaunal age assessments. It is intended to publish the detailed biostratigraphy of the borehole elsewhere.

SHEFFORD, CLOPHILL AND SHARPENHOE

Jukes-Brown (1900) records that a seam of phosphatic nodules was worked in the Lower Gault at Campton near Shefford. A well at the works, 8.5 m deep, penetrated through clay into sand, indicating that the nodule bed must lie about 7 m above the base of the Gault. The nodules occurred through a thickness varying between 0.23 m and 0.6 m. Calcareous shields of 'Belemnites' minimus were so abundant that they had to be picked out by hand from the washed nodules.

Jukes-Brown (1900) also mentions that a small pit near the old Church at Clophill [presumably TL 0913 3880]) revealed in 1884, 'several feet of grey clay with phosphatic nodules passing down through sandy clay into clayey sand, the last enclosing large arenaceo-phosphatic nodules like those which occur in the zone of *Ammonites mammillaris* at Folkestone and elsewhere. This bed rests on yellow and brown sand'. The clay and sand with nodules almost certainly correspond to the 'Junction Beds' at Leighton Buzzard.

A nodule bed overlain by light grey marly clay was recorded (Jukes-Brown, 1900) in the shallow excavation by the roadside north-west of Grange Mill near Sharpenhoe. The same bed was seen at the surface 'north-west of Great Faldo Farm, and has been found by trial borings about 5.5 m below the surface in the area near Brookend, and not so far from the outcrop of the nodule bed at the base of the Chalk Marl, which was formerly dug for 'coprolites' at this place'.

SIX
Cretaceous: Chalk

The Chalk crops out over about 100 km² in the south-east of the area, where it forms a part of the Chilterns escarpment. During the recent survey the long established lithostratigraphical subdivisions of Lower, Middle and Upper Chalk have been mapped by the use of feature-forming rock units, namely the Melbourn Rock and the Chalk Rock, which mark the base of the Middle and Upper Chalk respectively. The Lower, Middle and Upper Chalk are considered as having formational status within the 'Chalk Group' but have never been formally defined. There are few natural exposures, but a fairly complete lithostratigraphical sequence in the Chalk has been built up from the sections in large quarries at Barton, Sundon, Houghton Regis, Totternhoe

and Kensworth (Figure 18), supplemented by a cored borehole through the lower part of the Lower Chalk at Sundon Quarry.

The total thickness of the Chalk within the district is 190 to 200 m, of which about 70 m are Lower Chalk, up to 85 m are Middle Chalk and about 35 m represent the lower part of the Upper Chalk. Significant local variations in thickness have been noted and are discussed below.

The Chalk mainly comprises pure microporous limestone built up of the skeletal remains of calcareous algae (coccoliths). It was deposited in a relatively shallow epicontinental sea that extended over much of north-west Europe in Late Cretaceous times. The surrounding land

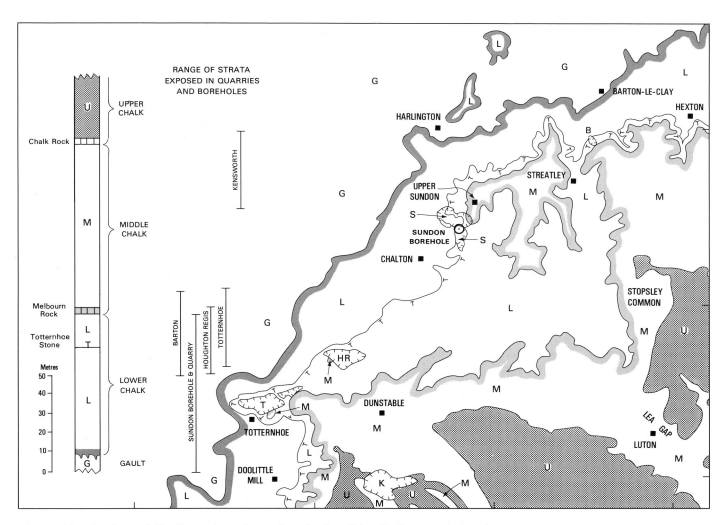

Figure 18 Outline of Chalk stratigraphy and major localities. B: Barton; S: Sundon; HR: Houghton Regis; T: Totternhoe; K: Kensworth.

was probably arid and of low relief, since very little terrigenous sediment appears to have been supplied to the depositional area; sea depths of 100 to 600 m have been estimated (Hancock, 1975).

In addition to the dominant coccolith component, the Chalk includes varying amounts of clay, fine detrital quartz, glauconite, phosphatic material, pyrite and shell and fish debris. Syndepositional and later diagenesis of the Chalk sediments has led to the development of flint, nodular chalk and chalkstones at some levels (Bromley and Gale, 1982). The Chalk is well stratified, although bedding plane partings are weakly developed. The common occurrence of layers of flint nodules, nodular chalks, chalkstones and marl seams enables the dip of the strata to be determined in medium to large exposures. Chalk sedimentation was cyclic on a small scale, but this is often cryptic because of the lack of obvious lithological or colour variation. In the Lower Chalk, cycles in the Chalk Marl are easily distinguished by the alternation of dark grey marly chalk and pale, harder limestone (p.60). This cyclicity may reflect variations in the strength of tidal currents linked to the Earth's orbital cycles (Robinson, 1986b).

Some of the distinctive lithological units within the Chalk, such as the Chalk Rock, Melbourn Rock, Plenus Marls and Totternhoe Stone, as well as some lesser marl seams, are laterally persistent over much of the Chilterns and southern England. Most of these marker horizons have characteristic signatures on geophysical borehole logs which enable them to be correlated regionally, albeit with some problems (Murray, 1986).

Invertebrate fossils are common in the Chalk, but tend to be concentrated at certain levels. The chief macrofaunal components include the various molluscan groups, brachiopods, echinoderms, sponges, serpulids and bryozoans. The preservation of molluscan species depends on whether their original shell material was calcitic or aragonitic calcium carbonate; the aragonitic shells are lost by solution in diagenesis so that ammonite species are generally represented only by stained impressions or moulds. In some chalkstones, aragonitic shells are preserved as hollow moulds showing detailed impressions of the original shell surfaces. Overall, bivalves are the commonest of the shelly fossils in the Chalk. Foraminifera and ostracods are important microfaunal elements, while coccoliths (Coccolithophoridae) are ubiquitous at most levels. Fish remains are also common locally. Trace fossils are common in the Chalk at all levels, but are readily observable only where there is a sufficient colour contrast. In the Middle and Upper Chalk, flint nodules often replace the fill of thalassinidian burrows and are referred to as 'burrow-form' flints. Crustacean burrows, including *Thalassinoides,* are a common form of bioturbation in the Chalk. The zonation of the Chalk is mainly based on its macrofauna, but complementary zonal schemes based on its microfauna (Carter and Hart, 1977, Hart et al., *in* Jenkins and Murray, 1989) and microflora are also available. The relationships between the current macrofaunal zones and the lithostratigraphical sequence is shown in Figure 19. In the Lower Chalk ammonites and inoceramid bivalves are the most useful fossil groups for zonal

purposes, while in the Middle and Upper Chalk inoceramids, brachiopods and echinoderms are important.

In the Chilterns outcrops the international chronostratigraphical stages of the Cenomanian, Turonian and part of the Coniacian are broadly represented by the Lower, Middle and Upper Chalk respectively, although the boundaries do not coincide exactly (Figure 19).

Within the district the Chalk has, at various times, been exploited for lime burning, cement manufacture, phosphatic nodules for fertiliser manufacture and building stone. Lime is still produced at Totternhoe, where, in the last decade, the working of Totternhoe Stone has been revived for restoration work in old buildings. The Chalk worked in Kensworth Quarry is crushed and slurried before being pumped via a 90 km pipeline to cement works at Rugby. A considerable portion of the district's water supply is extracted from wells in the Chalk aquifer (Chapter Nine).

Surprisingly little has been published on the stratigraphy of the Chalk in the district, since early work by Whitaker (1865), Jukes-Browne (1875), Hill and Jukes-Browne (1886) and Jukes-Browne and Hill (1903). Recent studies which refer to sites within the district include those of Bromley and Gale (1982) on the Chalk Rock, Mortimore and Wood (1986) on the development of flint and marl seams around the Middle–Upper Chalk junction, Murray (1986) on the correlation of the Lower and Middle Chalk by resistivity log marker bands and Hart (1973) on the Cambridge Greensand. A general account of the Chalk of the East Midlands was given by Keen (1968) making reference to several sites within the district.

LOWER CHALK

The Lower Chalk rests on Upper Greensand or Gault strata of late Albian age, along the foot of the Chalk escarpment for 20 km between Edlesborough in the southwest and Barton-le-Clay in the north-east. It ranges in thickness from about 65 m near Totternhoe to 80 m near Barton-le-Clay. The generalised lithostratigraphy and biostratigraphical zonation of the Lower Chalk are shown in Figure 20, from which it will be seen that it more or less corresponds to the Cenomanian stage.

Generally the Lower Chalk is notably more argillaceous and greyer in colour than the Middle and Upper Chalk, and is devoid of flints. The content of clay minerals and other noncarbonate detritus decreases upwards from more than 30 per cent at the base to less than 5 per cent at the top of the sequence, and a similar variation is shown within each of the small-scale sedimentary cycles that characterise the formation (Destombes and Shephard-Thorn, 1971).

At the base of the Lower Chalk, the Glauconitic Marl, which forms a useful marker in the North Downs of Kent and Surrey, is weakly developed, and locally absent. North-east of the A5, the lithological contrast between the marls (silty calcareous mudstone) of the basal Lower Chalk and the underlying muddy siltstones of the Upper Greensand is very slight and the junction has thus

Figure 19
Stratigraphy of the
Chalk of the Leighton
Buzzard district. (Only
selected marker
horizons shown —
most flint bands
omitted).

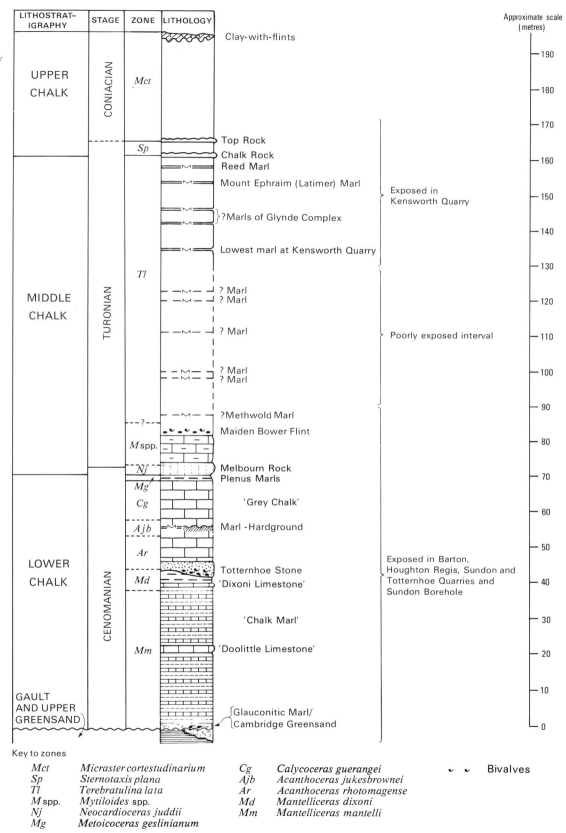

Key to zones

Mct	*Micraster cortestudinarium*	*Cg*	*Calycoceras guerangei*	↝ ↝ Bivalves
Sp	*Sternotaxis plana*	*Ajb*	*Acanthoceras jukesbrownei*	
Tl	*Terebratulina lata*	*Ar*	*Acanthoceras rhotomagense*	
M spp.	*Mytiloides* spp.	*Md*	*Mantelliceras dixoni*	
Nj	*Neocardioceras juddii*	*Mm*	*Mantelliceras mantelli*	
Mg	*Metoicoceras geslinianum*			

proved difficult to locate in the field. The Sundon Borehole [TL 0405 2724] was drilled to address this problem; it proved the presence of a thin, weakly glauconitic marl at the base of the Lower Chalk, which was not readily traceable in the field. Subsequently mapping and the examination of sections in ditches and road cuttings to the south-west (Aldiss, 1990) has enabled the junction to be located; the base of the Chalk shows no particular concentrations of glauconite there.

In the north-east, between Harlington and Barton-le-Clay, the base of the Lower Chalk is marked by the Cambridge Greensand (Jukes-Browne, 1875; Hart, 1973), a thin bed of sandy glauconitic marl containing numerous phosphatic nodules and phosphatised fossils derived from the Upper Gault. The phosphatic nodules or 'coprolites' were extracted extensively in the 19th century for the manufacture of superphosphate fertiliser, and little of the Cambridge Greensand now remains near the surface. The Cambridge Greensand, north-east of Barton, rests on Upper Gault strata, the Upper Greensand having been lost by pre-Cenomanian erosion. The extent of the Cambridge Greensand to the south-west appears to be limited by the Lilley Bottom structure which was active during the Albian/Cenomanian (Figure 32).

Above the basal bed, the sequence of cyclically alternating dark marl and pale limestone extending up to the base of the Totternhoe Stone is traditionally but informally known as the 'Chalk Marl'. However, the 'Chalk Marl' of the Chilterns is not exactly equivalent stratigraphically to the unit of the same name in east Kent (Shephard-Thorn, 1988). In this district the 'Chalk Marl' is 30 to 40 m thick around Totternhoe but increases to 54 m in the Sundon area. The top of the Chalk Marl is a major erosion surface on which the Totternhoe Stone was deposited (Figure 20).

Chalk Marl cycles are typically up to one metre in thickness. A basal dark, clay-rich, pyritous, marly chalk showing considerable bioturbation usually rests on a burrowed erosion surface at the top of the preceding cycle. The marl becomes paler and more calcareous upwards and passes into a pale, compact, argillaceous limestone at the top of the cycle. Traces of glauconite and white mica are present in both the marls and the limestones. Limestone dominates the sequence in places and may form mappable units. For example, south of Totternhoe and also south-west of Chalton a thin hard limestone, or group of limestones occurs, and is here given the informal name 'Doolittle Limestone' from its occurrence near Doolittle Mill [SP 990 202] (Aldiss, 1990). The limestone is up to 1 m thick and occurs about 20 m above the base of the Lower Chalk (Figure 20). It gives rise to a distinctive fossiliferous soil brash; the fossils include 'Inoceramus' crippsi, Schloenbachia varians and subordinate Hypoturrilites tuberculatus. The brash has also been noted low in the combes near Sundon and Sharpenhoe, where the bed is not readily mappable. It may possibly correlate with a similar bed in the Lower Chalk sequence at Folkestone, designated marker M3 by Gale (1989, fig. 2). Another, weakly cemented limestone, here referred to informally as the 'Dixoni Limestone', is 0.5 m thick,

and has been noted about 3.5 m below the base of the Totternhoe Stone (Figure 22) in Sundon and Barton quarries (Figure 18). It contains common Inoceramus ex gr. virgatus and other fossils indicative of the Mantelliceras dixoni Zone, including rare examples of the zonal index. This limestone may correlate with the marker M6 of the Folkestone sequence (Gale, 1989, figs. 2 and 3).

The Doolittle and Dixoni limestones have been used to demonstrate that the depth of pre-Totternhoe Stone erosion varies considerably. Locally both of the limestones have been cut out by differential erosion. In addition, some of the thickness variations of the 'Chalk Marl' may be accounted for by accumulation in local troughs, for example around Sundon. South-westwards from Sundon to Totternhoe there appears to be a reduction in thickness of the Chalk Marl below the Doolittle Limestone.

The Chalk Marl is relatively impermeable and yields little groundwater. Springs emerge locally from the Totternhoe Stone and also from the Doolittle Limestone, on the scarp faces of the Chilterns.

The Totternhoe Stone (0.8 to 5 m thick) is exposed in several large quarries in the district (Figure 18). It is a massive greyish brown calcarenite with brown phosphatic pebbles in its lower part. Typically, it is a freestone, and has been extracted for use as a building stone at Totternhoe, where it is thickest. It forms only a weak topographical feature and gives rise to a relatively sparse soil brash. Indeed, in some areas (such as from Totternhoe village southwards) the feature and brash associated with the Doolittle Limestone are far more conspicuous, and in the past have been mistaken for those of the Totternhoe Stone.

The Totternhoe Stone reflects a major episode of erosion and deposition during the early Middle Cenomanian; its greatest thickness corresponds to a channel in the Chalk Marl (Aldiss, 1990; Wood, 1990b; and p.74). The surface of the underlying Chalk Marl typically contains a Thalassinoides burrow system infilled with Totternhoe Stone sediment indicating a hiatus before the deposition of the Totternhoe Stone. The phosphatic pebbles in the lower part of the Totternhoe Stone tend to be concentrated close to the base of the bed, and fossil debris, much of it reworked, is locally abundant. Autochthonous fossil material is usually relatively sparse, but in most localities it includes the small brachiopod Orbirhynchia mantelliana in the upper part of the Totternhoe Stone; the trace fossil Teichichnus is common.

The Totternhoe Stone is only one of a series of detrital, bioturbated chalk beds in this part of the sequence. Each rests on a scoured surface and passes up typically into marly chalk. The Totternhoe Stone is distinguished from the other beds by its relative coarseness, a greater abundance of phosphatic pebbles, the development of Thalassinoides, and, in most places, the occurrence of abundant O. mantelliana. It is also the thickest and most prominent of the detrital chalks in this part of the sequence, and seems to be the only such bed which persists throughout the Leighton Buzzard district.

The Lower Chalk above the Totternhoe Stone is known informally as the 'Grey Chalk' but it is not exactly

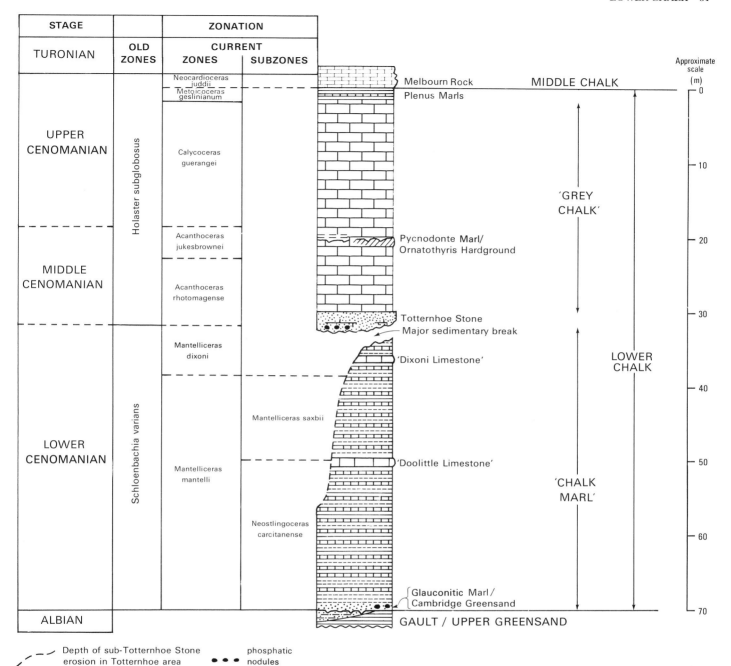

Figure 20   Generalised lithostratigraphy and biostratigraphy of the Lower Chalk.

equivalent stratigraphically to the 'Grey Chalk' of east Kent (Shephard-Thorn, 1988). It comprises 20 to 30 m of mostly uniform, massive, yellowish grey, marly chalk. A thin grey-green marl rich in pycnodonteine oysters and with sparse crushed inoceramids forms an important marker a few metres above the Totternhoe Stone at Totternhoe. This marl rests on a burrowed erosion surface which, in the Lime Quarry (Figure 25), is locally mineralised to form a hardground with associated terebratulid brachiopods (*Ornatothyris sulcifera*). It correlates with the Nettleton *Pycnodonte* Marl of Eastern England (Gaunt et al., 1992), and probably also with the basal part of Jukes-Browne's Bed 7 in the Folkestone sequence (Smart et al., 1966; Shephard-Thorn, 1988), and thus it represents an event of inter-regional significance. Thin beds of calcarenite with phosphatised pebbles lithologically similar to the Totternhoe Stone have also been recorded (Hill and Jukes-Browne, 1886). The relationships of these beds to the Totternhoe Stone are described and discussed below in the details (p.70 and Aldiss, 1990).

The top of the Lower Chalk is marked by the Plenus Marls, up to 1.65 m thick, a widely persistent group of greenish grey marls and thin marly limestones (Jefferies, 1963).

Macrofaunal zonation of the Lower Chalk

The traditional and current macrofaunal zonation of the Lower Chalk is shown in Figure 20, in relation to the divisions of the Cenomanian chronostratigraphical stage. The obsolete zones of *Schloenbachia varians* and *Holaster subglobosus* were superseded by a more refined zonation based on ammonites (Kennedy, 1969; Wright and Kennedy, 1984), which facilitates international correlation. Over the years Kennedy's scheme has been further refined within the framework of the international ammonite zonal scheme to the version shown in Figure 20. In practice, the zonal ammonite species may be rare or poorly preserved due to the loss of the original aragonite shell material, and it has been found that inoceramid bivalve faunas provide a useful complementary zonal scheme. Further, a number of bands rich in particular fossil species have been shown to have widespread occurrence and so to provide valuable correlation markers. An example is the rhynchonellid brachiopod *Orbirhynchia mantelliana* which, in the Folkestone succession, occurs in abundance at three discrete levels close to the Lower–Middle Cenomanian boundary; one in the *Mantelliceras dixoni* Zone above the equivalent of the 'Dixoni Limestone', one near the base of the Middle Cenomanian and a third below the mid-Cenomanian non-sequence. It should be noted, however, that in the Folkestone area this species is found in fine-grained chalk and limestone (where it is thought to be autochthonous), whereas in the Leighton Buzzard district it occurs uncharacteristically in detrital, calcarenitic chalks, probably as a result of intraformational reworking.

In the recent survey of the district enough material has been collected to establish the presence of the zones and subzones shown in Figure 20, but in some instances the precise zonal boundary has not been defined. In recent years new work on the Lower Chalk of southern England has necessitated some modifications to the standard ammonite zonal scheme for the Lower and Middle Cenomanian. These are discussed below.

LOWER CENOMANIAN

At Folkestone, the *Neostlingoceras carcitanense* Subzone can be divided informally into two parts (Gale and Friedrich *in* Gale, 1989). The lower part yields a low-diversity fauna with *Aucellina* spp. and '*Inoceramus*' ex gr. *anglicus* as well as heteromorph ammonites such as *Anisoceras*, *Idiohamites*, *Sciponoceras* and the subzonal index. The upper part contains a high-diversity fauna including the brachiopod *Tropeothyris? carteri*, the oyster *Rastellum colubrinum* and the ammonites *Hypoturrilites*, *Mantelliceras*, *Sharpeiceras* and abundant *Schloenbachia*, the last occurring in profusion in the limestone (marker horizon M3 of Gale, 1989, fig. 2) at the top of the subzone. The higher part of the subzone marks the entry in

flood abundance of '*Inoceramus*' *crippsi*, a bioevent that finds its expression in the Inoceramus beds of the condensed succession of eastern England. It is probable that a new zonal/subzonal nomenclature will need to be introduced for this basal part of the Chalk Marl succession. In the Chilterns, the two subdivisions of the *carcitanense* Subzone are probably represented by the beds below the Doolittle Limestone and the Doolittle Limestone respectively.

Unpublished work on the sequence at Folkestone (Gale, personal communication) and elsewhere shows that, contrary to the indications given by Gale (1989), the base of the range of *Mantelliceras dixoni* and of the eponymous ammonite zone is more or less coincident with the base of the range of *Inoceramus* ex gr. *virgatus*, and that the entry of the latter can be used to recognise the base of the zone in the absence of the zonal index.

MIDDLE CENOMANIAN

Unpublished work by Gale on the Middle Cenomanian in southern England shows that the base of the substage can be recognised by the appearance of the ammonite genus *Cunningtoniceras*, approximately coincident with the base of the second of the three *Orbirhynchia mantelliana* bands, with the basal Middle Cenomanian zonal index *Acanthoceras rhotomagense* first appearing higher in the succession, in the 'Tenuis limestone' (this informal term is as yet unpublished) beneath the 'Cast Bed'. In any future revision of the zonal scheme it will probably be necessary to introduce a *Cunningtoniceras* (partial-range) Zone at the base of the Middle Cenomanian beneath the (revised) *rhotomagense* Zone. In the Chilterns, phosphatised *Cunningtoniceras* and *Acanthoceras* are found at the base of the Totternhoe Stone at Houghton Regis [TL 005 236]; for practical purposes the base of the Totternhoe Stone in this area can be regarded as marking the base of the Middle Cenomanian *rhotomagense* Zone.

The base of the *Acanthoceras jukesbrownei* Zone, as recognised by the presence of the zonal index, appears to be more or less coincident with that of thin-shelled inoceramids grouped around '*Inoceramus*' *atlanticus*. In the Kent and Sussex successions this faunal change occurs 1 to 2 m beneath the base of Jukes-Browne Bed 7.

In the Totternhoe Central Quarry (p.74) '*Inoceramus*' *atlanticus* has been found 18 cm below a marl (15 cm thick) rich in *Pycnodonte*, that is taken to correlate with the equivalent of the basal part of Jukes-Browne Bed 7 and with the Nettleton Pycnodonte Marl at the base of the Nettleton Stone in Eastern England (Gaunt et al., 1992). The marl itself contains both '*Inoceramus*' ex gr. *atlanticus* and *Inoceramus* ex gr. *pictus* and almost certainly equates with the Pycnodonte Event bed of northern Germany (Ernst, Schmid and Seibertz, 1983), which has yielded *Acanthoceras jukesbrownei* (Wiedmann et al., 1989, fig. 2.0).

Microfaunal zonation of the Lower Chalk

Foraminifera, ostracods and nannoplankton are abundant in the Chalk and can be used to complement the macrofaunal zones. Microfaunal zonation is especially valuable where macrofaunal evidence is lacking or non-diagnostic, although some care has to be taken in interpreting the results because of reworking of the sediments by burrowing organisms and by sedimentary processes. Studies of uninterrupted sequences can also provide a record of environmental changes during deposition.

Carter and Hart (1977) detailed a zonal scheme for the Gault and Lower Chalk (derived from an earlier scheme developed from Channel Tunnel boreholes) based on benthonic foraminifera and allied to studies of benthonic/planktonic foraminifera ratios. Their zones 7 to 14 inclusive cover the Lower Chalk interval.

As part of the recent survey microfaunal studies have been carried out on the continuous cores from the Sundon Borehole (p.65) (Wilkinson, 1989), on samples collected from quarry sections of strata associated with the Totternhoe Stone (pp.70–73) (Wilkinson, 1991) and on samples from the contact of the basal beds of the Lower Chalk with the underlying Albian strata (p.00) (Wilkinson, 1990). It has not, however, been possible to carry out a complete microfaunal study of the Lower Chalk of the district to define the zonal boundaries.

The work on the Sundon Borehole established the presence of Zones 8 and 9 in the Chalk Marl. The facies controlled assemblage characteristic of Zone 7, which is restricted to the Glauconitic Marl of east Kent (Carter and Hart, 1977) was not recognised.

Lithostratigraphical and macrofaunal studies of the beds immediately below the Totternhoe Stone (p.00) have demonstrated varying degrees of erosion prior to its deposition. The interpretation of the microfauna from these beds (Figure 26) is further complicated by bioturbation and probable sedimentary reworking at some localities, as discussed below.

Microfaunas from the Cambridge Greensand are mainly Cenomanian in age (Hart, 1973), although its derived phosphatic macrofauna includes Albian forms. According to Hart (1973), the entire foraminiferal microfauna is indigenous; this also seems to be true of the ostracods (Wilkinson, 1988).

MIDDLE CHALK

In marked contrast to the greyish, marly Lower Chalk, the Middle Chalk consists mainly of pure, white, massively bedded chalk. Bands of flint nodules occur at regular intervals in the upper part and there are several thin, but persistent, marl seams which form useful markers. The hard, nodular Melbourn Rock marks the base of the formation and its top is taken at the base of the Chalk Rock. So defined, the Middle Chalk coincides approximately with the Turonian Stage (see Figure 19).

Within the district, the Middle Chalk varies from about 75 to 90 m in thickness. Exposures are rare, but the topmost 30 m or so are well exposed in the Kensworth Quarry [TL 017 197] and the lowest 12 m are seen in the quarries near Totternhoe (Figure 18). The total thickness of the formation has been proved in a number of water boreholes, some of which have been geophysically logged, enabling the unexposed middle part of the formation to be correlated with sequences in adjoining areas (Murray, 1986).

The Middle Chalk crops out extensively in the urban areas of Dunstable and Luton, and around Stopsley and Barton-le-Clay; a sizeable outlier occurs between Upper Sundon and Streatley. Subaerial erosion, possibly linked to minor tectonic flexuring and fracturing (Figure 32), has produced an intricate outcrop pattern, with a major south-easterly re-entrant along the Lea gap in the Chalk escarpment. The Melbourn Rock, at the base of the formation, forms a strong positive feature on the scarp face and valley sides, and can be traced with reasonable confidence through the built-up areas of Dunstable and Luton. It defines the tops of the spectacular combes developed on the scarp face near Barton-le-Clay, Hexton and Pegsdon (Lewis, 1949; Sparks and Lewis, 1957).

The Melbourn Rock consists of very hard creamy-white nodular chalk in a softer matrix, with wisps of greenish grey marl surrounding the nodules; it has a rough, knobbly aspect on weathered quarry faces. The Melbourn Rock extends 2 to at least 4 m above the top of the Plenus Marls in the district. It is well exposed in Sewell Quarry [SP 9945 2236] near Totternhoe and was described by Hill and Jukes-Browne (1886) from a former lime-works pit at Leagrave Road, 3 km north of central Luton. Above the Melbourn Rock about 8 m of hard, white, variably nodular chalk with *Mytiloides* spp. occur, which lack the greenish grey marl wisps characteristic of the Melbourn Rock. A thin marl occurs at the top of this nodular chalk, in the Central Quarry [SP 985 219] at Totternhoe, and a discontinuous layer of flint nodules with associated *Mytiloides* ex gr. *mytiloides* occurs a further 0.5 m above (Aldiss, 1990). This is the lowest horizon at which flint is developed in the Chalk sequence of the Chilterns and is here informally named the 'Maiden Bower Flint' from its occurrence near the prehistoric fort of Maiden Bower [SP 997 226] which has been partly destroyed by the former workings in Sewell Quarry.

Above the Maiden Bower Flint, the Middle Chalk is not exposed for some 35 to 50 m, but is probably made up of uniform white chalk with a few flint layers, some pyrite nodules and several thin marl seams.

The uppermost 30 m of the Middle Chalk are well exposed in the Kensworth Quarry [TL 017 197] (Figure 28). It consist of massive white chalks with bands of flint nodules at intervals of a metre or so and several thin marl seams; sponges and inoceramids are common fossils at some levels.

The thin marl seams give a distinctive signature on resistivity and other geophysical logs of Chalk boreholes, which can be correlated over large distances (Murray, 1986). The sequence in this district is intermediate in character between those of the North Downs and East Anglia; the correlation of some marl seams is difficult because of lithological changes and the absence of cored boreholes (Wood *in* Murray, 1986). Recent work on the geochemical signature of trace elements in the marl seams (Wray and Gale, 1993) enable some of these marls to be correlated over large distances and offer a useful complement to Murray's work.

Macrofaunal zonation of the Middle Chalk

The Middle Chalk has traditionally been divided into two zones; that of *Inoceramus labiatus* below and that of *Terebratulina lata* above. These zones are thick and not sufficiently refined for detailed correlation, so that here, as in the Lower Chalk, inoceramid faunas provide valuable complementary indicators of horizon.

The term *Inoceramus* (correctly *Mytiloides*) *labiatus* Zone has been applied to all the strata between the top of the Plenus Marl and the appearance of the zonal index of the succeeding *lata* Zone, although the first occurrence of the genus *Mytiloides*, which can be taken to mark the base of the Turonian Stage, occurs within and not at the base of the Melbourn Rock. The greater part of this sequence (but not the basal beds) is characterised by inoceramids belonging to the genus *Mytiloides* which occur in great abundance at some horizons, but the use of *Mytiloides labiatus* as a zonal index for this interval is inappropriate for several reasons. *M. labiatus*, as generally understood, appears to have a rather restricted stratigraphical range, probably within the lower part of the sequence between the appearance of *Mytiloides* and the first occurrence of *Terebratulina lata*; but it almost certainly does not occur in the basal part, which is characterised by *M. columbianus*. The higher part of the sequence is characterised by abundant *M. mytiloides*. Current work suggests that several *Mytiloides* zones could well be recognised; thus in the absence of a definitive zonation, it has been decided to adopt the term 'Zone of *Mytiloides* spp.' for the lower part of the Turonian up to the appearance entry of *Terebratulina lata*. In terms of the international standard ammonite zonation (Hancock, 1991) this part of the Turonian succession would probably correspond to the successive zones of *Watinoceras* spp., *Mammites nodosoides* and the lower part of the *Collignoniceras woollgari* Zone. The basal part of the Melbourn Rock is characterised by *Inoceramus* ex gr. *pictus* and *Sciponoceras bohemicum anterius*, and can be inferred by extrapolation from expanded sequences elsewhere to belong to the uppermost Cenomanian *Neocardioceras juddii* Zone, although the zonal index has not been recorded from the Chilterns.

The first occurrence of the zonal index of the succeeding *Terebratulina lata* Zone in southern England occurs a few metres above the abrupt lithological change from shelly chalk with abundant *Mytiloides* to massive, poorly fossiliferous chalk. This lithological change also corresponds approximately to the lowest occurrence of flint and to the appearance of poorly preserved *Mytiloides subhercynicus* and *Collignoniceras woollgari* (Mortimore and Pomerol, 1990). The latter faunal change marks the beginning of the Middle Turonian. In the Chilterns and north Hertfordshire, the lithological change seen in southern England appears likewise to correspond to the lowest flint, represented by the Maid-

en Bower Flint at Totternhoe [SP 997 226] (p.74) and its equivalent at Steeple Morden [TL 300 405] in the Hitchin district. It is, therefore, probable that the base of the *lata* Zone in these areas can likewise be drawn some distance above the flint and the sudden disappearance of conspicuous *Mytiloides*.

UPPER CHALK

The Upper Chalk caps the Chilterns escarpment in the south-eastern corner of the district, where up to 35 m of the lower beds are preserved beneath a cover of Clay-with-flints. It is made up of massive white chalks with bands of black nodular flint, sheets of tabular flint and beds of hard nodular chalk; the last are highly indurated and form chalkstones in places. Fossils are abundant at some levels. The residual capping of Clay-with-flints is commonly let down into large solution hollows developed in the Chalk which are generally cylindrical or funnel-shaped.

For practical mapping purposes the base of the Upper Chalk is taken at the base of the Chalk Rock (Bromley and Gale, 1982). The representative of this unit in the district is a highly condensed version of the Chalk Rock sequence developed more fully to the south of the district. It usually comprises indurated chalkstones 'welded' into a single bed which is up to a metre thick, penetrated by an open meshwork of *Thalassinoides* burrows and capped by a mineralised hardground. It incorporates only the uppermost hardgrounds of the type section at Ogbourne Maizey (Bromley and Gale, 1982, fig. 3). The base of the *Sternotaxis plana* Zone lies within the condensed Chalk Rock of the Chilterns. At some localities, notably Kensworth and the Luton railway cutting, the Chalk Rock has yielded a rich fauna of aragonite-shelled mollusca preserved as finely detailed hollow moulds (H Woods, 1896). The bed gives rise to a mappable feature and distinctive soil brash just below the crest of the Chilterns escarpment and on the valley sides.

A thinner hardground, the Top Rock, occurs 3 m above the Chalk Rock and has been mapped locally. It comprises a chalkstone, 0.3 to 0.5 m thick, capped by a glauconitised hardground strewn with glauconitised pebbles. The basal Upper Chalk, including the Chalk Rock and Top Rock, is exposed for 10 m in the top workings of Kensworth Quarry [TL 017 197] and is described in detail below. The Top Rock represents a condensed sequence in a similar manner to the Chalk Rock, and the junction of the *Sternotaxis plana* and *Micraster cortestudinarium* zones lies near its base.

The higher beds of the Upper Chalk preserved in the district are largely concealed by Clay-with-flints and are not exposed. Chalk of the *Micraster coranguinum* Zone has not been proved in this district.

The precise level of the Turonian–Coniacian stage boundary remains somewhat controversial (Bailey et al., 1983, 1984; Hancock, 1991); it may be taken at or just below the base of the Top Rock in the condensed sequence of this district.

DETAILS

The detailed lithostratigraphy and biostratigraphy of the Chalk of the district has been established for the most part in major quarry sections at Sundon, Barton, Houghton Regis, Totternhoe and Kensworth, and a cored borehole drilled in the floor of Sundon Quarry. The stratigraphical range of the beds exposed in each case, and the location of the quarries is shown in Figure 18.

For ease of reference each quarry section is described separately below.

SUNDON QUARRY AND BOREHOLE

The Lower Chalk was quarried for cement manufacture at Sundon over a long period up to the late 1970s, when the works were closed by the Blue Circle company. At the time of survey in 1987, the abandoned quarry faces had become more or less degraded, with the best remaining sections lying in the more recently worked area [TL 041 267], where the Totternhoe Stone was accessible at several locations. The Sundon Borehole [TL 0405 2724], drilled on the floor of the quarry, commenced at approximately 8 m below the base of the Totternhoe Stone and was completed at a depth of 55.65 m in Gault, having proved the base of the Lower Chalk at 46.20 m and that of the Upper Greensand at 49.61 m (Figure 21). Wireline geophysical logs were run in the borehole and the cores have since been studied for their macro- and microfaunas, calcimetry and clay mineralogy; these results will be published in detail elsewhere.

The Lower Chalk sequence in the Sundon Borehole

The base of the Lower Chalk is marked by the Glauconitic Marl, which here comprises 0.6 m of slightly glauconitic calcareous muddy silt, resting on pale calcareous siltstone of the Upper Greensand. The Glauconitic Marl contains sparse fragments of thin-shelled inoceramids and scattered dark and pale brown, phosphatised pebbles. There are no indications of the large, black, *Atreta*-encrusted phosphatised pebbles, and reworked Upper Albian fossils, that characterise the Cambridge Greensand, the feather-edge of which crops out about 3 km to the north-east near Barton-le-Clay (Jukes-Browne, 1875).

The Glauconitic Marl is succeeded by the Chalk Marl, a poorly defined rhythmic succession of alternating silty marls and marly limestones (Figure 21). The lowest beds contain a low-diversity fauna comprising *Aucellina* ex gr. *gryphaeoides* and *A.* ex gr. *uerpmanni*, as well as sparse occurrences of '*Inoceramus*' ex gr. *crippsi*, '*I*'. ex gr. *anglicus–comancheanus* and poorly preserved moulds of *Schloenbachia*. In addition, there are isolated records of *Monticlarella carteri*, terebratulids of uncertain affinities and the giant isopod *Palaega carteri*.

About 20 m above the base of the Chalk Marl, the sequence passes abruptly into mainly marly beds, about 2 m in thickness, with much reduced calcimetry values compared with those of the underlying beds. This calcimetry change is approximately coincident with the highest record of *Aucellina*, about 0.6 m higher. The occurrence of *Aucellina* and '*Inoceramus*' ex gr. *anglicus–comancheanus*, taken together with an isolated record of a poorly preserved *Idiohamites* or *Anisoceras* about 16 m above the base of the Chalk, indicates that the basal 20 m can be assigned to the 'lower part' (Gale and Friedrich, 1989) of the *Neostlingoceras carcitanense* Subzone of the *Mantelliceras mantelli* Zone, and equates with the Porcellanous Beds of eastern England borehole successions (see Morter and Wood, 1983 for further discussion). Compared with other areas in southern England (e.g. the Aycliff Borehole, Dover), the *Aucellina*-bearing

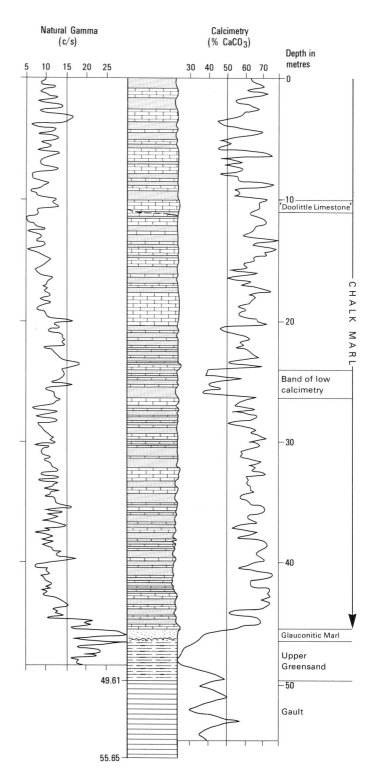

Figure 21 The lithological sequence in the Sundon Borehole. The natural gamma-ray log and calcimetry plot illustrate the rhythmic character of the Chalk Marl.

beds are here considerably thicker and may represent the thickest basal Cenomanian succession in England.

Above the marly beds (2 m) with reduced calcimetry values, rhythmic alternations of marl and marly limestone continue to about 4 m above the point where calcimetry values increase; these beds have yielded sparse 'Inoceramus' ex gr. crippsi and 'I'. ex gr. anglicus–comancheanus as in the underlying beds, but Aucellina, has not been recorded.

The overlying 10 m unit is characterised by thick beds of limestones alternating with marls; the base and top are marked by thicker limestone beds, 2.7 m and 1.4 m thick respectively. This unit contains a relatively high-diversity fauna dominated by 'I'. ex gr. crippsi (including 'I'. crippsi s.s.) and Schloenbachia varians, together with Grasirhynchia grasiana, Terebratulina proto-striatula, Entolium sp., Limaria sp., Plicatula cf. minuta and pyn-odonteine oysters. This fauna with its abundance of 'I'. ex gr. crippsi indicates the higher part of the carcitanense Subzone, an interpretation supported by a single record of a possible Tropeothyris? carteri, a brachiopod particularly characteristic of this subzone.

Unflattened Schloenbachia are preserved in abundance in the top limestone about 18 m beneath the base of the Totternhoe Stone, which probably equates with the brash-forming lime-stone that crops out 15 to 20 m below the Totternhoe Stone in the combes near Barton-le-Clay. These occurrences are be-lieved to represent the Doolittle Limestone of the Totternhoe outcrops.

The highest, rather weathered, 10 m of the borehole succes-sion comprises ill-defined rhythms of poorly fossiliferous silty marl and marly limestone. By analogy with the Folkestone suc-cession (Gale and Friedrich, 1989), these beds presumably equate with the basal part of the Mantelliceras saxbii Subzone of the Mantelliceras mantelli Zone above marker horizon M3. There is no indication of the horizon rich in large M. saxbii that is found in this subzone in Sussex and the Isle of Wight and which is also known from the southern Chilterns at Chinnor Quarry. The complete absence of Inoceramus ex gr. virgatus from the borehole succession indicates that no part of it can be attributed to the overlying Mantelliceras dixoni Zone, which is identifiable in the adjoining quarry section and also at Barton Quarry.

Lower Chalk exposures in Sundon Quarry

About 3 m of strata above the top of the Sundon Borehole are obscured by talus at the foot of the nearby face; above this the beds are fairly well exposed for 5 m up to the base of the Tot-ternhoe Stone (Figure 22). Elsewhere in the quarry floor exca-vations had been made to depths of 10 m or more below the base of the Totternhoe Stone in dark grey, silty, marly chalk, which has yielded specimens of Grasirhynchia grasiana, Monti-clarella? rectifrons and a group of associated cirripede plates (Zeugmatolepas).

The 5 m section below the Totternhoe Stone, near the bore-hole site, is shown with a diagrammatic summary of the faunal elements in Figure 22; it comprises medium to dark grey, marly chalk with poorly cemented limestone bands and a thin marl seam. The lower limestone band is the Dixoni Limestone, which previously formed a more prominent band elsewhere in the quarry (A S Gale, personal communication). The faunal evidence (Figure 22) indicates that pre-Totternhoe Stone erosion has cut down to a level in the higher part of the Mantelliceras dixoni Zone here.

The Totternhoe Stone is now poorly exposed and rather in-accessible. It is much affected by fracturing and minor dis-placements, but can be traced as a band about a metre thick in the old quarry faces. The basal surface is sharp with a marked

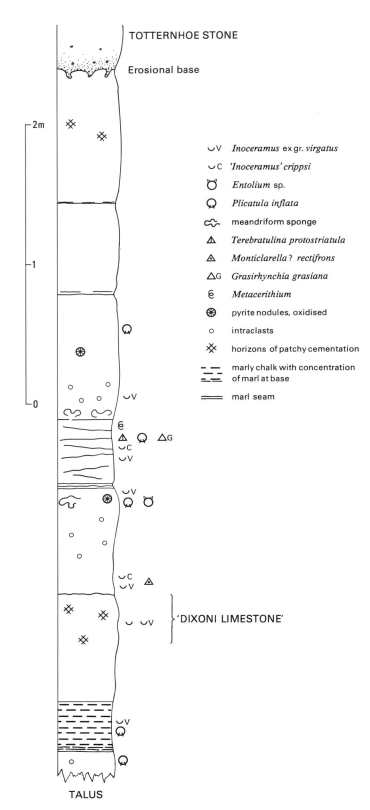

Figure 22   Section below the Totternhoe Stone in Sundon Quarry.

colour contrast between the typical grey-brown gritty, cal-carenitic lithology and that of the underlying dark grey, marly chalk. Scattered small brown phosphatic pebbles occur in the lower part of the Totternhoe Stone.

Beds above the Totternhoe Stone are poorly exposed in steep degraded and inaccessible faces for 15 to 20 m in the quarry. They are relatively uniform, pale grey, slightly marly chalk of the 'Grey Chalk', but no fauna has been collected from them.

BARTON-LE-CLAY QUARRY [TL 079 296]

At the time of this survey, this former limeworks pit was being actively backfilled as a landfill site, so that only limited sections were accessible (Figure 23). However, it was possible to record a partial section from the base of the Melbourn Rock down to a level about 9 m below the base of the Totternhoe Stone, to-talling about 35 m. Earlier observations by Smart (1957, 1958, and personal communication 1991) complement those of the present survey. He also recorded sections made during the im-provements to the A6 (Barton Bypass) and records a large *Parapuzosia* in the Totternhoe Stone (Smart, 1990) there. The composite section for Barton Quarry drawn in Figure 23 is based on a number of smaller sections numbered 1 to 7 (see also Wood, 1990a for details of sections and faunas), which were visible in 1988 to 1989.

The lower part of the Chalk Marl succession underlying the Totternhoe Stone was well exposed in a sloping section (sec-tion 1) on the north side of the gully leading off from the ac-cess road. The basal 1.5 m is rather silty, marly chalk with a sparse fauna including *Grasirhynchia grasiana* and *Entolium* sp. Above this are two weakly cemented lenticular beds, the lower of which passes laterally into spongiferous masses which yielded poorly preserved *Hypoturrilites* and bivalves including '*Inoceramus*' *crippsi*. Some 3.5 m higher, a prominent, patchily cemented, fossiliferous limestone, the Dixoni Limestone, up to 0.5 m thick provides a conspicuous and readily accessible marker horizon that can be followed on either side of the gully, and in section 2 on the east side of the access road. This bed yielded a fauna including common, large *Inoceramus* ex gr. *virgatus* indicating the *Mantelliceras dixoni* Zone together with *Schloenbachia varians* and rare examples of the zonal index. *In-oceramus* ex gr. *virgatus* was noted down to 1.7 m below the base of the limestone, suggesting that this interval should also be as-signed to the *dixoni* Zone. It is succeeded by 0.8 m of relatively marly chalk overlain by a conspicuous, dark, 0.1 m marl; a con-centration of small intraclasts together with small brachiopods including *Orbirhynchia mantelliana* was found 0.4 m beneath the marl. This bed is the correlative of the lowest of the three *Orbirhynchia* bands of the Folkestone succession.

The Totternhoe Stone, 3.5 m above the top of the Dixoni limestone, was best exposed in a weathered section (section 3) adjacent to the gully, and less well exposed in sections 2 and 4. The Totternhoe Stone is a prominent bed, about 1.15 m thick, of coarse-grained sandy chalk ; it passes upwards into some-what more marly chalk. The base of the stone is marked by a conspicuous erosion surface and the Totternhoe Stone sedi-ment is piped down into the Chalk Marl by the *Thalassinoides* burrow-system to depths of 0.9 m below the erosion surface. The lowest 0.4 m of the Totternhoe Stone is much more sandy and rough-textured than the remainder of the bed, particularly at the base. Small, dark brown, phosphatised intraclasts are common in this basal part of the stone, but become less numerous upwards, the highest is noted at 0.7 m above the basal erosion surface; rare glauconitised chalk pebbles are also found at the base. The Totternhoe Stone is rich in small bra-chiopods, notably *Orbirhynchia mantelliana*, with subordinate

Kingena concinna, Terebratulina protostriatula and terebratulids of uncertain affinities. *O. mantelliana* is common 0.45 m above the base in section 3, and ranges up to the top of the stone, becom-ing less common upwards. The highest record was from the base of the more marly chalk immediately overlying the Tot-ternhoe Stone.

Observations at Barton by Smart (1957, 1958 and personal communication, 1991) include the recording of a horizon with numerous large ammonites, of the genus *Parapuzosia (Aus-tiniceras)*, about 0.3 m below the top of the Totternhoe Stone. A specimen of *P. (A.) austeni*, 743 mm in diameter, was recov-ered from the Totternhoe Stone in excavations for the Barton Bypass (Smart, 1990) about 200 m south of the quarry.

The succession was traced for some 8 m above the base of the Totternhoe Stone in Section 5, which was very degraded and overgrown. The highest part of this section yielded a fauna of indifferently preserved inoceramids indicative of the higher part of the *rhotomagense* Zone.

An estimated 6 m of beds overlying the latter section was un-exposed, but a block of highly fossiliferous, gritty chalk, with inoceramids and ammonites indicative of the *jukesbrownei* Zone, found loose on the floor of the quarry between sections 4/5 and the back face, almost certainly came from here.

The highest part of the succession was poorly exposed and relatively inaccessible on the back face and behind the advanc-ing wall of dumped rubbish. An *Amphidonte* shell bed 5.4 m be-neath the Melbourn Rock in the south-east corner of the quar-ry is indicative of the *Calycoceras guerangeri* Zone. However, in the local absence of Plenus Marls underlying the Melbourn Rock, due to post-Cretaceous slumping, the exact stratigraphi-cal horizon of this oyster bed relative to the base of the former could not be determined.

The contact between the Plenus Marls and the hard, nodular Melbourn Rock was poorly visible in a very degraded exposure (section 7) behind the rubbish. The Plenus Marls, 0.2 m thick, at this point rest on a weakly glauconitised convolute erosion surface, and are overlain by a unit, 0.2 m thick, consisting of three thin marls alternating with marly chalks. The section was not sufficiently well exposed to establish whether the miner-alised surface was the sub-Plenus erosion surface, with the over-lying marls and marly chalks corresponding to beds 1–3 of Jef-feries (1963), or whether only Bed 3 is present. However, a fauna of *Orbirhynchia multicostata* and small pycnodonteine oys-ters collected from above the erosion surface suggests the pres-ence of Jefferies' Bed 1. The higher unit clearly corresponds to the upper part of the Plenus Marls, i.e. Jefferies' beds 4–8 in-clusive. Farther along the section, the Plenus Marls appeared to be as much as 0.7 m thick, with no signs of the mineralised erosion surface.

HOUGHTON REGIS QUARRY [TL 005 236]

This large quarry, extending over about half a square kilome-tre, was formerly worked for cement manufacture by Blue Cir-cle plc. The abandoned workings are much degraded and part-ly flooded, but still provide some useful sections. A sequence totalling about 30 m of the Lower Chalk is exposed, ranging from some 5 m below the base of the Totternhoe Stone up to the basal part of the Melbourn Rock (Figure 24), which is pre-served as a small capping at the highest point (near the north-west end of the south-west face) [TL 0051 2344]. The most ac-cessible sections are in the north-west of the quarry. The Tot-ternhoe Stone forms a massive bed up to 0.9 m thick that stands slightly proud of the quarry faces at the bottom of a prominent group of beds about 4.5 m thick (Figure 24). From the exposures in the quarry, it can be demonstrated that the regional dip is reversed here, and is about 2° to the north-west.

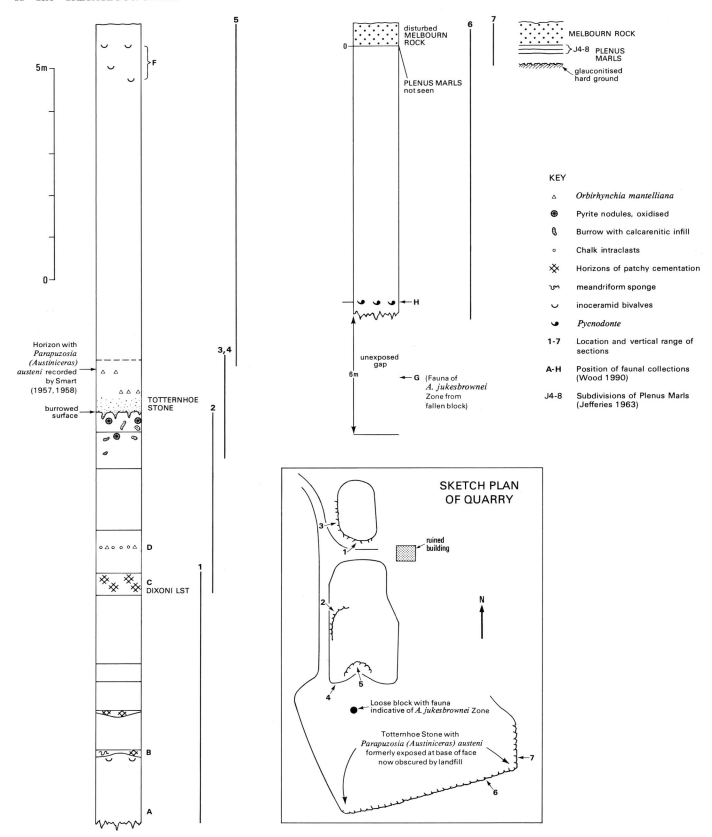

Figure 23 Composite diagram of sections recorded in Barton-le-Clay Limeworks Quarry, 1988–89. (There is a 6 m gap between the top of section 5 and the base of section 6).

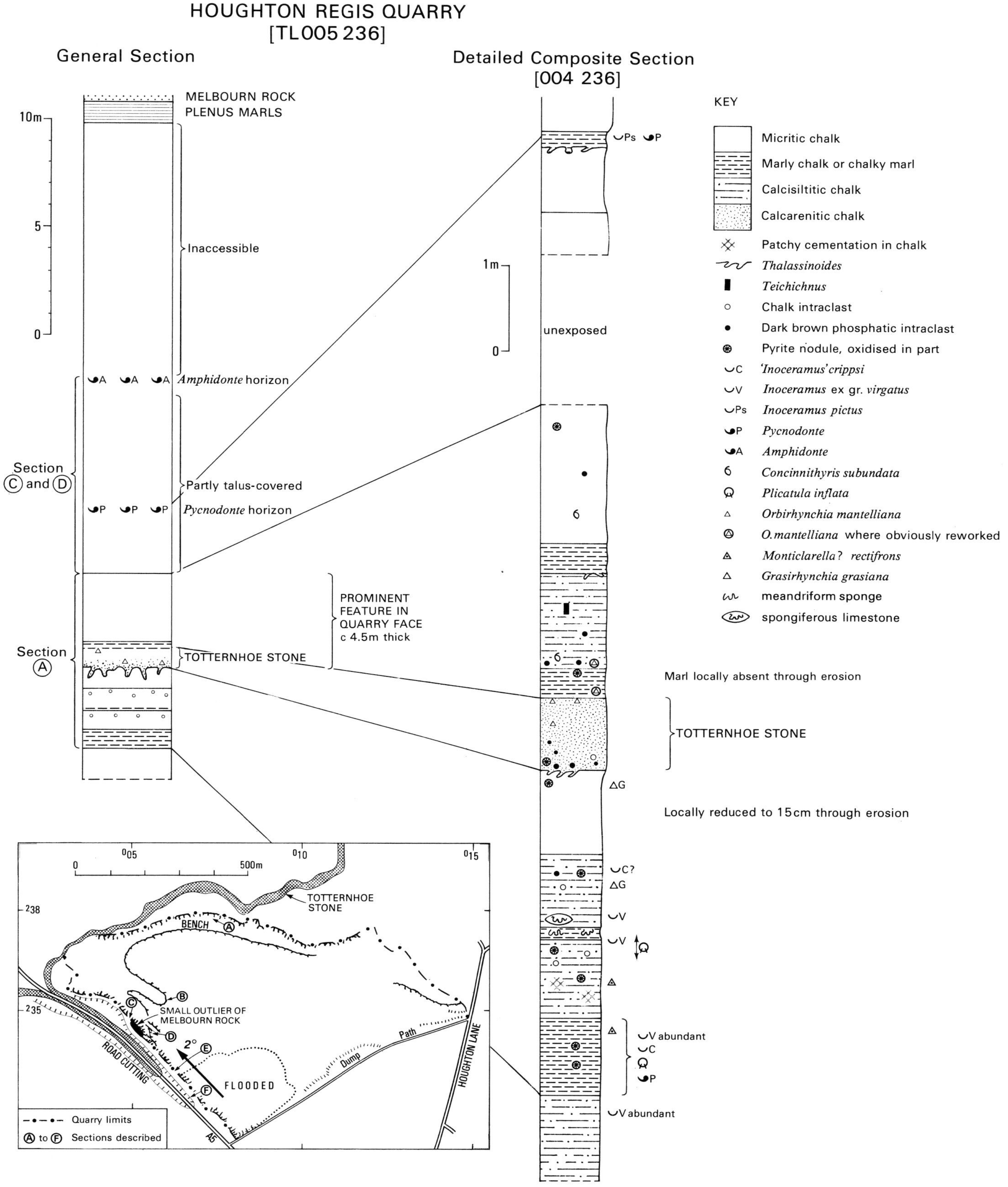

HOUGHTON REGIS QUARRY
[TL 005 236]

General Section

Detailed Composite Section
[004 236]

KEY

Figure 24   Lower Chalk sections in Houghton Regis Quarry.

Lithostratigraphical details of the Chalk Marl strata exposed at Houghton Regis, together with the limited faunal records (based mainly on field observations) are given in Figure 24.

The Chalk Marl succession below the Totternhoe Stone at Houghton Regis differs in detail from those at Barton and Sundon. It comprises alternations of marly chalks and slightly gritty, locally patchily cemented, detrital chalks (calcisiltites) with pale phosphatised and nonphosphatised intraclasts, and rare plant debris. The more calcareous beds exhibit much more evidence of resedimentation than at the other two localities and there is no indication of either the Dixoni Limestone or of the overlying chalk with abundant *Orbirhynchia mantelliana*. The macrofauna is, however, generally similar. *Inoceramus* ex gr. *virgatus* is common at the top of the lowest exposed bed and in the overlying marly chalk, where it occurs together with *Plicatula inflata* and subordinate '*Inoceramus*' *crippsi*. It becomes less common upwards, ranging to an horizon about 1.5 m beneath the base of the Totternhoe Stone. *Monticlarella? rectifrons* is present in the lower part of the exposed succession, but is apparently absent from the highest bed of calcisiltite and the overlying marly chalk, which are characterised instead by *Grasirhynchia grasiana*. The remaining fauna is of low diversity.

It is unclear whether the part of the Chalk Marl succession exposed at Houghton Regis is expanded, or whether pre-Totternhoe Stone erosion has cut down to below the Dixoni Limestone. The occurrence of *Inoceramus* ex gr. *virgatus* and *Monticlarella? rectifrons* near to the base suggests that these beds can be no older than the *dixoni* Zone. However, the upward replacement of *M? rectifrons* by *Grasirhynchia grasiana* in the higher beds is somewhat suggestive of the succession above the lowest of the three '*Orbirhynchia* horizons' elsewhere. It would then be above the Dixoni Limestone, which could be represented in an uncemented state, or could occur below the present level of exposure.

Whereas the presence of *I. virgatus* and '*I.*' *crippsi* demonstrate that the lowest part of the section is in Lower Cenomanian strata, the bed immediately beneath the Totternhoe Stone has yielded an assemblage of benthonic foraminifera diagnostic of Zone 11(i) (Wilkinson, 1990a), which apparently places it in the lowest Middle Cenomanian. In the absence of a significant macrofauna it is unclear if this bed is indeed composed of Middle Cenomanian sediment, or if it is part of the Lower Cenomanian which has been contaminated by a younger microfauna, for example through bioturbation, as suggested for the Totternhoe 'Stone Quarry' section.

The Totternhoe Stone rests on a well-marked erosion surface which locally (as in Section B, Figure 24) cuts down to near the base of the underlying bed of marly chalk. This underlying marly chalk is also penetrated by *Thalassinoides* burrows, infilled by calcarenitic sediment piped down from the base of the Totternhoe Stone. Pale and dark brown phosphatic intraclasts are concentrated in the basal 0.4 m of the Totternhoe Stone but occur sporadically up to 0.7 m above the base. Well-preserved (but probably remanié) *Orbirhynchia mantelliana* are also common, ranging up to the top of the Totternhoe Stone, where it passes rapidly upwards into more fissile, marly chalk.

This is, however, overlain by a bed composed of rather similar rock to that of the Totternhoe Stone, although it is finer grained and contains only a few phosphatic pebbles. This calcisiltite rests on a scoured surface which locally cuts out the underlying marl, so that (following bioturbation of the sediment) the Totternhoe Stone appears to pass gradationally into the overlying calcisiltite. The two beds can nevertheless be distinguished by the absence (except for rare, broken specimens) of *Orbirhynchia mantelliana* in the upper one. The calcisiltite itself passes rapidly upwards into marly chalk before the succession

gives way to more uniform pale grey chalks with *Concinnithyris subundata*. The occurrence of sedimentary rock of similar aspect as the Totternhoe Stone in the overlying beds suggests an explanation for observations such as that of Whitaker (1872, p.41) who recorded that the Totternhoe Stone formed two beds (each 0.9 m thick) where it was seen at the western end of the disused railway cutting at Sewell Quarry (Figure 25). It seems possible that the upper of the beds observed by Whitaker would not be included in the Totternhoe Stone as described here.

The Totternhoe Stone at Houghton Regis is highly fossiliferous, particularly in the basal part, and an extensive collection made in the early part of this century by the amateur geologist E A Martin is preserved at BGS, Keyworth. The thin-shelled pectinacean *Entolium* sp. is abundant, as are *Plicatula inflata* and terebratulids of uncertain affinities. The greater part of the fauna, even though apparently well preserved and indigenous, must be reworked. This is clear in the case of the more or less strongly phosphatised internal moulds of gastropods, ammonites and other originally aragonite-shelled molluscs that are found concentrated in the basal part of the bed, but is less obvious where the fossils have not been mineralised and exhibit no obvious signs of having been rolled or abraded, for example many of the brachiopods and bivalves. The extent of reworking is shown by the presence of the belemnite *Actinocamax primus* and phosphatised moulds of ammonites including *Acanthoceras rhotomagense*, *Cunningtoniceras* sp., *Turrilites costatus* and common *Sciponoceras baculoides*. *Actinocamax primus* is restricted to the equivalent of the Cast Bed (Gale, 1989, fig. 3) of the Folkestone succession. The abundant *Orbirhynchia mantelliana* in the Totternhoe Stone can therefore be inferred to have been reworked from the topmost *O. mantelliana* band (which overlies the horizon of *A. primus*), as can the *Turrilites* and the *Sciponoceras*. It is also possible that some *O. mantelliana* may have been reworked from the second of the three bands recognised in southern England. The minimum downward extent of reworking is shown by the occurrence of *Inoceramus tenuis*, which is largely restricted to the limestone underlying the Cast Bed and which lies within the *costatus* Subzone (Wood, 1990b).

The age of the Totternhoe Stone sediment, as distinct from that of its contained fossils, probably postdates the mid-Cenomanian non-sequence (Carter and Hart, 1977) at the top of the topmost *Orbirhynchia mantelliana* band in the Folkestone succession.

A bed rich in *Chondrites* and *Pycnodonte* occurs c.7.5 m above the base of the Totternhoe Stone (Section C and E, Figure 24). This may indicate the topmost Middle Cenomanian *jukesbrownei* Zone by analogy with the '15-cm Marl' of the Totternhoe succession, but there is no indication of the shell beds with '*Inoceramus*' *atlanticus* found at Barton and Totternhoe, or of the mineralised hardground at Totternhoe. A second oyster bed, some 6 m higher (Section C, Figure 24), comprising relatively coarse-grained chalk with *Amphidonte* almost certainly falls within the basal Upper Cenomanian *guerangeri* Zone, and represents one of the *Amphidonte* events (Ernst, Schmid and Seibertz, 1983) characterising this zone. The overlying beds are inaccessible, but yellowish green 'Plenus Marls' and the nodular base of the Melbourn Rock can be discerned at the highest point of the north-west face with the aid of binoculars.

TOTTERNHOE QUARRIES [SP 988 222]

To the north of Totternhoe village lie three quarries, totalling about two-thirds of a square kilometre in area (Figure 25). Only the most westerly remains in operation, where the Grey Chalk is taken by the Totternhoe Lime and Stone Co. Ltd,

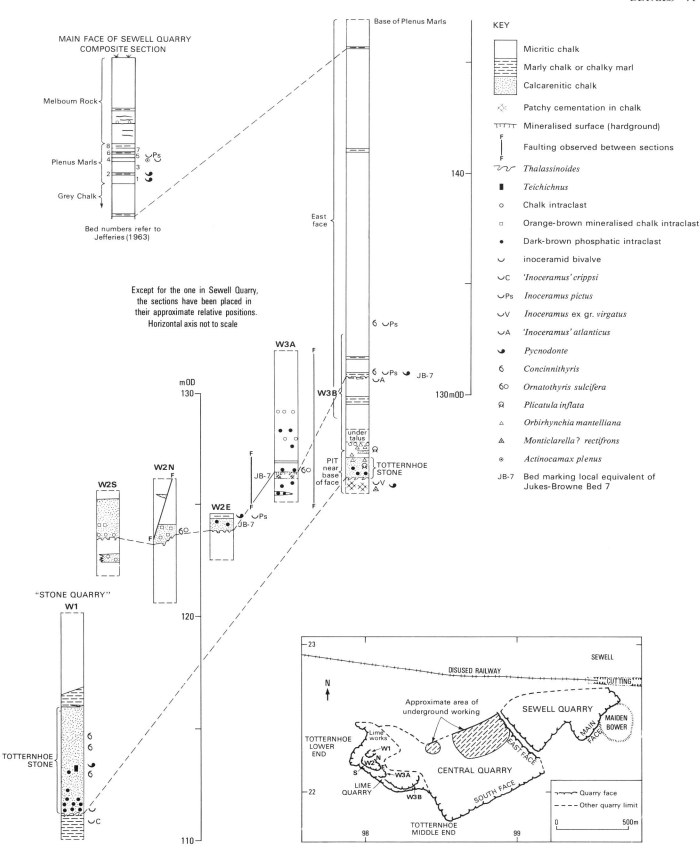

Figure 25 Sections exposed in the Totternhoe group of quarries.

principally for lime production, and the Totternhoe Stone is extracted for building stone as a separate, small-scale concession (Plate 7). The Central Quarry is the largest of the three. Previously, it was worked for cement manufacture by Rugby Cement plc but has now been returned to agriculture, without having been backfilled. The floor of this old quarry is partly underlain by pre-19th century adits in the Totternhoe Stone, but these have long been blocked-off. In the east, the Sewell Quarry, formerly worked by Blue Circle plc for cement manufacture, has been partly restored, with only limited backfill.

Although many parts of these quarries have been degraded, or are too steep to allow access, together their faces expose a nearly complete section from just below the base of the Totternhoe Stone to the lowest flint bed in the Middle Chalk, about 8 m above the Melbourn Rock, a total of some 35 m (Figures 25 and 27). Several of the exposed sections, particularly in the Lime Quarry, reveal minor faults displacing the Chalk by up to 3 m, and also display local increases in dip to about 5°, in some cases oblique to the regional dip.

The pebbly basal layer of the Totternhoe Stone is not taken for building-stone purposes, and the beds beneath the Totternhoe Stone in the Stone Quarry are therefore not always visible. A 2 m section was excavated during the recent survey, exposing the structurally lowest strata seen at Totternhoe (Face W1 in Figure 25). They comprise dark grey calcareous, glauconitic muddy siltstones, rich in fossil debris and intensely bioturbated. These are not like the beds seen elsewhere beneath the Totternhoe Stone. Amongst other forms, the macrofauna includes '*Inoceramus*' *crippsi* and *Aucellina* sp., whose co-occurrence suggests that the sediment was deposited during the *carcitanense* Subzone in the Lower Cenomanian (Wood, 1990a). The benthonic foraminifera, however, indicate instead Zone 11(i) of Carter and Hart (1977), which would place it in the basal Middle Cenomanian (Wilkinson, 1990a). This apparent contradiction can be accounted for if the sediment (and contained macrofauna) was originally deposited during the Lower Cenomanian, but was then contaminated by Middle Cenomanian sediment (together with its microfaunal elements), most probably by bioturbation, after early mid-Cenomanian erosion but before the deposition of the Totternhoe Stone. Although many of the macrofossils are broken, the preservation of some relatively delicate Lower Cenomanian faunal elements would

Plate 7 General view of the Totternhoe Lime and Stone Company quarry at Totternhoe [SP 980 222]. Blocks of Totternhoe Stone for building use are excavated from the lowest face, where the top of the unit is marked by a thin dark band. The 'Grey Chalk' above is used for lime making and fill. The section extends up to the Melbourn Rock, which is obscured by vegetation in the photograph (ERST).

seem to preclude significant transport during any Middle Cenomanian reworking (Aldiss, 1990).

In addition to the pervasive bioturbation of these siltstones by *Planolites* and *Chondrites*, the topmost 20 cm has been penetrated by a wide-diameter (c.20 mm) horizontal *Thalassinoides* burrow system, infilled with Totternhoe Stone sediment. As seen in the Stone Quarry the basal 0.5 m of the Totternhoe Stone includes a concentration of dark brown phosphatic pebbles up to 30 mm in diameter, many of which display adnate oysters, together with varied invertebrate and vertebrate fossil debris, including an impressive variety of fish teeth. This material decreases in abundance upwards, and the rest of the 4.7 m thick bed is in massive, brownish-grey calcarenite composed mainly of comminuted shell debris with glauconitic and phosphatic grains, and sparse pyrite nodules. The trace fossil *Teichichnus* is fairly common, but macrofossils (of which the most usual is *Concinnithyris subundata*) are relatively rare. Only one macrofossil specimen which could indicate the age of the Totternhoe Stone has been collected from the Stone Quarry section. This is a small brachiopod steinkern (phosphatised internal mould) cf. *Capillithyris squamosa*, which (if correctly identified) is one of the stratigraphically restricted Middle Cenomanian brachiopods that are found in the Totternhoe Stone or equivalent beds elsewhere (Lake et al., 1987, p.50).

The Totternhoe Stone is overlain on a sharply defined surface by dark marly chalk, above which is a fairly complex sequence of some 7 m of interbedded marly and arenitic chalks, in some cases separated by scoured surfaces. Jukes-Browne and Hill (1903) record that the Totternhoe Stone forms several beds, totalling some 6.7 m, where it was quarried to the east of the present section. It seems possible that the topmost of these would not now be included with the Totternhoe Stone, as defined here.

The Totternhoe Stone is also seen in a topographically higher part of the Lime Quarry, about 300 m to the south-east, but there it is only 0.9 m thick (Face W3B in Figure 25 and 26). The constituent sediment, with dark phosphatic pebbles, is similar to that seen in the Stone Quarry (although the basal concentration of coarse material is not well developed), and the underlying *Thalassinoides* system is likewise present, but here the Totternhoe Stone rests on slightly arenitic marly chalk. This contains, amongst other macrofossils, *Inoceramus* ex gr. *virgatus* and *Monticlarella? rectifrons*, indicating the *dixoni* Zone, and its microfauna is compatible with this, indicating benthonic Zone 9 or 10 (Wilkinson, 1991). Indeed, the relative abundance of inoceramids, and its patchy cementation, suggest that this bed is the Dixoni Limestone (Wood, 1990a).

As at Houghton Regis and other localities in the Chilterns, in the south-east of the Lime Quarry the upper part of the Totternhoe Stone contains numerous specimens of *Orbirhynchia mantelliana*, although by analogy with the Houghton Regis sequence these are probably not autochthonous, having been reworked from the topmost and possibly also the middle *O. mantelliana* band. Similarities with the Houghton Regis sections continue in the immediately overlying beds, which at Totternhoe include at least 0.7 m of marly chalks interbedded with thin calcarenites. These contain *Concinnithyris subundata*, *Orbirhynchia mantelliana*, *Inoceramus tenuistriatus* (sensu Keller) and

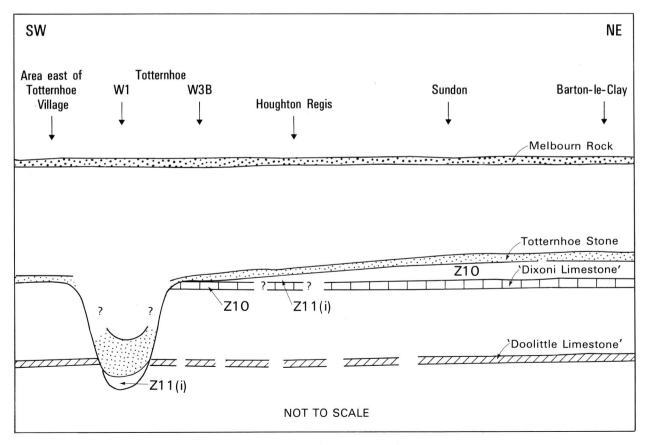

Figure 26 Sketch showing the relationships between the Totternhoe Stone and marker beds in the Lower Chalk of the Leighton Buzzard district.

Plicatula inflata, indicating deposition in the *costatus* Subzone of the *rhotomagense* Zone.

This thin bed of the Totternhoe Stone continues into unexposed ground to the south-east of the quarries, where it forms a sparse brash associated with a barely discernible topographic feature about 10 m above the Doolittle Limestone. In contrast, the thick bed of Totternhoe Stone in the 'Stone Quarry' lies at about the same level as the Doolittle Limestone in Totternhoe village, suggesting that the limestone has been removed from the section by erosion before the deposition of the Totternhoe Stone, and that the exceptional local thickness of the Totternhoe Stone is the result of deposition within a channel (Figure 26). It therefore seems that the Totternhoe Stone occurs in two main forms: a 'regional' facies, which is typically less than 1 m thick, and a much thicker 'channel' facies. Whereas the regional facies is found throughout the district, the 'channel' facies has so far been observed only at Totternhoe; unfortunately it is the channel facies which must be regarded as the stratotype. The position of the southern edge of this channel is constrained by the occurrence of the regional development of the Totternhoe Stone in Face W3B, and possibly also indicated by the extent of the disused adit system beneath the Central Quarry (Figure 26 and Aldiss, 1990), but its dimensions and orientation are otherwise unknown. It possibly lies parallel to north-easterly regional lineaments (Figure 30).

In Face W3B of the Lime Quarry, the thin calcarenite beds die out within 1.3 m above the Totternhoe Stone, and the succession passes into more uniform, rather unfossiliferous, pale grey chalk containing up to three beds of chalky marl (Figure 25). The second of these (here informally named the '15 cm Marl') rests on a burrowed surface and includes *Inoceramus* ex gr. *pictus*, small pycnodonteine oysters, and *Concinnithyris subundata*.

This marl bed almost certainly correlates with the Nettleton *Pycnodonte* Marl, which occurs at the base of the Nettleton Stone in the Northern Province Cenomanian succession of eastern England, and both can be inferred to correlate with the basal part of the Jukes-Browne Bed 7 of the Folkestone–Dover succession. This marks a shallowing event dated to the later part of the *jukesbrownei* Zone (Gaunt et al., 1992). '*Inoceramus*' *atlanticus* has been collected from 0.25 m below the marl where it occurs in the East Face of the Central Quarry, indicating the *jukesbrownei* Zone (Wood, 1991).

Notwithstanding this correlation, remarkable lithofacies variations occur at this horizon within the area of the Totternhoe Lime Quarry. In Face W3A, less than 200 m to the west of Face W3B, the marl bed is absent, and the underlying burrowed surface is represented by a convolute glauconitised hardground above some 0.3 m of orange-brown nodular chalkstone with abundant *Ornatothyris sulcifera*. In Face W2, however, the marl is replaced by a calcarenite bed up to 1.7 m in thickness. Although this rests on an unmineralised, burrowed surface, it contains clasts of orange-brown mineralised chalk, and also *Ornatothyris* sp. At one end of Face W2 this calcarenite bed passes into the complex succession overlying the maximum development of the Totternhoe Stone, while at the other end it is pinched out.

Although the base of the Melbourn Rock is visible in the highest part of the Lime Quarry, the Grey Chalk is better exposed in the East Face of the Central Quarry, where the 15-cm Marl is again exposed. The marl is overlain by about 16 m of relatively uniform massive chalk extending up to the Plenus Marls which are weakly exposed at the very top of the face.

A complete section through the Plenus Marls is very clearly exposed in the Sewell Quarry, although access to the face is hazardous. Each of the beds in Jefferies's (1963) standard succession can be observed (Figure 25). Some 3.8 m of the Melbourn Rock extends to the top of the quarry; it comprises

mainly unfossiliferous, pale creamy-white nodular chalkstone with wispy marl partings.

The Plenus Marls and the lower part of the Melbourn Rock are also exposed in the South Face of the Central Quarry, but in an inaccessible position. The top of the Melbourn Rock and the immediately overlying beds are obscured by talus on a narrow bench preserved near the top of this South Face. With care, access can be gained to the short section above, which exposes some 5 m of highly fossiliferous bedded chalks, including abundant *Mytiloides* sp. (Figure 27).

Almost at the top of this section, about 8 m above the Melbourn Rock, there is a layer of large flint nodules which contain fragments of *Mytiloides* ex gr. *mytiloides*, informally named the 'Maiden Bower Flint' (Aldiss, 1990).

KENSWORTH QUARRY [TL 017 197]

This extensive quarry, on the crest of the Chilterns south of Dunstable, has been worked by the Rugby Cement company since the 1950s. Cement is not manufactured at Kensworth, the quarried chalk being slurried and conveyed by pipeline to the company's works at Rugby. Beneath a capping of clay-with-flints, a total of about 39 m of highest Middle Chalk and basal Upper Chalk were exposed in four vertical faces in 1988–89. The sections recorded in these faces have been combined into a composite section (Figure 28), although the difficulties of access to parts of the vertical faces and the connections between face sections leave some minor uncertainties in correlation. In the following account the faces have been numbered 1 to 4 in ascending order. The relationship of this section to others measured between 1969 and 1988 is discussed in Wood (1990c, fig. 1).

The sequence illustrated in Figure 28 consists mainly of pure white blocky chalk in which several thin but persistent marl seams, bands of chalkstone with hardgrounds on their upper surfaces, and bands of nodular and tabular flint occur at intervals as shown. Fossils are common at some horizons.

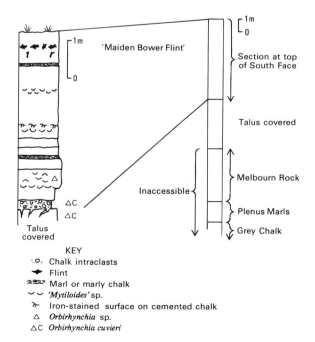

KEY
- `.○.` Chalk intraclasts
- Flint
- Marl or marly chalk
- '*Mytiloides*' sp.
- Iron-stained surface on cemented chalk
- △ *Orbirhynchia* sp.
- △C *Orbirhynchia cuvieri*

Figure 27 Details of the Middle Chalk in Totternhoe Central Quarry [TL 9884 2193].

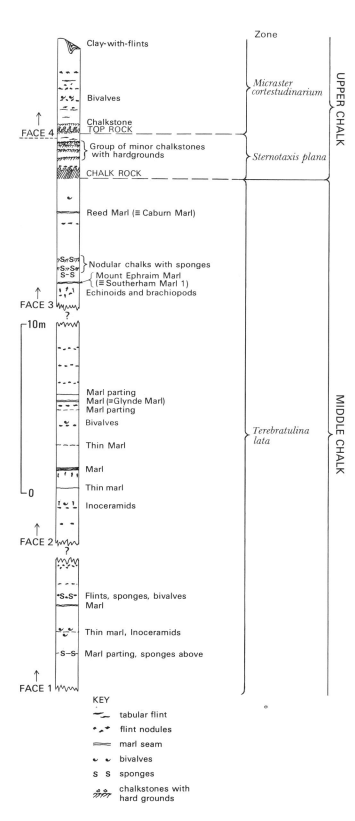

Figure 28 Composite section in Kensworth Quarry, 1988–89.

The succession begins in the *Terebratulina lata* Zone of the Middle Chalk at an horizon 30 m below the top of the Chalk Rock, and extends up to an horizon in the higher part of the *Micraster cortestudinarium* Zone of the Upper Chalk, 5 m above the top of the Top Rock. The top of the *lata* Zone and the basal part of the overlying *Sternotaxis plana* [formerly *Holaster planus*] Zone of the Upper Chalk are represented in condensed form within the complex comprising the Chalk Rock; the lower part of the *cortestudinarium* Zone is likewise condensed and incorporated in the Top Rock.

In the higher part of the quarry, the massive chalkstones and associated glauconitised and phosphatised hardgrounds of the Chalk Rock (0.7 m) and Top Rock (0.15 m) form conspicuous marker horizons near the top of face 3 (Plate 8) and near the base of face 4 respectively. Several marl seams are seen in the succession beneath the Chalk Rock, notably the 5 cm Reed Marl and the 10 cm Mount Ephraim Marl (the Latimer Marl of Bromley and Gale, 1982). The geochemical characteristics of the marl bands have been used to correlate them with those of the Sussex Chalk sequences (Wray and Gale, 1993).

Middle Chalk

Terebratulina lata Zone   The correlation between the marl seams in face 1 and any of the Turonian marl seams recognised elsewhere is unclear. A conspicuous nodular burrow-form flint preserving hexactinellid sponges, the zonal index fossil *Terebratulina lata* and common *Inoceramus cuvieri*, provides a useful marker horizon.

Inoceramid bivalves, including *I. cuvieri*, are common at the base of face 2 above the talus at an horizon of vertically elongate, digitate burrow-form flints. In the middle of the face, there is a pair of marl seams about 1 m apart, the upper of which is up to 10 cm thick, and underlain by similar small flints. At 4.5 m beneath the top of the face, a conspicuous thin marl seam is underlain by a 1.1 m sequence with minor marl seams and courses of nodular flints.

Mortimore and Wood (1986, figs. 2.3 and 2.4) suggested that the marl seams in face 2 correlated broadly with the sequence of marls comprising the Glynde marls of the South Downs (Mortimore, 1986), with the 10 cm marl corresponding to the Glynde Marl 1 of the Sussex succession (Plate 9). On purely stratigraphical grounds, the 10 cm marl at Kensworth could also be interpreted as one of the New Pit marls of southern England (Mortimore, 1986). However, clay mineral trace-element characterisation studies (Wray and Gale, 1993) tend to confirm the Mortimore and Wood interpretation: results show that the 10 cm marl-seam probably equates with Glynde Marl 1 of Sussex, and that the thin, dark marl underlain by flints higher in the face could correspond to one of the higher of the six marls comprising the Maxton Marls (Robinson, 1986a) of the North Downs succession, equivalent to a higher Glynde Marl in Sussex.

The marl seam in face 3 and in the new bridge section adjacent to Luton railway cutting ('Luton') [TL 109 204], identified as the Latimer Marl by Bromley and Gale (1982, figs. 13 and 14), cannot safely be correlated with the Latimer Marl at its type locality. The name, Southerham Marl 1, taken from the standard southern England marl-seam nomenclature (Mortimore, 1986) or, preferably, the nearest geographical equivalent in East Anglia, the Mount Ephraim Marl (Ward et al., 1968)—as recommended by Mortimore and Wood (1986)—has been adopted here. The Southerham Marl 1/Mount Ephraim Marl at Kensworth contains common specimens of the large complex lituolid foraminifer *Coskinophragma* and is underlain by the characteristic association of small, subvertical, digitate burrow-form flints and large nodular flints (Mortimore

Plate 8 Junction of the Middle and Upper Chalk exposed in Face 3, Kensworth Quarry [TL 017 197]; see also Figure 28. The Chalk Rock marking the base of the Upper Chalk, is the thin dark band displaced by the minor faulting in the 10 m face. Solution pipes filled with clay-with-flints are also visible (ERST).

and Wood, 1986). Thin-tested echinoids including *Micraster corbovis* of '*lata* Zone type' (Stokes, 1977, p.106, figs. 4–6) and *Sternotaxis plana* occur at the level of these flints. Several discontinuous beds of iron-stained indurated chalk in the lowest 2 m above the Mount Ephraim Marl yield a diverse fauna of hexactinellid sponges including *Eurete, Porochonia simplex* and *Tremabolites polystoma.*

Given that the 'Latimer Marl' at Kensworth correlates with the Southerham 1/Mount Ephraim Marl, the next higher marl seam in the Kensworth and Luton successions (inferred to be the Reed Marl by Bromley and Gale, 1982) can be presumed to equate with the Caburn Marl (Mortimore, 1986) of southern England, both correlations being confirmed by the clay mineral trace-element characterisation studies. Two further lines of evidence to support the correlation of the Reed Marl with the Caburn Marl are supplied from the macrofauna. *Romaniceras deverianum* has been found in a weakly nodular horizon overlying the Reed Marl at a small exposure close to the railway cutting at Luton (A S Gale, personal communication) and has also been recorded from an approximately equivalent level in Sussex (Lake et al., 1987). The beds between the Reed Marl and the base of the Chalk Rock at Kensworth yield the small echinoid *Epiaster michelini* sensu Stokes (e.g. the specimen figured by Stokes, 1977, p.107, figs. 4–6), a species that charac-

terises the interval between the Caburn Marl and Bridgewick Marl 1 in southern England.

At Kensworth, a concentration of large fragments of *Inoceramus* 0.33 m above the Reed Marl was used by Bromley and Gale (1982, p.288 and fig. 13) to establish the correlation with the Reed Marl at its type locality in north Hertfordshire. This shell-rich horizon is absent from the bridge section adjacent to the Luton railway cutting, where small *Sciponoceras* occur in hard yellow chalk just above the Reed Marl. *Spondylus spinosus* is common in the interval between the Reed Marl and the base of the Chalk Rock at Kensworth.

Upper Chalk

Sternotaxis plana Zone   The 'Basal Complex' succession of chalks with large flints and discrete marl seams (Bridgewick Marls) used by BGS to recognise the base of the *Sternotaxis plana* Zone and of the Upper Chalk in the North Downs is probably represented at Kensworth in extremely condensed form within the Chalk Rock, with all the flints and marl seams having been occluded (Mortimore and Wood, 1986, pp.11–12, figs. 2.2–2.4).

The Chalk Rock, 0.7 m thick at Kensworth (Plate 8), comprises a 'welded' sequence of chalkstones with associated weak-

Plate 9 Middle Chalk exposed in Face 2, Kensworth Quarry [TL 017 197] (Rugby Cement Ltd); see also Figure 28. The prominent marl seams belong to the Glynde group of marls; the face is about 12 m high (ERST).

ly glauconitised hardgrounds and is penetrated by a *Thalassinoides* burrow system. The terminal (Hitch Wood) hardground of the Chalk Rock at this locality exhibits a complex topography of mushroom-like bosses, and is strongly phosphatised and glauconitised. It is locally extremely fossiliferous, and has yielded a large fauna of originally aragonite-shelled molluscs, notably ammonites, but also including scaphopods, gastropods and bivalves, superbly preserved as phosphatised and part-glauconitised internal moulds and external moulds. This is the *Hyphantoceras reussianum* fauna of the older literature, so named after a highly ornamented spinose heteromorph ammonite that is relatively common at Kensworth. Associated with this fauna is a diverse assemblage of sponges, corals, brachiopods [notably *Cretirhynchia cuneiformis* and *Gibbithyris subrotunda*], calcitic bivalves and echinoids including small phosphatised *Micraster leskei*. The fossils (notably ammonites) for which the locality is renowned were found in pockets in the Hitch Wood Hardground during an earlier period of working; few such pockets have been encountered in recent years in the present working area and fossil collecting from the Chalk Rock has been rather unrewarding. Large collections of Chalk Rock fossils from this locality are preserved at BGS, Keyworth.

The Chalk Rock ammonite assemblage belongs to the Upper Turonian *Subprionocyclus neptuni* Zone of the international ammonite zonal scheme (see Wright, 1979; Kaplan, 1986; Hancock, 1991 for details), and practically all the 24 species recorded from the Chalk Rock have been found at Kensworth. Some of these are of exceptional rarity, notably the magnificent specimen of *Tongoboryoceras rhodanicum* [BGS Zr 9330] figured by Wright (*ibid.*, pl. 6, figs. 1a–b). The occurrence here of taxa such as *Baculites undulatus*, *Subprionocyclus normalis* and the large *Puzosia curvatisulcata* suggests that the (derived) ammonite assemblage at Kensworth includes elements that characterise a relatively high level in the expanded correlative ammonite-bearing beds (Scaphiten-Schichten) in Germany (see Kaplan, 1986). The derived inoceramid bivalve assemblage at Kensworth is also apparently younger than elsewhere, being dominated by *Mytiloides incertus* [= *M. fiegei*] rather than by the (earlier) *Inoceramus* ex gr. *costellatus* assemblage that characterises the Chalk Rock at the famous Hill End (Hitch Wood) pit [TL 197 240] in the adjoining Hitchin district. The Hitch Wood Hardground at the top of the Chalk Rock is presumed to equate with the highest of the beds of nodular chalk (Kingston Nodular Chalks) found in southern England successions (Mortimore, 1986) immediately beneath the Lewes Marl; the latter marker-horizon is not present in the Chilterns, but reappears to the north-east, away from the area of condensation, as the West Tofts Marl (Ward et al., 1968) of the East Anglian succession (Mortimore and Wood, 1986, figs 2.3, 2.4).

The higher part of the *plana* Zone is represented by the beds between the top of the Chalk Rock and the base of the Top Rock. This interval is more condensed here than elsewhere in the Chilterns—north Hertfordshire area (Bromley and Gale, 1982); it includes a chalkstone with a glauconitised and phosphatised hardground, overlain by glauconitised pebbles, and a group of three, closely spaced, less strongly indurated beds with weakly glauconitised surfaces. No fauna has been collected from this poorly exposed and relatively inaccessible interval at Kensworth.

Micraster cortestudinarium Zone   The intensely hard chalkstones of the Top Rock at Kensworth contain small, uniplicate terebratulid brachiopods (*Concinnithyris?*), but no other fauna has been collected. At the Redbournbury Quarry [TL 123 103], 13 km to the south-east in the Hertford (Sheet 239) district, weathered Top Rock exposed in a trench in the floor of the quarry has yielded a *remanié* assemblage of basal Coniacian inoceramid bivalves including *Cremnoceramus? waltersdorfensis hannovrensis* and *C? rotundatus* (BGS collection). This assemblage characterises the lower part of the *M. cortestudinarium* Zone in southern England, i.e. the interval between the Navigation hardground(s) and the Hope Gap Hardground of Mortimore's (1986) terminology. In terms of the southern England succession, the Top Rock of the Chilterns and adjacent areas probably represents condensation of the beds from the Navigation Hardground(s) up to and including the Hope Gap, Beeding and Light Point hardgrounds, with the latter group having cut down to rest on and coalesce with the Navigation Hardground. Using the succession at Langdon Stairs, near Dover (Shephard-Thorn, 1988), as a framework of reference, this condensation would involve the loss of 9 m of beds; in the more basinal, and consequently thicker, sequences in Sussex, the equivalent figure would be of the order of 15 m.

The extremely hard chalkstones of the Top Rock have a slight pink coloration, and can be distinguished from those of the Chalk Rock (particularly that underlying the Hitch Wood Hardground) by the absence of conspicuous glauconite grains. The Top Rock is surmounted by a glauconitised convolute hardground which is overlain by a concentration of dark green glauconitised pebbles. Many of these pebbles are extremely rolled and corroded *M. cortestudinarium* of a type indicative of a relatively high level in the *cortestudinarium* Zone.

The Top Rock is overlain by some 5 m of white chalk with courses of large nodular, burrow-form flints and several sub-horizontal tabular flints. No fossils have been collected from these beds at Kensworth, but equivalent beds elsewhere (e.g. at the Redbournbury Quarry) have yielded large inoceramid bivalves such as *Cremnoceramus schloenbachii* and *Tethyoceramus* ex gr. *humboldti*. There is no evidence for the presence of the succeeding *Micraster coranguinum* Zone at Kensworth.

Recent trial boreholes indicate a total thickness of the Middle Chalk of about 85 m in the area of Kensworth Quarry.

Other details

KIMPTON LANE, NEAR LUTON AIRPORT

The junction between the Middle and Upper Chalk was exposed temporarily in excavations for a new building [TL 1135 2085] on the south side of a Kimpton Lane leading from Luton Airport.

The section was as follows:

	Thickness m
UPPER CHALK	
Chalk, white, rubbly weathered	about 1.5
Top Rock; hard chalkstone, slightly greenish, weathered	0.4
Chalk, blocky, weathered	about 2.0
Chalk Rock; very hard chalkstone, rubbly appearance	up to 0.6
MIDDLE CHALK	
Chalk, rubbly nodular with trace of marl at base (possibly Reed Marl)	0.9
Chalk, massive, blocky with band of black flint nodules 1.5 m below the top	about 4.5
Mount Ephraim/Southerham Marl 1 ('Latimer Marl') greenish grey marl	about 0.1
Chalk	1.0
Flint, nodules with incipient tabular band	0.05
Chalk, massive	seen for 1.0

Several small pipes filled with clay-with-flints were noted, as were oblique joints and fissures parallel to the bedding apparently injected with brown silty clay.

SEVEN
Structure

The district is situated on the north-western flank of the London Basin, as defined by the Chilterns Chalk escarpment. The structure of the Mesozoic formations at outcrop is relatively simple; in general, beds dip gently towards the south-east with only minor faulting and folding. The Mesozoic strata rest unconformably on the eroded surface of the Lower Palaeozoic basement rocks at depths between 50 and 140 m below OD. Basement rocks range from Tremadoc to Devonian in age (see Chapter Two).

In the following pages the evidence of structural trends in the concealed Palaeozoic basement rocks, derived from geophysical and borehole evidence, is reviewed and certain 'lineaments' are identified. (Here 'lineament' is used as a general term for linear gradients and anomalies identified from regional geophysical data). These are compared with structural features in the exposed formations in order to examine the extent to which they have influenced Mesozoic sedimentation.

STRUCTURES OF THE CONCEALED FORMATIONS

The Leighton Buzzard district is located on the Midlands Microcraton (Tucker and Pharaoh, 1991), a block of relatively undeformed platform rocks bordered on the east by folded basinal rocks of the eastern Caledonides (Allsop and Smith, 1988), (Figure 29). The boundaries of the microcraton are most clearly defined in the south and west by the Variscan Front and the Church Stretton Fault System respectively. However, in the east the boundary cannot be precisely defined on the available evidence. Within the district, the Mesozoic rocks thin over the west-south-west-trending Charlton Axis. The core of the axis comprises Tremadoc and igneous rocks in the west and Devonian rocks in the east. Few boreholes penetrate the base of the Mesozoic succession and a wider area has been considered to strengthen the structural interpretation. Figure 30 has been compiled from all the available geological and geophysical data (see Chapter Two and Figures 3 and 4). It shows three major structural trends; these are north to south, east-north-east to west-south-west, and north-west to south-east. In addition, a weakly developed north-east-trending feature underlies the Lower Chalk (p.84, C'–C Figure 30).

North–south-trending structures

A major north–south-trending lineament (A–A') crosses the western part of the district (Figure 30). Evidence for this can be identified on the aeromagnetic map and as a

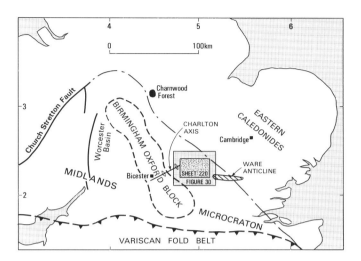

Figure 29 Simplified basement features of Central England (after Tucker and Pharaoh, 1991; Smith, 1985; Reid et al., 1990).

gradient on the residual gravity map. This lineament may coincide with the junction between Lower Palaeozoic rocks of Tremadoc age to the west and Upper Palaeozoic Devonian rocks to the east. The apparent south-easterly offset of the Charlton Axis (B–B') suggests that it is a major fault.

In the south of the district the lineament, A–A', veers south-south-east and continues as a strong gravity gradient to the south-east of Tring where it coincides with strong gradients on the eastern margin of a series of high frequency magnetic anomalies. These anomalies are likely to indicate shallow intrusive bodies within the pre-Mesozoic basement rocks.

To the east of the district, a second lineament, a–a', (Figure 30) subparallel with A–A' is indicated from the gravity data. This feature is weaker and discontinuous and there is no corresponding aeromagnetic feature, possibly due to a greater depth to magnetic basement, over 5 km below ground level. The gravity gradient associated with it could be related to variation in density contrasts between the Silurian and Devonian rocks on either side.

The trend of the lineament a–a' appears to mirror the general north–south trend of the Silurian subcrop, although, like A–A', it may also follow a fault direction in the upper part of the basement. Such faults could have been a major controlling influence on the formation of deep Devonian basins in eastern England (Allsop, 1985a). It is possible that any north–south faulting, as

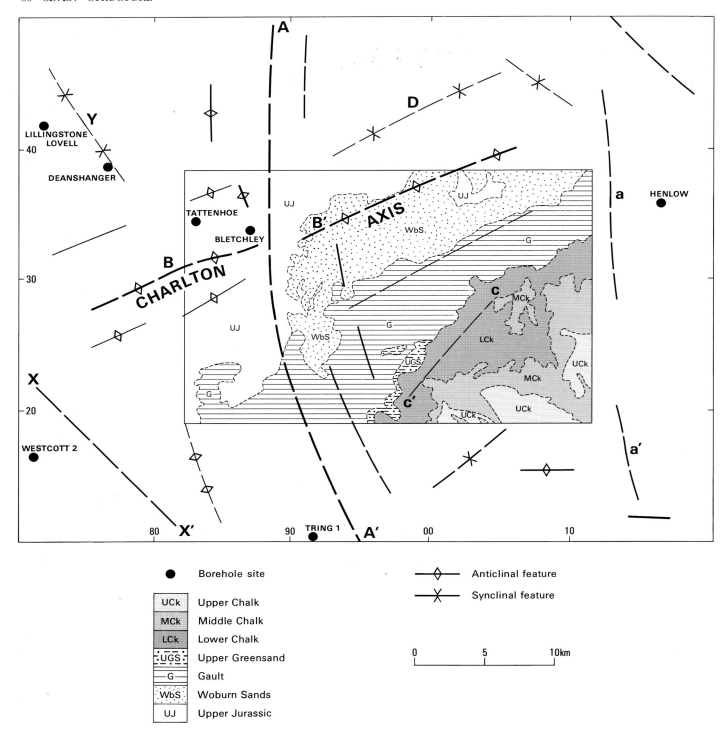

Figure 30 Possible structural lineaments, associated with pre-Mesozoic features, deduced from gravity and aeromagnetic anomaly maps in the Leighton Buzzard district and surrounding country. (Strength of line indicates intensity of anomaly). Outline of surface geology is also shown.

represented by lineament A–A′, could have been reactivated at later times, for example the western limit of the Woburn Sands outcrop (Figure 30) coincides with the location of lineament A–A′ suggesting that there might have been some movement in Upper Jurassic to Lower Cretaceous times.

West-south-west-trending structures

Several lineaments trending west-south-west to east-north-east are indicated by the potential field data, mainly gravity. The most notable of these lineaments is the Charlton Axis (B–B′, Figure 30) which has influenced the thickness of the Jurassic and Cretaceous rocks and also the strike of the Cretaceous formations. In the west of the district, the centre of the axis (B) may be partly composed of igneous rocks within the basement. Igneous rocks have been proved in the Bicester area (Figure 29) and are indicated there by the high frequency aeromagnetic anomalies originating from shallow sources. The aeromagnetic map indicates a continuation of these magnetic rocks towards the district but they appear to be separated from the shallow igneous rocks near the Tattenhoe Borehole.

The continuation of the Charlton Axis (B–B′) across the northern part of the district (Figure 30) is indicated on both aeromagnetic and gravity maps. The geophysical evidence suggests a slight south-eastwards offset of the axis along the line of A–A′. High-frequency aeromagnetic anomalies from near-surface sources do not occur to the east of A–A′, but the west-south-west trends are still apparent in the gravity field, although they are weaker and discontinuous.

North of the Charlton Axis, an elongated gravity low, represented by lineament D in Figure 30, parallels the Charlton Axis. This may be related to the presence of additional low-density sedimentary rocks within the Mesozoic or to low-density rocks immediately below the Mesozoic strata.

North-west-trending structures

North-west-trending lineaments are normally associated with the Palaeozoic rocks of the eastern Caledonides and the eastern margin of the Midlands Microcraton has this trend. Lineaments of similar trend occur within the Midlands Microcraton (Figures 29, 30).

To the south-west of the district (Figure 30), a strong north-west-trending lineament (X–X′) indicates the edge of steep gradients in both gravity and magnetic maps. It represents the north-eastern boundary of an area of shallow magnetic basement. In the north-west of the district (Y in Figure 30), a similar, but weaker, north-west-trending lineament is indicated from the gravity data. This appears to terminate to the south-east near the features associated with the Charlton Axis. Such weaker lineaments may, in fact, be related to the gentle north-west- or west-north-west-trending fold axes observed in the Upper Jurassic rocks at Stoke Hammond and Soulbury (Figure 31) and local basins in the Woburn Sands formation.

STRUCTURES IN THE EXPOSED FORMATIONS

The Mesozoic sequence is broken by a number of unconformities of varying magnitude; the most important is that between the Upper Jurassic and Lower Cretaceous formations. Gentle folds trending west-north-west affected the Upper Jurassic clay formations in the Stoke Hammond–Soulbury area, (Figure 31), prior to the deposition of the Woburn Sands. The Woburn Sands, deposited during the Upper Aptian transgression, thus overstepped a folded and eroded surface of Upper Jurassic rocks. The western limit of the Woburn Sands, although obscured by drift cover, is quite abrupt and roughly falls on a north–south line at about Easting 90, closely coincident with a major basement lineament (A–A′ in Figure 30). There is, however, no direct surface evidence for a fault at the western limit of the Woburn Sands.

Fault control of small depositional basins has been advocated (Eyers, 1991; Ruffell and Wignall, 1991) to account for thickness variations in the Woburn Sands of the district. There is very little evidence for the presence of such faults at the surface other than those shown on the published map.

The Cretaceous strata generally dip towards the southeast and dip readings are consistently low. However, gentle flexures or 'rolls' produce local reversals of dip within the Chalk (Figure 32). The strike of the Lower Cretaceous formations is broadly parallel to certain basement lineaments (Figure 30) suggesting a possible causal relationship between the structural features identified in the basement and those of the Mesozoic rocks. Structural control of sedimentation probably occurred during the deposition of some of the Mesozoic formations, notably the Woburn Sands and Lower Chalk; these aspects are further discussed in the following pages.

STRUCTURES IN THE UPPER JURASSIC FORMATIONS

It is rarely possible to map structures in the Jurassic rocks in the field due to poor exposure, partial drift cover and lack of marker horizons in the dominantly argillaceous sequence. An exception is in the area around Soulbury and Stoke Hammond, north-west of Leighton Buzzard, where a feature caused by a thin cementstone band at the base of the West Walton and Ampthill Clay formations has enabled tentative structural contours to be drawn on this horizon (Figure 31). These contours delimit a north-west–south-east-aligned synclinal flexure with its axis along the Ouzel Valley, east of Stoke Hammond. The dip on the south-western limb of this fold is approximately 1 in 80, less than 1°. An associated anticlinal roll is postulated south of Soulbury, in an area of heavy drift cover, to take the West Walton and Ampthill Clay formations down below the Kimmeridge Clay to the south-west. These folded Upper Jurassic clay formations were eroded prior to the deposition of the Woburn Sands in the late Aptian transgression. A little beyond the south-west corner of the district (1:10 000 Sheet SP81NW) a shallow NNW–SSE syncline with associated faulting, the East Bierton syncline (Bristow, 1963; Barron, 1988), preserves the Portland Formation, which is overstepped by the Gault. There is evidence to suggest that the faults were active both prior to and later than the deposition of the Gault. It is likely that both these folds were formed during the same episode of early

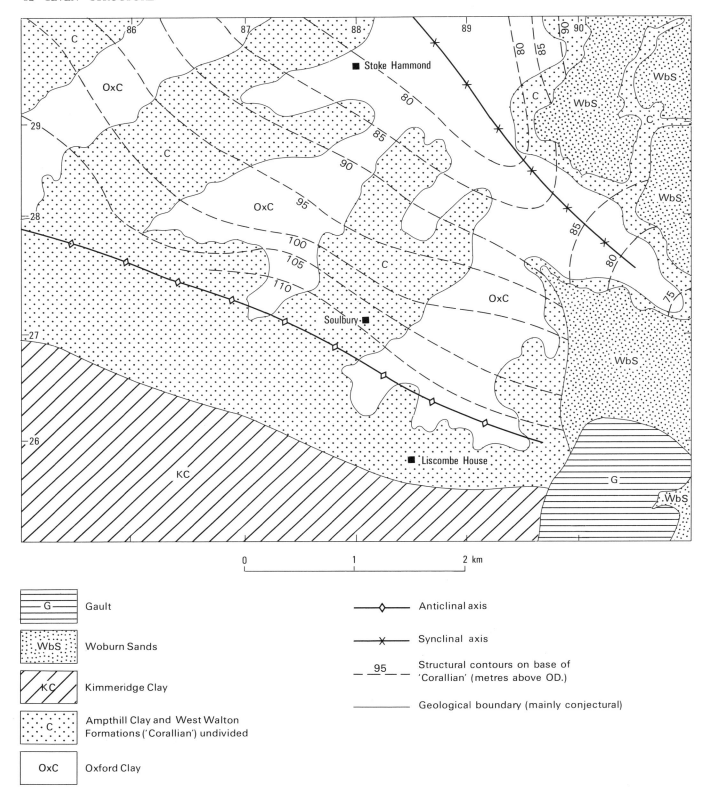

Figure 31 Structural contours on the base of the West Walton Formation around Stoke Hammond and Soulbury illustrating the effects of pre-Aptian folding and the magnitude of the Jurassic–Cretaceous unconformity.

Cretaceous tectonism; both are associated with basement features.

STRUCTURES OF THE WOBURN SANDS

Structural contours drawn on the base of the formation (Figure 12) show a very gentle dip towards the south-east. The surface is by no means uniform, however, and the contours demonstrate the presence of a north-west–south-east-trending erosional trough centred on Woburn and a north-east–south-west-trending ridge south of Ampthill. Information from BGS boreholes and from outcrop between Leighton Buzzard and Clophill shows that the Woburn Sands Formation rests uncomfortably on strata ranging from the lower part of the Middle Oxford Clay up to the Ampthill Clay. The distribution of these Upper Jurassic formations below the Woburn Sands, and the observed variations in depositional thickness (60 to 120 m) of the sands, can be explained solely in terms of pre-Woburn Sands erosion. It is not necessary to invoke tectonic inversion of the Jurassic rocks and fault-control of Woburn Sands deposition as proposed by Ruffell and Wignall (1990) and Eyers (1991); in general, this survey does not support the presence of the synsedimentary faults postulated by these authors. However, there may be an element of 'basement control' on the form of the eroded pre-Woburn Sands surface. For example, the western margin of the Woburn 'trough' dips at 4°, steep for this area, and is defined by closely spaced, north–south-aligned contours (Figure 12), which are parallel to a basement lineament in this area (A–A' Figure 30), and

may in turn be linked to a group of minor, generally north–south-trending faults which displace the base of the formation at Woburn Sands Village. Thus north-south fracturing or faulting may have had a part in the location of the Woburn 'trough', but might not have been active during the deposition of the Woburn Sands.

The Ampthill 'ridge' (Figure 12) was also a significant feature of the pre-Woburn Sands surface effecting the deposition of the formation. The ridge separates the deep Woburn trough from a lesser basin around Clophill and the total formational thickness is considerably reduced over it. Both depressions provided suitable environments for the deposition and preservation of fuller's earth seams, which appear to die out over the ridge.

Erosion surfaces overlain by derived pebbles and phosphatised fossils within the Woburn Sands, as for example that seen in the Clophill workings, (p.44) point to regional tectonic activity at this period, which possibly rejuvenated the source areas of detritus on the London Platform.

STRUCTURES AFFECTING THE CHALK

The structure of the Chalk formations in the south-east corner of the district shows some interesting variations from the regional pattern of the Chilterns Chalk escarpment, which probably relate to local basement features. In general, the Chalk dips gently in a south-easterly direction, but there are notable changes of strike and some dip reversals. Structural contours drawn on the base of the Middle Chalk (Figure 32) demon-

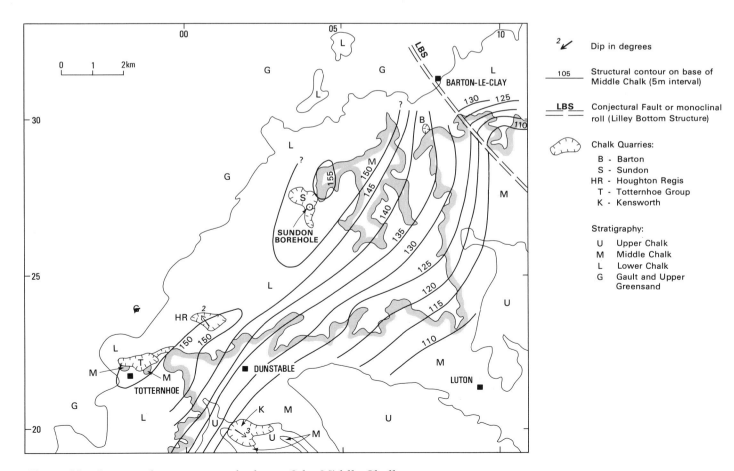

Figure 32   Structural contours on the base of the Middle Chalk.

strate considerable variation of strike and the presence of a north-east–south-west-aligned anticlinal roll, running between Sundon and Houghton Regis. In Houghton Regis quarry the Lower Chalk dips at 2 to 3° to the north-west, while at Kensworth the beds dip at 3° towards the south-east. This anticlinal feature is associated with a gravity anomaly which cannot be explained by variations in the Mesozoic cover and a coincident basement structure (c–c' in Figure 30) is suspected.

A number of minor normal faults, each with a throw of about 1 m and hade of about 20°, were observed in Kensworth Quarry in 1989 (Plate 7). Conjugate joint sets are well developed. The pattern of faulting and jointing is consistent with an extensional regime.

Recent work on the adjoining Hitchin (221) Sheet to the east, indicates the likely presence of a north-west–south-east-trending dislocation running up the axis of the Lilley Bottom buried valley into the district and crossing the outcrop of the base of the Chalk near Barton-le-Clay. The precise nature of this structure has not been resolved from the available field evidence; it appears to be a normal fault downthrowing up to 10m to the north-east or a monoclinal roll of similar effect. It is here referred to as the Lilley Bottom structure (Figure 32). The aeromagnetic anomaly map shows that the Lilley Bottom structure can be related to a basement lineament suggesting faulting at depth.

The Lilley Bottom structure seems to have exercised significant control on Chalk sedimentation in several ways. It appears to separate a zone with a complete, thick Lower Chalk sequence of about 75 m (as typified in the Sundon Borehole and adjacent area) to the south-west, from a thinner sequence of about 60 m in the Hitchin area to the north-east. It also coincides with the south western limit of the Cambridge Greensand as the basal bed of the Lower Chalk. Furthermore, it appears to be on the south-western limit of the 'Anglian Trough' (Jefferies, 1963; Hart, 1973) in which a comparatively thick Plenus Marls sequence was deposited. This 'trough' however, coincides with the north-eastern zone of reduced Lower Chalk thickness around Hitchin. The reduced Lower Chalk thickness is problematical but could be linked to erosion prior to the deposition of the Cambridge Greensand and/or the Totternhoe Stone.

EIGHT
Quaternary

The Quaternary period, which covers the last 2 million years, has been one of extreme climatic variation, in which the landscape was moulded to its present form in response to weathering and depositional processes. It is the period in which the materials distinguished as 'drift deposits' on the geological map were laid down in a range of terrestrial environments, and in which the various superficial structures were formed.

During the Quaternary, many lines of evidence show that climate oscillated between severe glacial episodes, and temperate interglacial episodes. During the glacial episodes the polar ice caps expanded, continental ice sheets developed and sea level fell. During the interglacial episodes ice sheets and glaciers retreated, sea level rose and conditions were as warm or warmer than the present. Weathering processes and vegetation naturally varied in harmony with the climatic oscillations. We are fortunate to have continuous climatic records of the Quaternary, derived from oxygen isotope variations in the shells of foraminifera recovered from cores of deep ocean sediments (Shackleton and Opdyke, 1973). This work shows a sequence of over 20 cold and temperate periods during the Quaternary, which are tied to palaeomagnetic reversals and some absolute datings. The onshore drift sequence, characterised by numerous erosional events and the reworking of older deposits, is by its nature incomplete. In the British Isles, there are generally accepted to be deposits representing the last three major glacial stages and their associated interglacials, making up the Middle and Late Pleistocene (Table 3). The Early Pleistocene is partially represented by fluvial and marine deposits in East Anglia. Some differences of opinion still remain over the correlation of these stages with the deep oceanic record, due to the paucity of datable material and the presence of many sedimentary breaks (Bowen et al., 1987). Some problems attend the definition of the 'Wolstonian' glacial period, originally believed to have occurred between the Hoxnian and Ipswichian interglacials. Many workers currently accept the 'Wolstonian,' in its type area in the West Midlands, to be equivalent to the Anglian of East Anglia. However, it is conceded that a cold period did occur between the Hoxnian and Ipswichian, though a major ice-sheet did not develop over lowland Britain. No new stage name has yet been proposed to replace 'Wolstonian', which is thus used in parenthesis in this account.

The Quaternary stratigraphy is illustrated in Table 3. There are no certain representatives of the Cromerian, 'Wolstonian' or Ipswichian stages, nor indeed of the Early Pleistocene. Hoxnian interglacial deposits have not been discovered in the district, but are known from several localities in the Hitchin (Sheet 221) district to the east.

Although it has little relevance to the Leighton Buzzard district, it should be stated that the 'Wolstonian'–Ipswichian interval is probably more complicated than indicated in Table 3 In relation to the deep-ocean records three cold and three warm oscillations may be represented, as illustrated by Wymer (1985, fig. 107). Warm oscillations of lesser magnitude, known as interstadials also occurred within the glacial stages.

The oldest Quaternary deposits of the Chilterns are the clay-with-flints and associated high-level marine deposits preserved in solution hollows in the Chalk (at Rothamsted and Little Heath, near Berkhamstead). The latter are generally taken to be of Plio-Pleistocene age and hence predate most of the Early Pleistocene of East Anglia.

The glacial drifts of the area were laid down during the Anglian glacial stage, when a major ice sheet covered most of the British Isles but did not extend south of the river Thames. The ice sheet impinged on the Chilterns escarpment of the district and, judging by the lack of till on the dip slope, did not generally override it. The northern and western parts of the district were covered by thick deposits of till (chalky boulder clay) and associated sands and gravels, which were largely moulded to the preglacial topography. Ice lobes and glacial streams crossed the escarpment via the Lea gap at Luton and by that in Lilley Bottom. The channel of the River Ouzel was modified and overdeepened by subglacial stream erosion. The sites of former proglacial lakes in this depression are recorded by deposits of laminated silty clays.

Periglacial regimes prevailed on several occasions during the post-Anglian, 'Wolstonian' and Devensian stages, resulting in deep permafrost, the formation of head deposits, the development of superficial structures and landslips, the deposition of thin but widespread loessic deposits over much of the landscape and an overall rounding and smoothing of landforms.

The rivers of the district have played a major part in the development of the landscape since the overall blanket of Anglian till was laid down. Some of the rivers have reoccupied their pre-Anglian valleys, but in other instances the 'buried valley' has been abandoned in favour of a new course. Only two terraces of river gravels have been recognised, and are probably no older than the Devensian. Chalky, flinty washes, with land molluscan shells were deposited in the floor of the scarp-face combes at Barton, Hexton and Pegsdon, and spread out thence as flat apron-like fans over the outcrop of the Lower Chalk. This deposition commenced in the late-Glacial period at the end of the Devensian and has continued through the Flandrian. The molluscan faunas provide a record of climatic and ecological change through this time. The alluvium and peat of the flood-

Table 3   Drift deposits of the Leighton Buzzard district (and adjacent areas) in relation to the stages of the British Quaternary (simplified and not shown to scale).

	Stage (Approx age)	Environment		
		Glacial	Periglacial	Fluvial
Holocene	Flandrian (10 ka)		Landslips Combe	Alluvium Peat dry valley deposits
Late Pleistocene	Late Glacial (12 ka)	Not glaciated but very cold, with warm interstadials	deposits ?Local permafrost Head–solifluction ?Loessic deposits Cryoturbation	First terrace deposits Second terrace deposits
	Devensian (79 ka)			
	Ipswichian (132 ka)		?'Brickearths' of Caddington etc.	
Middle Pleistocene	'Wolstonian' (367 ka)	Not glaciated but very cold	?Combe deposits ?Loessic deposits ?Permafrost ?Older Head	
	Hoxnian (400 ka)		?'Brickearths' of Caddington etc.	Interglacial organic deposits and tufa at Hitchin, Stevenage and Hatfield
	Anglian (472 ka)	Till (chalky boulder clay) Glacial sand and gravel Glacial lake deposits Buried channels of Ouzel and Lea	?Permafrost in extraglacial areas	
	'Cromerian Complex'		Pedogenetic development of clay-with-flints	High-level deposits at Sugworth, near Oxford
Early Pleistocene	(2 Ma)		Early development of clay-with-flints from Reading Beds clays	
Plio-Pleistocene		High-level 'marine' deposits at Rothamsted and Little Heath		

Temperate stages

plains has accumulated during the Flandrian period up to the present day.

CLAY-WITH-FLINTS

As its name conveys, this deposit comprises a mixture of reddish or yellowish brown clay with numerous flints, the latter being either directly derived from the Chalk or re-cycled from Tertiary formations. It occurs as a dissected capping on the dip-slope interfluves of the Chilterns Chalk escarpment, being generally 5 to 6 m thick, although much greater thicknesses are encountered in solution pipe infills.

Various theories have been advanced to explain its origin, in the past, including dissolution of the Upper Chalk and glaciation (reviewed by Catt, 1986), but it is now accepted to result from the virtually in-situ alter-ation of former outcrops of the Palaeocene Woolwich and Reading Beds, by periglacial and pedological pro-cesses over a very long period. A minor component of clay and flints may be attributable to solution of the chalk below.

In support of its derivation from Palaeocene rocks, it can be demonstrated that the clay-with-flints rests on an extrapolated extension of the sub-Tertiary erosion sur-face cut in the Chalk of the Chilterns. The transforma-tion from 'solid' formation to 'drift' deposit occurred over a period of time and must postdate the deposition, folding and partial erosion of the Tertiary rocks of the London Basin. Pedological evidence (Catt, 1986) sug-gests that the alteration processes commenced no earlier than the Cromerian interglacial period.

Just to the south of the district, residual deposits of high-level marine sands are preserved in Chalk solution hollows associated with the clay-with-flints at Rothamsted (Dines and Chatwin, 1930) and Little Heath [TL 017 083] (Moffatt and Catt, 1983). Fossil shells from the Rothamsted deposit link it with the Waltonian Red Crag of Essex of Plio-Pleistocene age. This may suggest an ear-lier origin of the clay-with-flints, but it could equally be argued that the 'weathering' processes linked to its for-mation postdate the Plio-Pliocene marine event.

Much discussion has taken place over the last century on the status, definition and origin of the clay-with-flints, which has been fully reviewed by Catt (1986). The de-posit is somewhat heterogenous in detail and variable from place to place. In this survey no attempt has been made to subdivide the deposit on the 1:10 000 maps, al-though variations in the proportions of broken flints and rounded flint pebbles and the occasional occurrence in ploughed soils of fragments of Hertfordshire pudding-stone (silicified flint pebble conglomerate) derived from Tertiary formations have been noted. Similarly, the prac-tical difficulties of augering stony clays have made it im-possible to delimit the deposits of 'brickearth' formerly exploited around Caddington and Luton, although their general locations are documented (Smith, 1894; Cox, 1979a). On some earlier geological maps the Woolwich and Reading Beds are shown resting on the Upper Chalk below clay-with-flints cover in the south-east of the

district, but the presence of these beds has not been con-firmed, either by surface features or by the limited expo-sures. Rarely, traces of displaced pebbly sands and mot-tled clays of Woolwich and Readings Beds aspect have been preserved on the sides of solution pipes, but no positive evidence for continuous spreads of the unal-tered formation has come to hand.

The deposits of 'brickearth' preserved in depressions in the clay-with-flints land surface, reflecting solution collapse features (dolines) in the Chalk, were widely ex-ploited in the 19th and early 20th centuries (see also Chapters Six and Nine). They seem to have developed as ponded hollows in which waterlain sediments mainly of silt grade were deposited over a period. Large collec-tions of Palaeolithic artifacts from several sites were made by Smith (1894, 1916), and actual working floors identified, from which the flint flakes could be painstak-ingly reconstructed to reveal the form of the original nodule from which the hand-axe was manufactured on the spot. A number of such sites in the Chilterns, in-cluding one at Caddington [TL 054 193], have been restudied by Avery et al. (1982) and Sampson (1978). The researches of Avery and colleagues indicate that much of the fine sand and silt material in the 'brick-earths' was probably derived from the local Woolwich and Reading Beds, although coarse silt and fine sand from other sources is generally also present. Some of this latter could be loessic material deposited over the Chilterns at intervals during the Anglian, 'Wolstonian' and Devensian glacial periods. The artifacts themselves do not provide positive dating evidence for the 'brick-earth' in which they occur; they fall in the Acheulian tradition. In some cases evidence of pedogenesis affect-ing the 'brickearths' during the Ipswichian interglacial suggests that they were emplaced in the Anglian and 'Wolstonian' cold periods. On general grounds a post-Anglian–pre-Devensian age seems most likely for the ar-tifact-bearing brickearths at Caddington and nearby sites. Very often the final stage of infilling of the solu-tion hollows appears to result from Devensian solifluc-tion of stony clays, from the surrounding clay-with-flints, which has helped to preserve the 'brickearth' deposits from recent erosion.

TILL

The Anglian ice sheet extended at least as far south as the Chilterns escarpment and laid down a thick lodge-ment till, with associated glaciofluvial deposits, over the northern and western parts of the district. This till, known as the Chalky Boulder Clay, is coeval with the Lowestoft Till of East Anglia. It is typically a bluish grey, overconsolidated clay with clasts of chalk, flint, 'Bunter' pebbles from the Trias, and blocks of Jurassic limestone and fossils (notably thick *Gryphaea* shells and belemnite guards). Igneous erratics of mainly northerly prove-nance also occur rarely.

The proportion of clasts to clay in the till is variable, but generally there are more and larger clasts in its basal portion. At the surface it weathers to a brownish grey, stony, sandy clay with most of the chalk lost by solution; it gives rise to heavy, stiff clay soils, once mainly left in pasture, but now mostly under intensive arable culture. Irregular sheets and pockets of glacial sand and gravel occur beneath, within or above the till. The thickness of the till varies considerably, in part because of pre-Anglian relief and post-Anglian erosion. It rarely exceeds 15 m except where preserved in channel fills. In the Tattenhoe Borehole [SP 8289 3437] till was proved to a depth of 29.38 m (73.05 m above OD), overlying about 9.5 m of glacial lake deposits, apparently in a channel cut in the Oxford Clay.

GLACIAL SAND AND GRAVEL

This term encompasses a highly variable range of sands and gravels, with subordinate silts and clays, laid down in what may broadly be described as glaciofluvial environments. They are intimately related to the Anglian till of the district, occurring as irregular sheets or bodies, below, within and above the till. The sediments were deposited by subglacial and englacial streams, and proglacial outwash marginal to the ice sheet; some are possibly morainic in origin. It is impossible to recognise any Anglian glacial depositional landforms in the district, due to modification by subsequent erosion.

All grades of sediment are represented: clay, silt, fine to coarse sand, fine to coarse gravel, cobbles and boulders. The suite of derived clasts is virtually identical to that of the till, reflecting their common source areas. Flint and chalk predominate, but notable proportions of 'Bunter' quartzite pebbles, Carboniferous limestones and sandstones, Jurassic cementstone nodules, limestones and thick-shelled fossils and Cretaceous 'carstone' also occur; igneous rocks are found more rarely.

As is typical of glaciofluvial deposits, the sands and gravels tend to be poorly sorted and irregularly stratified. They contain high proportions of clay fines and chalk, which limit their usefulness as constructional materials. Some lenticular bodies of fairly clean sand occur within the deposits. Frequent abandoned pits witness the former widespread exploitation of the deposits on a farm or village scale, but because of their variable distribution, thickness and quality, and the presence of chalk they are no longer of economic significance. The thickness of the deposits is highly variable, rarely exceeding 5 m, except within channels.

The sands and gravels are highly permeable and act as minor aquifers, giving rise to permanent springs at some sites. Sometimes the gravels or sands have been cemented by the secondary deposition of calcite from percolating waters.

SAND AND GRAVEL OF UNKNOWN AGE

During the survey of the Milton Keynes area (Horton et al., 1974) spreads of reddish brown, clayey, sandy, flint gravel were mapped in the Ouzel Valley around Bletchley and Fenny Stratford. The deposit overlies glacial lake deposits preserved in the buried channel of the Ouzel. The field relationships suggest that it may postdate the till since its form is related to the modern drainage system. It occurs at a slightly higher level than the Second terrace gravels. The age and origin of these gravels remain uncertain; they could represent a glaciofluvial event following the retreat of the ice sheet, or more probably the remnants of an early terrace deposit preserved in an old channel when the Ouzel was diverted to the east of Fenny Stratford, prior to the aggradation responsible for the Second terrace gravels.

GLACIAL LAKE DEPOSITS

The presence of a buried valley, incised for 40 m or more into the Jurassic bedrock of the Ouzel Valley, was demonstrated during the survey of the Milton Keynes new town area (Horton et al., 1974). It would seem that the pre-Anglian Ouzel Valley, draining northward to join the Ouse, was first dammed to form a finger lake as the Anglian ice sheet encroached from the north. The lake and its early deposits were later entirely overridden by the ice sheet. At this time, a subglacial stream under hydrostatic head appears to have scoured out and overdeepened the preglacial valley in the manner of the tunnel valleys of East Anglia (Woodland, 1971). As the Anglian ice began to retreat, with strong seasonal melt periods, the laminated lake deposits were laid down in a proglacial situation. They consist of very finely laminated (varved), grey, clayey silts and silty clays with some bands of coarser material and minor slumped horizons (see Plate 4, Horton et al., 1974). Sandy layers with cross-bedding of fluvial character are also intercalated with the silts locally. In addition, dropstones and water-lain till-like clays occur, suggesting deposition from the basal layers of floating ice in the proglacial lake.

The geotechnical properties of the clayey silts are generally poor and they are not very stable in excavations or when wet. Special care is needed in designing the foundations of structures to be built on their outcrop.

BURIED VALLEYS

Traces of three major drift-filled hollows associated with the advance and retreat of the Anglian ice sheet occur within the district, and have been referred to briefly in preceding sections of this chapter. A few smaller-scale channels at the base of the till have been observed in the sand pits around Heath and Reach (Plate 10).

The three major features are indicated in the inset diagram on the published 1:50 000 geological map of the district; they fall into two categories. The buried valley of the Ouzel seems to represent a proglacial lake, modified by subglacial erosion and then infilled with laminated clays and other glacial sediments. The features in the Lea headwaters and Lilley Bottom mark the sites of gaps in the Chilterns escarpment, through which outwash from the Anglian ice sheet was channelled. Minor ice lobes penetrated the gaps depositing till and glacioflu-

Plate 10   Minor subglacial channel, about 6 m deep, cut into the 'Silver Sands' division of the Woburn Sands, Stone Lane Quarry, Heath and Reach [SP 929 289] (Joseph Arnold & Sons Ltd). The channel is filled with interlayered chalky till and sands and gravels (ERST).

vial sediments, much of which have been removed by subsequent erosion. In Lilley Bottom the present dry valley has been cut some distance to the east of the old gap and this feature continues onto the Hitchin (Sheet 221) district.

The thick drift sequence in the Tattenhoe Borehole [SP 8289 3437] comprising 29.38 m of till above 9.67 m of glacial lake deposits suggests the presence of a channel tributary to that of the Ouzel, but no further evidence is available in that area.

The buried valley of the Ouzel, between Woughton on the Green in the north and Stoke Hammond in the south, was studied during the survey of the Milton Keynes new town area (Horton et al., 1974). Over this 8 km distance mapping and numerous trial boreholes allowed the buried channel to be fairly closely defined. It is up to 500 m in width and locally depths of over 40 m of glacial lake deposits were proved in boreholes. South of Stoke Hammond the channel is less well defined and difficult to locate below the floodplain and river terraces in the valley bottom. The inference is that the channel, as an overdeepened feature, terminated near Stoke

Hammond, or that all trace of its former presence has been destroyed by post-Anglian erosion.

The River Lea now rises at a major spring [TL 0609 2475] north of Leagrave Common, adjacent to the ancient earthwork known as Wanlud's Bank. Evidence for the position of a former gap across the Chilterns escarpment is preserved in a north–south string of glacial sand and gravel and till deposits. These extend from the summit of Sharpenhoe Clappers [TL 067 300] in the north, through Streatley to Limbury and thence to Luton Hoo. At Luton the outcrop of the resistant Chalk Rock in the gap gives it a narrow gorge-like character. Much of the drift formerly plugging this old channel has been removed by more recent erosion, so that typical thicknesses of glacial sand and gravel in central Luton are 5 to 6 m. Elsewhere, however, near Biscot and around Little Bramingham Farm [TL 073 254] boreholes have proved over 20 m of drift in the channel, which suggests that it may have had an irregular thalweg with isolated hollows. The deposits in Lilley Bottom are analogous to those of the Lea valley and at a similar level, implying that the two channels were contemporary. The presence of the glaciofluvial deposits in the Lea valley around Luton indicates that the major re-entrant in the Chalk escarpment there was already in existence by the Anglian period.

HEAD

A variety of slope deposits formed by solifluction and hill wash under mainly periglacial conditions are grouped together as head. The composition of these deposits is closely related to that of their local sources, although some admixture has occurred. The head deposits of the district are believed to have originated mainly in the Devensian glacial period, though deposition by hillwash, since man began to cultivate the land, is no doubt still active.

Head occurs mainly on the lower valley sides and valley bottoms and also on the Upper Jurassic clay slopes below the Woburn Sands escarpment. It generally thickens downslope so that the deposits are wedge-like in section. The deposits are somewhat dissected by Flandrian erosion and surface streams may be entrenched in them for several metres, possibly as a result of human interference with river flow. Combe deposits considered in the next section, are a special category of head which originated in combes on the face of the Chalk escarpment.

On clay outcrops solifluction can occur on slopes of only 3° (Weeks, 1969). It commonly affects the top metre or so, which probably corresponds to the depth of seasonal thawing under permafrost conditions. The clay in this layer has been remobilised and has moved downslope with the development of shear planes at the basal contact with in-situ material. It is not always easy to detect this kind of head by augering when both it and the parent clay are affected by weathering; it may thus be more extensive than indicated on the geological maps of the district. The presence of basal shear planes below this type of head can pose severe problems for civil engineers designing structures or excavations.

The friable sands of the Woburn Sands Formation give rise to thick and extensive deposits of a sandy head with clasts of ferruginous carstone and of flint and other rocks derived from glacial drift. Where the Woburn Sands overlies Upper Jurassic clay formations, the head can completely obscure the junction and also the underlying clays for considerable distances downslope. The base of the Woburn Sands can normally be traced by a combination of spring-line and break-of-slope features.

Till and glacial sand and gravel give rise to head, which may be difficult to differentiate unless it rests on bedrock of contrasting character. Thus tills give rise to grey-brown, sandy stony clays, resembling weathered tills, from which chalk clasts have generally been lost by solution.

In sections, the base of head deposits is often marked by a concentration of coarse clasts; in other cases the head may be disturbed by cryoturbation structures and festooned into the underlying bedrock.

By infilling and smoothing out irregularities in the landscape head deposits have contributed to a general softening of the relief of the district.

COMBE DEPOSITS

At several localities along the Chalk escarpment, short dry valleys have been cut back into the scarp face producing narrow steep-sided combes, which have relatively flat floors and exhibit some sharp right-angled bends. The material eroded during the formation of the combes is in part spread out as broad apron-like fans on the lower slopes of the escarpment, and in part fills the narrow floors of the combes. These combe deposits comprise water-lain chalk gravel in a fine chalky-clayey matrix with some flint and erratic pebbles, usually overlain by a metre or more of pale brown, silty, chalky loam. Shells of land mollusca are often preserved in the deposits and analysis of the faunas can give an indication of climatic changes during the formation and partial filling of the combes.

Two large spreads of combe deposits occur south of Totternhoe, and a number of smaller ones have been mapped between Upper Sundon, Barton-le-Clay and Hexton. The combes near Barton, Hexton and Pegsdon (the latter just to the east of the district, on the Hitchin (221) sheet) have been described by Lewis (1949) and Sparks and Lewis (1957). Their work included the sinking of boreholes and trial pits to sample the deposits in the combe bottoms. They confirmed that the flat floors of this group of combes are due to infilling, possibly emphasised by prehistoric to recent ploughing, rather than their having originated as glacial meltwater channels. The sharp bends were suggested to be a reflection of major joints in the Chalk. Spring sapping at a time of higher regional water table in the Chalk was adduced to be the most likely origin of the combes. Rapid hillwash on the sparsely vegetated combe sides during the cold, late-Glacial period could also have contributed to the erosion and partial infilling of the combes and to the spread of combe deposits below. The terrestrial molluscan faunas indicate possible cold conditions during the early stages of deposition in the combe bottoms (possibly late-Glacial) and generally warmer conditions through the ensuing Flandrian period. The faunas of the now dry Pegsdon combe sections confirm that a spring was active there up to the warm Atlantic period (c.6000 yr BP). The change to loamy material in the upper metre of so of the combe bottom infills is problematical, but could be the result of increased soil wash following cultivation.

South of Totternhoe near Eaton Bray, the combe deposits form large spreads with a basal layer of chalky, flinty gravel overlain by varied, clayey, chalky silts with some flint chips. The basal gravels in this area vary from 0.1 to 1.8 m in thickness, with the whole deposit up to 3 m in thickness.

Combe deposits may occur on the Lower Chalk outcrops in Dunstable and Luton, but it has not been possible to map the deposits in the built-up areas.

DRY VALLEY DEPOSITS

These typically occur as narrow ribbons on the floors of dry valleys cut into the dip slopes of the Chalk, in the south-east of the district around Kensworth, Caddington and Luton. The dry valleys tend to be steep sided and asymmetrical in cross-profile. They may have been cut by semipermanent streams, at a time when the regional water table in the Chalk was higher than at present, or during a permafrost period when the frozen ground would have enhanced surface run-off and erosion.

The deposits are rarely exposed except in temporary excavations. They are generally several metres thick, with a coarse, flinty gravel in a red-brown, clayey matrix at the base, overlain by a metre or more of brown, silty loam with scattered flints. The chalk in the valley bottom below the deposits is typically fractured and badly weathered.

The deposits include material derived from the clay-with-flints redistributed by hill wash, solifluction and ephemeral streams. They appear to postdate the Anglian glacial deposits which plug the old Lilley Bottom valley. Bourne flows no longer occur in the dry valleys of the district, probably due to the recent lowering of the water table in the Chalk by pumping for public and industrial water supplies.

RIVER TERRACE DEPOSITS

River terrace deposits of sands and gravels, representing the eroded remnants of former floodplain aggradations, are of fairly limited extent; they are restricted to the catchments of the larger streams, the Ouzel, Flit, Lea and Thame. Within the district, terrace deposits are preserved at two levels in the Ouzel catchment, but at a single level in the valleys of the Thame, the Flit and the Lea.

The sands and gravels of the terrace deposits, rarely exceed 2 to 3 m and are usually overlain by a thin capping of sandy loam. In the Ouzel and Flit catchments, the alluvium is entrenched into the first terrace, which locally survives beneath it.

The outcropping solid formations, older head deposits and Anglian glacial drifts are the source of the clasts making up the terrace gravels; their proportions vary with location. The dominantly clayey, Upper Jurassic formations yield little in the way of durable clasts, and it is probable that fragments of Jurassic limestones and thick-shelled fossils in the gravel have been glacially transported from outside the district. Hard ferruginous 'carstone' and 'boxstones', derived from the Woburn Sands and the basal Gault, are locally present in appreciable proportions. Overall, however, the terrace deposits of the district have flint, chalk and 'Bunter' pebbles, recycled from the glacial deposits, as their major constituents.

The terrace deposits are post-Anglian in age and probably both terraces date from the Devensian glacial period, but no direct evidence of the age is available.

The Ouzel catchment

The Ouzel, the most important river of the district, drains northwards to join the River Ouse near Newport

Pagnell. The present valley more or less coincides with that of the Anglian buried valley (p.89), so that in places the terrace deposits directly overlie those in the buried channel. The floodplain falls from about 90 m above OD in the south to 60 m above OD in the north over a straight line distance of 20 km, giving an average gradient of 1 in 66. The top of the First and Second terrace deposits are up to approximately 2 and 5 m respectively above the floodplain surface. The base of the terrace deposits are irregular, because they infill channels cut at periods of lowered sea level. The floor of the First terrace extends beneath the alluvial fill of the modern floodplain and appears to be graded to a lower sea level than that currently prevailing. The floor of the Second terrace is generally 1 to 2 m above the floodplain surface. In the Ouzel valley, it is possible that there could be three channels below the Second and First terraces, and the alluvium. The terraces of the Milton Keynes new town area have been described by Horton et al. (1974) who suggest that, on regional evidence, the Second terrace could correspond to a mid-Devensian temperate interstadial around 42 000 years BP. The First terrace probably predates the Late Devensian glacial advance, while the channel in which alluvium rests was cut during the Devensian period of low sea level, and infilled in pace with the Flandrian rise of sea level over the past 10 000 years.

Remnants of First and Second terrace deposits are present in a small unnamed tributary of the Ouzel which flows from near Woburn to Ridgmont Station, in the north of the district.

Because of their limited extent, thinness and poor quality the gravels of the Ouzel catchment have little economic potential. The Second terrace gravels have been dug on a small scale in the past and exploited commercially near Milton Keynes village, just outside the district (Horton et al., 1974). The First terrace deposits are thin with a clayey matrix and in places have an overburden of alluvium; they have rarely been exploited in the district.

Cryoturbation has affected the upper parts of both First and Second terrace deposits.

The River Flit

The Flit, a tributary of the River Ivel, drains the north-eastern part of the district. Several isolated remnants of First terrace deposits occur on the northern side of the valley between Maulden and Clophill, where it is possible that head may conceal other terrace remnants. The top of the terrace deposits lies at about 5 m above that of the adjacent floodplain alluvium. It is probable that the terrace deposits are continuous below the alluvium for the most part. The gravels are up to 2 m thick, but are generally of low quality and hence of little economic significance.

The River Lea

The Lea rises at Leagrave north of Luton, and drains the south-eastern part of the district via the gap at Luton, eventually joining the Thames. A few small gravel remnants have been classified as First terrace deposits, on their topographical position and flat-topped form. The terrace tops lie about 10 m about the flood plain.

ALLUVIUM

Alluvium, deposited during the Flandrian period, is present in the valleys of the Ouzel, the Thame, the Flit, the Lea and their tributaries. In the floodplains of the Ouzel and the Flit, the alluvium rests in channels cut into or through the First terrace deposits. The alluvium of the Lea occupies a channel cut mostly in the glacial deposits of the buried valley. The alluvium is thin rarely exceeding 2 m.

The composition of the alluvium varies, reflecting the locally exposed solid formations and older drifts from which it is derived. Thus it tends to be dominantly clayey in the Ouzel catchment, where till and Jurassic clays are the main sources, and more sandy in the Lea. In the Flit Valley, east of Flitton, dark peaty silts predominate. Chalky detritus is typical of the Whistle Brook, a tributary of the Ouzel, which drains from the Chalk escarpment at Ivinghoe, south of the district.

The alluvium consists of dark grey, laminated, silty or sandy clay with variable organic content; commonly a thin, sandy, gravelly, lag deposit marks the base. Organic material includes molluscan shells and traces of vegetation, which locally form thin peat layers. Extensive peat in the Flit valley is described in the following section.

The floodplains are still subject to periodic seasonal flooding, but probably less so than in the past due to flood protection measures.

PEAT

Extensive areas of peat have been mapped along the floodplain of the River Flit between Flitton and Clophill. The deposit comprises a dark brown to almost black silt, very rich in peaty organic matter. It passes laterally into alluvium, and may also be interbedded with alluvial brown silt or clay. The thickness varies up to several metres. The reasons for the formation of peat in the Flit valley are not clear. It could be linked to high water levels in the underlying Woburn Sands giving rise to fairly permanent water-logged conditions in the past.

At Flitwick Moor [TL 048 352], the peat is largely undrained and supports a fen type of vegetation, with abundant birch trees, sedge and rushes. Here it is seen to be underlain by gravel at depths ranging from about 0.5 m up to several metres.

DETAILS

CLAY-WITH-FLINTS

Good sections in these deposits are rare in the district. At Kensworth Quarry [TL 017 197] some 5 to 6 m are removed as overburden, before the Chalk is excavated for cement manufacture. In the highest working face of the quarry a number of truncated solution pipes in the Chalk, infilled with collapsed clay-with-flints and 'brickearth' are usually visible. The pipes are irregularly conical in form, and often have flinty clay let down parallel to their walls; the central cavity of the larger pipes may be infilled with brown, silty, loamy 'brickearth' with very few flints (Plate 11).

At Capability Green [TL 098 197] near Luton, cuttings for the widening of the A1081 road, revealed sections through a number of infilled solution pipes, similar to those at Kensworth. The silty infilling of these pipes was unstable, so that special measures were necessary to stabilise the sides of the cuttings. On the adjacent Capability Green business park [TL 095 196] trial boreholes proved clay-with-flints up to 6 m thick in general, but with up to 15.5 m in solution pipes.

There are no longer any exposures of the 'brickearth' in solution collapse features formerly worked around Caddington, Slip End, Luton, Round Green and Stopsley, from which Smith (1894, 1916) collected Palaeolithic artifacts. For the most part the pits have been backfilled and levelled or built over, though degraded old pits remain around Caddington. Details of the sites and working histories of these brickworks were given by Cox (1979a).

TILL

Ampthill, Woburn, Sundon

Till covers the plateau which extends from north-east of Ampthill eastwards to near Chicksands. Much of it lies 100 m at more than above OD but, locally, for example around Beadlow [TL 105 385], its base descends about 50 m into the valley of the River Flit. It falls a similar amount into the valley south-east of Upper Gravenhurst.

At Kiln Farm [TL 0845 3860], to the north of Clophill, the basal part of the till appears to have been dug in the past as a brick clay.

To the north of Steppingley a narrow east–west aligned strip of till occupies a channel cut into the underlying Woburn Sands.

Till overlies the Gault on the high ground to the north and north-east of Hockliffe. Small isolated outcrops also occur at lower heights of about 100 m above OD in the valley of the Clipstone Brook to the west of Hockliffe, demonstrating either that the valley was eroded by the advancing ice sheet or that it is of preglacial origin.

At Upper Sundon [TL 045 284] the till to the north of Home Farm is draped over the margin of the glacial sand and gravel.

An extensive spread [TL 040 260] of till has been mapped to the south-east of Chalton. The deposit comprises an orange to red-brown pebbly clay, apparently chalk free. The presence of derived Jurassic fossils and exotic pebbles demonstrates that it is not weathered bedrock. Locally the deposit becomes quite gravelly. Evidence from the adjacent railway cutting suggests that the clay is less that 2 m thick.

Most of the M1 motorway cuttings through the till are now completely grown over. Trial borehole logs for the road show that the thickness of the deposit on the plateaux is less than 10 m.

Exposures in the banks of the ponds in Woburn Park show heterogeneous bluish grey and brown weathered, variably sandy, stony clays with gravelly sand intercalations. Near the Safari Park [SP 9739 3385] the basal 1 m or so consists of similar material overlying crudely interbedded, slightly chalky clay and orange-brown, slightly, gravelly sand, possibly a flow till incorporating local Woburn Sands bedrock.

South of Woburn Abbey there is an extensive tract of till carrying a typical suite of erratic and local rocks. However, about 600 m west-north-west of Brook End, Eversholt [SP 978 328], there is a preponderance of Jurassic cementstones, septarian nodules and shelly limestones. A water well in Woburn Park [SP 9657 3133] encountered 32.3 m of till containing beds of sand.

Heath and Reach to Leighton Buzzard

The higher ground around Heath and Reach, and north to the A5, is capped by till, which is exposed as overburden in some of the working sand quarries. Thin remnants of till also occur on Shenley Hill [SP 933 269]. The till is typically a stiff blue-grey clay with clasts of chalk, flint, 'Bunter' pebbles, Jurassic rocks and some far-travelled erratics. Locally, layers of lenticular pockets of brown sandy chalky gravel occur within it.

In the A5 Pit of P Bennie Ltd [SP 932 304] the overburden of till is up to 3.5 m thick, increasing from north to south. The thickest sequence recorded is as follows:

	Thickness m
Till, blue-grey and grey-brown chalky clay, with 'flints', 'Bunter' pebbles and *Gryphaea*. Chalk clasts up to 7 cm	seen up to 3
Clay, sandy, compact, brown, faintly stratified with a few small clasts of flint and chalk	up to 0.5

On the north-west face, beneath the beds described above, a small channel about 3 m wide and 1 m deep cuts into the Woburn Sands; it is filled with sandy stony clay. The base of the till undulates slightly in this pit.

At the northern limit of the workings in Hall's Fox Corner Pit [SP 9277 2936] typical blue-grey, chalky till infills a steep-sided channel, 25 m wide by 6 m deep, cut into the Woburn Sands. On the eastern face there was another channel (or a continuation of the same) [SP 9279 2929] of similar dimensions which was traced into the adjacent Buckland's Fox Corner Pit [SP 9278 2924] where it is 2 m deep and filled with grey-brown sandy clay containing chalk and flint clasts.

In Arnold's Stone Lane Quarry [SP 929 289], the overburden comprises up to 10 m of till and up to 6 m of glacial sand and gravel. The latter fills a steep-sided channel about 50 m wide (Plate 10), cut into the Woburn Sands and trending approximately west-north-west; it was seen in the eastern part of the working. The till comprises typical blue-grey chalky till with clasts of flint, 'Bunter' pebbles and Jurassic limestones. The glacial sand and gravel infilling the channel comprises medium brown, sandy, clayey gravel interbedded with layers of till. In some parts of the pit its top is cemented by calcite to a depth of 0.5 m, producing massive concrete-like slabs with clasts of chalk, flint and Jurassic rocks in a hard sandy matrix. Beneath this channel the 'Brown Sands' of the Woburn Sands are stained crimson. This may result from the oxidation of iron minerals in the sands by waters percolating from the gravels. Similar staining occurs at Buckland's Fox Corner Pit, where it affects the 'Silver Sands.'

In the L B Silica Sand Co.'s Bryants Lane Pit [SP 929 286] up to 10 m of typical till is removed as overburden. About a metre above the base it includes an interbedded layer of sandy gravel 1 to 2 m thick. Farther south, in Buckland's Reach Lane Quarry [SP 933 284] recent earth-moving has exposed up to 12 m of till at the eastern extremity of the workings. The till includes irregular pockets and layers of brown sandy gravel, which are sometimes waterbearing.

Till is also exposed at Garside's Mundays Hill Quarry [SP 937 282] where it comprises up to 6 m of blue-grey and grey-brown chalky, flinty till, resting with a sharp planar junction on the Gault.

West of the Ouzel valley at Leighton Buzzard, till in a complex association with glacial sand and gravel is present on much of the higher ground, but there are few exposures of any size. In some places near Stoke Hammond and Soulbury, the till has steep contacts with the underlying solid rocks, suggesting the presence of extensions to the buried channels of the Ouzel valley in the Milton Keynes area (Horton et al., 1974). There is no borehole information to provide supporting evidence for such channels.

In the Ouzel valley there are lower-lying patches of chalky till at 85 m to 90 m above OD. The most northerly of these [SP 921 241] adjoins the flooded sand pit close to Grovebury Road. This is almost certainly the 'Rockley Hill' pit referred to by Lamplugh (1915) in which he recorded stiff bluish boulder clay filling a deep-sided 'ravine' in the Woburn Sands. The till exceeded 6 m in thickness and contained much chalk, flint and 'Oolitic' (i.e. Jurassic) detritus, including *Gryphaea* shells; ice-scratched boulders of Carboniferous Limestone and basalt were also noted.

Just north of Slapton [SP 933 212] a thin spread of very chalky till, probably no more than 2 m thick, floors the Ouzel valley.

Wing to Ascott

In the vicinity of Wing the till contains extensive beds of glacial sand and gravel. The basal part contains much clay of local derivation and is thus difficult to differentiate from the underlying bedrock. In addition, to the south-west of the village, the till contains intercalations of buff silts and clayey silts, probably subaqueous in origin. Boreholes for the southern bypass revealed that these silts are associated with a channel, which contains sandy gravels in the lower part. To the south-east of Wing, the bedrock surface typically lies at about 110 to 117 m above OD beneath the drift, but near the axis of the channel [near 8825 2215] it lies below 93 m; the channel slopes towards the south-westwards hereabouts. The section below may possibly lie near the northward continuation of the channel.

The former brickworks pit in Wing [881 232] was recorded by Davies (1915, p.92) as follows:

	Thickness m
Coarse morainic gravels	2.4
Chalky Boulder Clay (till)	0.8
Sands and finer gravels	c.3
Boulder Clay (till)	9.1
Gault	—

It was noted that to the north, the 'lowest beds rose up and the lower till disappeared altogether, while on the other side of the brook they apparently dipped down again.' The valley side succession [SP 880 229] nearest to this site shows a simpler sequence of gravels (about 8 m) overlying till (about 2.5 m) which in turn rests on bedrock. Thus both of the tills may be lenticular in form.

In the vicinity of Ascott Home Farm [SP 990 231] a fourfold succession of drift is present; in descending order this is till, glacial sand and gravel, till, glacial sand and gravel. The bedrock surface is lower in this area and there may be a genetic link between the presence of such multilayer sequences and of broad-scale channelling of the bedrock surface.

Buff stoneless silts occur locally, particularly in the area [SP 878 219] south of Wing where they apparently show interdigitating relationships. Although there are no exposures it is thought that these sediments may be bedded and perhaps represent phases of subaqueous deposition.

GLACIAL SAND AND GRAVEL

Ampthill, Flitwick and Toddington

To the north-east of Flitwick [TL 035 350] an extensive area of glacial sand and gravel caps much of the higher ground, masking the junction between the underlying Woburn Sands and the 'Corallian' clays. A partially degraded section [TL 0353 3521], with over 2 m of poorly sorted sand and gravel composed mainly of angular and subangular flints, was noted off Brookes Road, Flitwick. The sand and gravel hereabouts probably does not exceeds a few metres in thickness.

An east–west train of gravel is present along the south side of the stream to the north of Steppingley [TL 012 354]. The gravels, although following the course of the present-day stream, occur at variable heights above the floodplain and are thus believed not to be River terrace deposits, but more likely to represent the eroded basal infill of a preglacial valley along the line of the present valley.

At Millbrook Golf Club, glacial sand and gravel crops out from below the margins of a small patch of till [TL 002 383]. The gravel consists mainly of subangular flints with subordinate rounded pebbles of 'Bunter' quartzite. Similar patches of sand and gravel are present around the margin of the more extensive area of till to the north-east of Ampthill.

In the Hockliffe area the glacial sand and gravel consists mainly of poorly sorted, fine- to medium-grained, silty sands with lenses of chalk and flint gravel, and of buff silt; the maximum thickness in this area is about 4 m. The glacial sand and gravel occurs in lenses at the base of the till, for example one occurrence [SP 977 278] near Watergate Farm apparently occupies a channel within the basal part of the till. The sand and gravel also occurs above the till as isolated patches on higher ground, where the deposits are very flinty at the surface, probably degraded and of variable thickness due to the effects of cryoturbation.

In the area between Tingrith and Toddington, an impersistent bed of sand and gravel lies about 5 m above the base of the till. In places it has extensive outcrop, but this may not reflect its true thickness; it is possible that the sand and gravel and the overlying drift may be 'draped' over an inclined bedrock surface. To the north-east of Toddington, and locally elsewhere, this sand and gravel rests directly on the Gault. The lithology is dominantly sandy and field relationships in the vicinity of old workings [TL 019 281] near White Hart Farm indicate that the base may be markedly channelled.

Capping the higher ground at Toddington, and about 15 m higher in the succession, there is an extensive spread of sandy gravels which have been dug in the past. It is possible that, towards the margins of this spread, 'draping' may also have occurred, and thus the outcrop pattern may suggest an exaggerated thickness. It is estimated that there may be up to 10m present.

Around Westoning an extensive spread of sand and gravel occupies the low ground adjacent to the River Flit. Although some of these deposits occupy positions normally associated with river terraces, they do not display a typical terrace morphology and locally are overlain by till. In this area gravels and gravelly sands predominate; the gravel fraction consists mainly of rounded 'Bunter' pebbles and subangular flints up to about 5 cm in diameter.

Upper Sundon

An extensive tract of sand and gravel caps much of the higher ground around Upper Sundon. A pit section [TL 0442 2747] about 10 m high revealed a cross-bedded sequence of gravels composed predominantly of rounded 'Bunter' pebbles, sub angular flints and chalk pebbles, with diameters up to about 5 cm, although larger pebbles up to about 10 cm were also noted. The gravels have a variable sandy matrix. Several beds up to about 10 cm thick of slightly pebbly grey-brown clay occur within the sequence. Discontinuities within the deposit, emphasised by the cross-bedding, cannot be satisfactorily explained by changes in sediment transport direction or solution of the underlying chalk, and may result from glaciotectonic deformation caused by an over-riding ice sheet.

The surface expression of the sands and gravel around Upper Sundon might suggest that they have the form of a sheet-like body, but an examination of the east face [TL 0430 2710] of the Sundon Cement Works reveals a series of gravel-filled channels and pipes cut into the chalk. One channel [TL 0425 2683] contains a gravel with boulders of flint, sandstone, limestone and igneous rock, interbedded with sands and thin seams of grey-brown clay.

Eversholt, Milton Bryan

South of Eversholt several small lenticular bodies of slightly gravelly sand occur within the till in the vicinity of Oakhill Spinney [SP 994 311]. A larger body of similar material is present within Woburn Park at and near Speedwell Belt [SP 960 317]; small exposures are visible around Upper Hopgarden Pond [SP 964 319].

Small spreads of gravelly sand, locally rather clayey, occur at and near Milton Bryan [SP 963 303; 970 311 and 972 303]. Similar, but better-sorted material caps the ridge on which Berry End Farm stands [SP 983 343]. Small bodies of sand and gravel at the base of the till occur at Hills End [SP 977 332] and north-east of Eversholt [SP 993 338].

Leighton Buzzard, Wing

To the west and north west of Leighton Buzzard, glacial sand and gravel occurs extensively in association with till. It may occur at the base, within or on top of the till. It generally gives rise to fairly light, sandy gravelly soils, in contrast to the heavier clay soils characteristic of the till. Springs often issue where these deposits rest on impermeable till or bedrock.

Between Linslade and Stewkley North End, the deposits occur in an irregular swathe up to 2 km in width with an approximate west-north-west trend. The gravels and sands have been worked from several old pits north-east of Stewkley [SP 854 271, 857 269, 859 269 and 862 268]. The results of a commercial investigation for gravel near Vicarage Farm, Stewkley [SP 860 268], showed between 10 and 20 m of assorted sands, chalky gravel, sandy gravel and clay occupying a channel cut through the till to bedrock. The channel varies in width between 60 and 150 m and has a west-north-west trend.

The deposits have also been worked around Hill Farm, Hollingdon [SP 873 272], where an old pit up to 5.5 m deep is still evident though largely overgrown. In Soulbury, a large erratic block of Carboniferous Limestone (presumably from Derbyshire), measuring 1.1 by 0.7 m, is preserved [SP 8829 2709] in a minor lane off High Road. It may have come from a former pit north-west of the church [SP 882 271], but has reportedly been in its present position at least since Cromwellian times.

Large outcrops of gravelly sand occur around Wing [SP 882 239; 882 228], forming sheet-like bodies within the till. Locally, in this area, small pockets of sand were detected within the till which could not be delineated with confidence.

South of Leighton Linslade the glacial sand and gravel lies below the till and outcrops at the margin of the higher plateau. It varies from reddish and orange-brown medium-grained sands with little gravel, to very gravelly sands. Just north-east of Ascott Farm [SP 903 234] the deposit contains much chalk. Boreholes hereabouts proved up to 6.8 m of gravel. In one borehole [SP 9050 2365], 4.5 m of gravel overlie 3.7 m of till, which in turn rest on Gault. The till here is probably a local lens at the base of the glacial gravels.

Luton, Dunstable

In the Luton and Dunstable urban areas glacial sand and gravel occurs in the buried valley of the Lea (p.89) and in several isolated patches at higher levels. The gravels are mainly composed of angular or subangular flints in a reddish brown silty clay matrix; occasional *Gryphaea* shells, Jurassic limestone and igneous rock clasts testify to the glacial origin of the deposits as seen in temporary exposures and soil brash. They were probably deposited at or near the margin of the Anglian ice sheet in subglacial channels, outwash spreads or channels cutting through gaps in the Chilterns escarpment. As noted previously, it must be emphasised that the deposits in the buried channel of the Lea are only partial remnants of thicker sequences much reduced by post-Anglian erosion. In central Luton a number of trial boreholes and wells prove thicknesses of up to 10.7 m of glacial sand and gravel; the base ranges from at 98 to 104 m above OD. Farther north near Biscot, wells at Croda Colloids [TL 0862 2271] proved up to 24.23 m of these deposits, above the Chalk at c.90 m above OD. Two sites where these gravels were formerly exploited [TL 074 247 and 083 241] near Limbury have been restored to above the original level, presumably with landfill material. Small exposures of chalky gravel below alluvium are seen at intervals along the course of the River Lea upstream of New Bedford Road [TL 086 240].

HEAD

Ampthill, Flitwick and Great Brickhill

Head locally drapes the escarpment of the Woburn Sands in the area to the north of Ampthill. It consists of brown clayey sands, which become increasingly clayey downslope with the incorporation of material derived from the 'Corallian' and Oxford Clay.

Extensive deposits of head cover the lower ground between Ampthill and Flitwick. Here they are variable in composition, having been derived from different sources, and include sandy clay, pebbly clayey sand, and clayey gravel.

In the Hockliffe area the head deposits are dominantly soft to firm, brown, flinty, sandy clays and sandy loams; peaty silts are present below spring lines. Clayey flint gravels are common near the base of the head, which is typically 2 to 3 m thick. Lenses of redistributed Gault clay occur in places.

The gravelly, sandy nature of the head deposits along the lower slopes of the valley of the River Flit between Flitwick and its source near Chalton reflects their derivation mainly from the adjacent outcrops of glacial sand and gravel.

South of Toddington M1 Services the head deposits are derived mainly from the Gault and Upper Greensand and therefore slightly pebbly clays and silts predominate.

Between Great Brickhill and Lidlington, head composed of sand and variable admixtures of clay and containing 'carstone' fragments commonly extends downslope from the escarpment of the Woburn Sands, obscuring the junction between the lat-

ter and the Oxford Clay. The resulting tract of head is generally between 100 and 150 m wide, but is more extensive in some places, for example south-east of Husborne Crawley [SP 962 358] and west of Woburn Sands [SP 905 353]. The head is probably thickest adjacent to the Woburn Sands outcrop where it may be several metres thick but, more distant from the outcrop, thicknesses of less than 2 m are usual.

Deposits of brown sandy loam with 'carstone' debris and pebbles derived from the glacial deposits occur in the floors of valleys falling away from the Woburn Sands outcrop between Great Brickhill and Leighton Buzzard.

Wing, Eaton Bray

In the Wing area, the head is largely derived from the till, Gault and Kimmeridge clay, and thus consists dominantly of firm brown and grey flinty clay. Locally there is soft, stoneless, grey clay derived solely from bedrock lithologies. Where Portland Beds crop out on valley slopes the head includes a proportion of angular limestone debris.

These deposits fill valley bottoms and grade down to the river alluvium at Ledburn. Up to 5 m may be present in the major valleys and they may be composite, comprising multiple solifluction lobes of variable derivation. A basal gravelly bed is commonly present.

East of Ascott Farm [SP 906 232], the head consists of orange-brown clayey sand derived from till and glacial sand derived from till and glacial sand and gravel. Variable clayey, sandy and silty loams occur west of Southcourt Stud Farm, Leighton Linslade [SP 901 244].

Dissected deposits of relatively old head occur near Eaton Bray and Edlesborough overlying Chalk Marl, Upper Greensand and Gault at the foot of the chalk escarpment. The head forms extensive spreads on top of low flat spurs on either side of the brook which marks the Buckinghamshire–Bedfordshire border. Hereabouts, the head comprises generally fine-grained, chalky, flint gravels and gravelly chalky silts of pale greyish brown, yellow or orange colours; clay and sand also occur. The head shows a crude layering in exposures and is generally heterogeneous. Coarser flint gravel may be concentrated in the base of the deposit, or there may be a rapid gradation into the underlying rocks, suggesting cryoturbation. The chalky gravels and silts are generally overlain by greyish brown silty clays with scattered flint pebbles. In Northall [SP 9566 2021], blocks of pebbly sandstone with ferruginous cement have apparently been excavated from the base of the head; this cementation probably results from groundwater having been concentrated in the more permeable base of the deposit.

RIVER TERRACE DEPOSITS

Second terrace deposits

Second terrace deposits of a tributary of the Ouzel near Salford are separated from those of the First terrace by a valley slope of Oxford Clay. They attain a height of 2 to 4 m above the present floodplain. They have been dug for gravel, but there are no current exposures.

In the Ouzel valley there are small patches of Second terrace deposits near Nares Gladley Farm [SP 908 280] and at Oak Farm, Stoke Hammond [SP 887 293]. The largest deposit, in Leighton Buzzard between Page's Park [SP 929 243] and the industrial estate [SP 938 248], is built over except at Page's Park. A small exposure in the face of an old sand pit [SP 9273 2426] shows about 1 m of fine to medium sandy gravel with bands of bedded fine-grained sand containing gravelly strings.

First terrace deposits

The first terrace of an unnamed tributary of the Ouzel has a small outcrop [SP 943 382] where it reaches a maximum height of about 2 m above the level of the floodplain. Ditch and stream sections indicate that it is generally less than 2 m thick. The deposit consists mainly of patinated subangular flints and rounded 'Bunter' quartzite pebbles with a matrix of medium- to coarse-grained sand. Just south of Husborne Crawley the terrace appears, from surface indications, to be composed mainly of pebbly sand; the sand fraction is presumably derived from the nearby outcrop of the Woburn Sands.

There are extensive outcrops of the First terrace in and around Leighton Buzzard, in the valleys of the Ouzel and its tributary the Clipstone Brook. Downstream from Leighton Buzzard a number of separate outcrops occupy the slip-off slopes of meander cores in the Ouzel valley, facing degraded river cliffs on the opposite side of the floodplain.

In the river bank just north of Ledburn [SP 9052 2252] 1.2 m of medium gravel overlies Gault clay. It consists mainly of subangular flints and quartzite pebbles, with subordinate quartz, 'carstone' and jasper pebbles. The matrix is a poorly sorted, clayey, medium- to coarse-grained sand.

South-east of Grove Lock [SP 9201 2269] a temporary excavation revealed the following:

	Thickness m
Sand, brown, fine-grained, silty, with a few scattered subangular flints and 'Bunter' quartzite pebbles; more gravelly towards base, with pebbles up to 0.08 m across	1.0
Gravel, creamy brown, fine-grained, sandy, poorly sorted, comprising subangular flints and chalk detritus; chalk more dominant in top 0.3 m	0.9

The terrace deposit is exposed in the northern face of Tiddenfoot New Pit [SP 9120 2396] where the section is:

	Thickness m
Loam, dark greyish brown, containing scattered small flints and quartzite pebbles	0.4
Gravel, orange-brown, medium-grained, poorly sorted, with a slightly loamy sand matrix; mainly subangular flints and rounded flint pebbles, with 'Bunter' quartzite, quartz and 'carstone' pebbles; base slightly pocketed into underlying Woburn Sands	0.5–0.8

A trench section at Leighton Buzzard [SP 9189 2427] showed:

	Thickness m
Loam, dark greyish brown, gravelly	0.2
Sand, orange-brown, slightly clayey, slightly gravelly	0.7
Gravel, orange-brown, medium clayey, sandy	0.5 seen

A temporary section in Luton [TL 0887 2229] showed about 0.8 m of brown sandy loam overlying up to 2.0 m of fine to coarse, yellow-brown, chalky flints, sandy gravel with some 'Bunter' and Tertiary pebbles resting on Middle Chalk. The rounded and subangular chalk clasts in the gravel are up to 7 cm in size and probably of very local origin. The gravels show cross-bedding, picked out by silty layers, dipping at 10° in an easterly direction. It is likely that the nearby glaciofluvial sands and gravels have been a major source of these terrace deposits.

The terrace remnant referred to above was worked in a few small pits in Victorian times. The pits were backfilled with ashes and domestic waste and subsequently built over. A house built on the edge of one of these pits developed severe structural problems due to differential settlement.

ALLUVIUM

An unnamed stream, in the east–west-trending valley which separates Ampthill and Flitwick, joins the River Flit to the west of Flitton. The present-day stream is small and obviously a misfit. Patches of glacial sand and gravel along this valley to the north of Steppingley demonstrate its antiquity and suggest that in preglacial times this might have been the main river valley. Alluvial silts and clays have been deposited along the valley bottom. The floodplain is usually less than 200 m wide, but locally, for example to the south-west and south-east of Ampthill, it widens considerably. This may have resulted from ponding-up of the valley by glacial sand and gravel to the north of Ruxox Farm [TL 0475 3595]. The alluvial deposits, generally less than 2 m thick, are mainly silts and clays, becoming sandy or gravelly in places [TL 0425 3665] [TL 0430 3646].

The floodplain of the River Flit is typically several hundreds of metres across. Between Flitton and Shefford the floodplain deposits are composed largely of dark brown to almost black silts, very rich in organic matter. These have been differentiated from the general alluvium and are shown as peat on the map. The junction between the alluvium and the peat is gradational and arbitrary. In places, gravel underlies the alluvial silts and clays; this may represent a gravelly base to the alluvium or, alternatively, be part of an older terrace deposit underlying the alluvium.

An unnamed stream, with an alluvial tract some 10 to 150 m wide, flows north-east through Lower Gravenhurst to Shefford. Its alluvial deposits consist of dark brown silts, rich in organic matter. In many places the silts overlie gravel at depths of between 1 and 1.5 m. The gravels probably form an integral part of the alluvial sequence as there are no terrace gravels adjacent to the margins of the floodplain.

Narrow strips of alluvial silts and clays, up to about 100 m wide, occupy the bottom of several broad north-east-trending valleys, to the north-east of Barton-le-Clay. The edge of the alluvial deposits against the surrounding weathered Gault clay is difficult to determine in places as it is not always associated with a distinct break of slope.

The floodplain of the Ouzel is well developed. Below Woughton on the Green, to Fenny Stratford, the alluvium consists of soft brown silty clay with scattered pebbles, becoming dark grey with depth. Organic sandy silts and calcareous silty sands may be present in the lower parts; a bed of fibrous peat proved in a borehole [SP 8856 3645] near Simpson was 1.2 m thick.

Alluvial deposits floor the valley of the unnamed tributary of the River Ouzel downstream from Husborne Crawley; the alluvium consists mainly of brown silty clays, commonly with pebbles of flint and quartzite in 'stringers' near their base. In the upper reaches of this valley, just north-west of Woburn, clayey sand and sandy clay lithologies reflect the composition of the Woburn Sands over which the stream flows. Peat has been recorded within the deposits east of Birchmoor Farm [SP 9495 3448].

Near Old Linslade Manor the floodplain is notably boggy and three trial boreholes [SP 913 272] proved up to 5.5 m of alluvium. An area north of the Manor has been reclaimed by tipping of waste.

West of Nares Gladley Farm several river bank exposures provide useful sections in the alluvium. One [SP 9070 2761] shows 1.6 m of grey-brown sandy clay resting on 0.4 m of peat, with 0.1 m of gravel at the base overlying Oxford Clay. A little to the north [SP 9071 2770], another section shows grey-brown silty clay (0.9 m thick) resting on fine to medium gravel (up to 1.0 m) with clasts of flint, 'Bunter' pebbles and 'carstone' overlying Oxford Clay. The gravel has cobbles up to 0.2 m in diameter and some ferruginous staining and cementation. It probably represents a First terrace remnant for the most part.

North of Paper Mill Farm a river bank section [SP 8924 2951] shows up to 2 m of grey-brown, sandy, silty clay; the base is not seen. Approximately 0.5 km east of Stoke Hammond lock another river bank exposure [SP 8913 2990] shows 1.3 m of grey-brown silty clay on up to 1.3 m of brown, medium to coarse sandy gravel.

The headwaters of the River Ouzel, east of Slaptonbury Mill [SP 9368 2139], drain the Gault clay outcrop. Its alluvium consists of up to 1.5 m of brown silty and sandy clays containing freshwater gastropod shells, scattered small flints and a few small chalk pebbles. At the base there is a thin flinty gravel. A similar sequence occurs in the tributary valley passing through Slapton Lock [SP 9285 2015].

Whistle Brook drains from the chalk scarp at Ivinghoe and is confluent with the River Ouzel near Slaptonbury Mill. Its floodplain, and that of the River Ouzel, below the confluence is underlain by alluvium containing abundant chalk debris. This alluvium typically consists of a thin surface spread of brown silty clay, overlying white clayey chalk detritus containing scattered small angular flints, and quartzite and chalk pebbles. At the base there is commonly a thin gravel bed containing flint, quartzite and chalk clasts.

A total thickness of 2.5 m was proved in a borehole just north-west of Slaptonbury Mill [c.SP 9145 2335], below Grove Lock; boreholes have proved up to 5.9 of alluvium consisting mainly of grey and brown, silty and sandy clays with scattered chalk, flint and quartzite pebbles and some sand and gravel layers. The deposit becomes more gravelly towards the base. One of these boreholes [SP 9151 2341] encountered 3.5 m of alluvium resting on 1.2 m of gravelly sand with a thin clayey layer, overlying Woburn Sands. The gravelly sand probably represents a suballuvial First terrace deposit.

In the tributary valley through Ledburn to Grove Lock, brown sandy clay (up to 1 m thick) with scattered small flints overlies up to 0.5 m of poorly sorted, medium- to coarse-grained gravel (up to 0.5 m thick) containing mainly subangular flints and flint pebbles, quartzite and quartzitic sandstone pebbles up to 0.10 m in diameter; quartz and 'carstone' pebbles were also recorded.

The south-east face of Grovebury Sand Pit [SP 9151 2341] intersects a tract of alluvium in which dark brown loamy soil (0.5 m) overlies brown, slightly sandy clay with sporadic gravelly strings (up to 1.0 m), resting on a basal fine- to medium-grained flint and quartzite gravel (up to 0.9 m).

SUPERFICIAL STRUCTURES

These include such nontectonic phenomena as landslips, cryoturbation features formed in periglacial regimes, and solution collapse features in the Chalk. In so far as they relate closely to the present topography these features are assumed to have originated during the Quaternary period, mostly after the Anglian glaciation. Valley bulging and related cambering have been noted in the Milton Keynes new town area to the north (Hor-

ton et al., 1974), but no well-documented examples are known within the district.

Landslips

About twenty landslips have been mapped in the district during the recent survey. For the most part they are limited in extent and relatively superficial in character; that is to say they are dominantly shallow mudflow type (translational) slips rather than deeper-seated rotational slips. They are fairly randomly scattered on steep slopes cut in solid clay formations or till. Some of the steep slopes are capped by till or by the Woburn Sands; springs emerge rarely at the top of the slips and may have contributed to their formation.

About 1 km west of Upper Gravenhurst small translational slips occur in the Gault clay along a steep-sided ENE–WSW-trending ridge [TL 101 356] capped with till.

At Pulloxhill, slipped, hummocky and uneven scrubland is present on a steep slope [TL 064 337] in Gault clay to the south-east of the village church.

An area of slip [SP 959 286] near Battlesden Park, which affects mainly Gault and till, may have been induced by the impounding of the adjacent lake to the north.

A shallow translational slip of the Upper Greensand and Gault on the steep slope, about 100 m south-east of Samshill Farm, Westoning, has given rise to an area of extremely hummocky ground.

Large areas of landslipped Oxford Clay and possibly Ampthill Clay are present to the south and south-west of Lidlington, and to the south of Bow Brickhill, both on slopes of about 8°. There are also two small landslips in these clays to the north of Little Brickhill [SP 906 329 and 912 327]. The slips appear to be mainly of the translational type with the development of many small back scars, some more than 1 m high. Much of the slipping is still active, although some areas now appear to be stable. At Lidlington, some parts of the slip were bulldozed to produce a more uniform slope, but these areas were already showing considerable signs of renewed movement in 1988.

There is a small landslip in till on the valley slope, immediately north-west of Grange Farm, Milton Bryan [SP 970 315]. It is characterised by uneven hummocky ground, with a degraded back scar.

A small slip in Oxford Clay and Ampthill Clay, below the outcrop of the Woburn Sands, occurs on a 6° slope, 350 m north-east of Stapleford Farm [SP 897 286].

About 1 km south of Linslade [SP 906 237] there is a degraded landslip in Gault Clay on a slope of about 6°. A prominent scar at the back of the slip is aligned with the margin of the glacial sand and gravel outcrop, from whence numerous springs emerge, giving rise to saturated ground. The freshness of the back scar suggests that slipping has occurred relatively recently.

An area of the valleyside [SP 8775 2380] at Burcott shows evidence of landslipping in till. The angle of slope here is only 7°, but the instability of the ground is probably exacerbated by springs which emanate from the glacial sand and gravel upslope.

Slopes of up to 10° on the valleyside [SP 877 221] to the south-west of Wing, show no evidence of instability. Probably the presence of silts in the till here provides better drainage and hence stable conditions.

In an intervening tract [SP 877 225], where till overlies Kimmeridge Clay, a scar-like feature may have resulted from landslipping or from disturbance of the ground by man. The average angle of slope is here less than 6°.

Periglacial features

At several times during the Quaternary period it is probable that the district experienced an extremely cold, periglacial regime with the development of permafrost. Evidence of early Quaternary periglacial episodes was largely destroyed during the Anglian glacial period, when a major ice sheet overrode the district, so that the surviving features date from the 'Wolstonian' and Devensian cold periods.

Apart from deep weathering phenomena in the Chalk, the obvious signs of former periglacial conditions are patterned ground, ice-wedge casts and cryoturbation features. Of these only the latter is well represented in the district. Head deposits are periglacial features, largely formed by solifluction during annual freeze–thaw cycles, and have already been described (p.95).

Cryoturbation features fall into two main categories: induced structural deformation of the upper few metres of the solid rock, and involuted 'pockets' of gravelly deposits in clay substrate. Examples of both types were noted in the former brickworks pit [SP 861 325], near Newton Longville (Horton et al., 1974), but have now

been quarried away. Within the quarry, the cementstone nodule band, the Acutistriatum Band–Comptoni Bed horizon in the Oxford Clay, was tightly folded in two places (Figure 33). The folds extended down 3 to 4 m below the truncated surface of Oxford Clay, and have been attributed to valley bulge related to two small streams, which formerly merged just east of the working face. Above the Oxford Clay cryoturbated First terrace gravels had been stripped off as overburden.

Elsewhere, near Newton Longville, contorted involutions of First terrace sandy gravels are festooned down for 2 m or more into the Oxford Clay bedrock.

Stone stripes have been noted near Newton Longville and Wavendon on Oxford Clay slopes. They comprise mainly 'carstone' clasts from the Woburn Sands and individual stripes may be 0.5 to 0.7 m wide.

Solution features

Karstic solution features are widely developed on the Chalk dip slope, which generally has a capping of clay-with-flints. The term 'solution pipe' is commonly used to describe such features, which are irregularly cylindrical or conical in shape. Their dimensions vary considerably, from a few metres to 10 m in diameter and up to 10 or 20 m in depth below the Chalk surface; a few examples are larger, and are possibly compound reaching up to 200 m in diameter and with unproven depths of over 20 m. The 'pipes' occur singly or in groups and alignments, often related to the joint pattern in the Chalk. The solution of the Chalk seems always to have occurred below a capping layer of some kind, which has typically

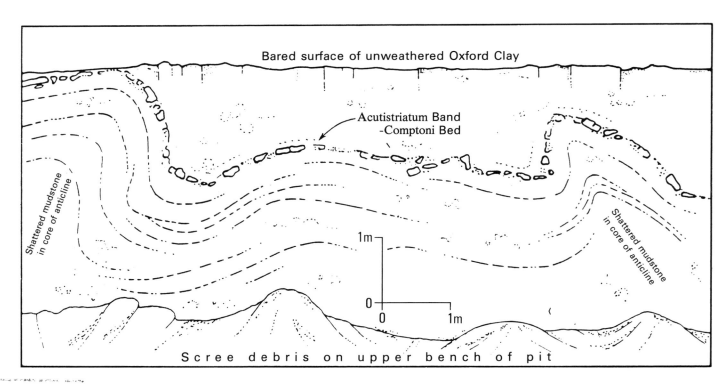

Figure 33   Superficial structures within the Oxford Clay at Newton Longville brick-pit.

been let down to infill the hollow as it formed. The sites of some of the larger pipes are marked by a shallow, closed, surface hollow. The subdued relief of such hollows is partly due to smoothing by periglacial processes and partly to their infilling by deposits of silty brickearth of loessic origin. Cross sections of a number of solution pipes were seen at the top of Kensworth Quarry [TL 017 197] (Plate 11) and in a road cutting at Capability Green, [TL 098 196], south of Luton.

A preliminary review of the occurrence of solution features on the English Chalk outcrops, with the aim of predicting subsidence risk, has been carried out by Edmonds (1983). His documentary research suggests that an average density of 22 solution features per 100 km^2 occurs in the Chilterns area. This figure seems unduly low, in relation to the observed frequency of solution

pipes at Kensworth and Capability Green, and probably reflects the paucity of recorded data.

In the Caddington and Luton areas, deposits of 'brickearth' which had accumulated in surface depressions related to solution features, were worked for brick manufacture in the late 19th and early 20th centuries (Smith, 1894; Cox, 1979a). The 'brickearth' comprises pale yellowish brown silty material, probably representing loessic sediment, redeposited by surface streams in the subsidence hollows to depths in excess of 10 m in some cases. Smith (1894) collected a large suite of Palaeolithic artifacts from these high-level sites (over 150 m above OD).

The subsidence risk associated with these features arises from the metastable nature of the infill material, if disturbed by excavations or by becoming excessively wet, as well as differential compaction effects.

Plate 11   Solution pipe in the Upper Chalk, Kensworth Quarry [TL 017 197] (Rugby Cement Ltd), about 6 m wide. The pipe has a draped lining of clay-with-flints about 1.5 m thick parallel to its sides; the inner fill is of 'brickearth', silty-clayey material of waterlain origin but with a probable aeolian component (ERST).

NINE
Economic geology

The rocks and drift deposits of the district have been widely exploited for bulk minerals and water supply, especially in the past century. Some resources have been worked out and some industries have declined and closed with changing economic conditions.

Those industries still active include the extraction of groundwater from the Chalk and Woburn Sands, the working of constructional and industrial sands from the Woburn Sands, fuller's earth production from the Woburn Sands, and quarrying of chalk for cement and lime manufacture.

Brickmaking became defunct in the district with the closure of the Newton Longville brickworks in 1991. Little trace now remains of the late 19th century 'coprolite' mining industry which worked phosphatic nodules for fertiliser manufacture. A limited amount of Totternhoe Stone is being quarried again, mainly to provide material for the restoration of old buildings.

The soils and land use of the area are directly related to the parent materials provided by the solid rocks and drift deposits of the district. The presence of drift deposits often has a profound effect on the soil at any given locality.

Large areas of worked-out or made ground occur on the sites of former chalk, clay and sand pits. Some quarries are being backfilled as landfill sites for the disposal of domestic waste.

Brief accounts of these past and present activities are given below.

SOILS AND LAND USE

Away from the urban centres of Dunstable, Luton, Leighton Buzzard and Milton Keynes, the landscape is dominated by arable farming but extensive areas have been quarried for brick clay, chalk, fuller's earth and sand; some of the quarries have been fully restored or built over.

A glance at the geological map of the district, with its range of Jurassic and Cretaceous formations and the varied drift deposits, demonstrates the difficulties of providing meaningful generalisations on the soils of the area. The 1:250 000 map of the Soil Survey of England and Wales (Sheet 4: Eastern England, 1983) provides a simplified picture of the distribution of soil associations in the district, which are described in the Soil Survey bulletin (Hodge, et al., 1984). Broad groupings of soils developed on Mesozoic clays (Upper Jurassic and Gault) and Cretaceous sands (Woburn Sands and Chalk) are depicted on this map, together with those formed on clay-with-flints, chalky drift, chalky till, glacial and river gravels and alluvium. Subgroupings, taking into account

drainage, soil depth and aspect, add some refinement to the broad picture.

In general the clay formations and chalky till give rise to heavy, variably calcareous soils with poor natural drainage. The clay-with-flints caps the Chilterns dip slope giving heavy, stony, noncalcareous clay soils. In the past such clay soils would have mostly been retained in permanent pasture, but nowadays, with improved drainage measures and mechanised farming, a large proportion is under arable cultivation.

Lighter free-draining soils are developed on the Woburn Sands outcrop and on the sandy and gravelly drifts. Such soils can be acidic, 'hungry' and subject to water erosion when ploughed. Much of the steeper ground on the Woburn Sands is under permanent woodland. The sandy soils are easily worked under most conditions and are used for arable farming or horticulture in preferred locations.

Light, shallow, calcareous soils are generally developed on the Chalk outcrop though the presence of drift deposits or thick hillwash can considerably modify this broad picture. The steeper ground on the scarp faces and valley sides may remain in permanent pasture but much of the land on the dip slope and lower scarp faces is under the plough.

SAND AND GRAVEL

Sand products

Over the past century the Woburn Sands outcrop around the town of Leighton Buzzard has been exploited to yield a variety of sand products. The facies variation within the area (Figure 14), and indeed within certain pits, is such as to yield products ranging from building and asphalting sand, and fine aggregate for concrete to foundry sand and filtration media. In 1988, 15 sizeable pits were extracting material from the Woburn Sands around Leighton Buzzard (Figure 13). A number of former pits have been backfilled, levelled or built over. In the past, a large number of small sand pits provided material for local use, but these have generally been backfilled or ploughed over. Large-scale exploitation commenced about a century ago when rail and canal links made the products accessible to wider markets.

It is difficult to obtain data on the output of sand products in the district for reasons of commercial confidentiality. Figures obtained from the Business Statistics Office for the whole of the Lower Greensand of Bedfordshire in 1984 were as follows: building sand, 471 359 tonnes; concreting sand and fill, 475 398 tonnes and industrial sand, 280 040 tonnes (Shephard-Thorn et al.,

1986). These figures refer mostly to sites within the district and may be taken as fairly typical, although output obviously varies with trade cycles.

Modern treatment plants operated by several major companies within the area are capable of washing, grading and blending sands to produce specified products. In general most high quality silica sand products are derived from the 'Silver Sands' division of the formation, while the building sands and concreting sands come from the 'Brown Sands' and the 'Red Sands' (p.35). These latter divisions are characterised by sands with considerable variation in grain size and degree of roundness, which contain much ferric oxide in the form of random iron-staining, iron-cemented concretions and dispersed goethite ooliths. Their broad grain-size distribution usually includes a proportion of silt-grade sediment.

Most of the constructional sands are used for building purposes. The screening out of the finer grades produces raw material suitable for the making of asphalt and mortar. Minor quantities are used for concrete roofing tiles and other applications, such as horticulture. The current British Standards for various types of constructional sands have been reviewed by Shephard-Thorn et al. (1986). Sands for use in mortar are covered by BS 1200:1976, as amended in 1984 (AMD 4510), which specifies two general purpose mortar sands. However, it emphasises that insufficient information exists to provide generalised guidance on the use of the specific sand grades. The most recent British Standards relating to sand used for asphalt (BS 594:Pt.1:1985) gives a series of grading requirements for mixtures of coarse and fine materials. Sand for concrete making is specified by BS 882:1983 in terms of three size ranges, but with some flexibility to allow the use of fine sand not complying with the specification.

A simple threefold classification of sand resources in terms of end use was adopted by Shephard-Thorn et al. (1986), based on the proportion of material retained on a 150 µm sieve. Sand with 75 per cent coarser than 150 µm was regarded as premium material likely to be used for concrete, mortar or asphalt. Sand with less than 50 per cent coarser than 150 µm was likely to be of little value. Sand with 50–75 per cent coarser than 150 µm was of intermediate value, and might well have some application in asphalt and, less likely, in concrete or mortar.

The silica (industrial) sands are derived from the 'Silver Sands' (see p.35) which lie near the top of the Woburn Sands succession and reach up to 15 m in thickness. These sands are restricted to a relatively small area centred on Shenley Hill, adjacent to the village of Heath and Reach, north-east of Leighton Buzzard. They have a silica content which exceeds 98 per cent and a ferric oxide content which is less than 1 per cent, except in and near sporadic carstone 'reefs'. Narrow ranges of particle size distribution are typical. Some of the silica sands are marketed as foundry sands which need to have a closely defined grain-size distribution, to be clean, and consistent in quality. Bands and lenses of coarse-grained, particularly well-rounded and well-sorted quartz sands are washed and screened to produce material which is ideal for filtration purposes in water treatment.

The sands were formerly used for glassmaking, but are not of the quality currently acceptable for colourless glass manufacture.

The sands are worked either 'dry' or 'wet' in open pits. The dry method involves the use of mechanical face shovels to dig the raw material from the quarry face where the water table lies below the pit floor. The wet method extracts the sand by suction dredger from below water level in flooded pits; a sand slurry is then pumped through a delivery pipe supported on pontoons to the processing plant.

The regional water-table level will determine whether a pit is worked wet or dry, and whether pumping is necessary. If pumping proves to be uneconomic or aquifer protection measures apply, the water table places an effective lower limit on extraction. At present only one pit in the district, the Grovebury Pit [SP 923 230], uses the wet method of working.

The Woburn Sands formation has an extensive outcrop and the potential resources of sand in the district are large. However, there are a number of constraints upon possible exploitation. Much of the outcrop is covered by a thick overburden of Gault clay or drift deposits and, where the prospective stripping ratio exceeds the currently acceptable economic value, the sands do not constitute a workable resource.

The variable thickness of the Woburn Sands formation also controls the available resources and location of sand deposits. A western limit, albeit approximate, is defined by the wedging out of the Woburn Sands beneath the overlying Gault to the west of Leighton Buzzard (Figure 12). The thickness to the east of this line ranges up to a maximum in excess of 120 m in the Woburn district. Lateral changes in lithology and quality may well be correlated with variations of thickness.

The bulk of the Woburn Sands, where known, consists of sands which are suitable for one or another of several traditional uses. Shephard-Thorn et al. (1986) point out, however, that the flexibility of the British Standards for construction sand specifications, together with the range of specialised sands which are possible as a result of mixing, selective working and washing, makes it difficult to equate resources in the ground with precise end uses. Sands suitable for industrial purposes should, on the other hand, be more easily identified because of their more precisely specified characteristics. Locally there are sands, such as the 'Compo' of the Mundays Hill area (Figure 14) which have limited potential use because of their fine grain size and high silt content.

Although several distinctive members within the Woburn Sands have been recognised in the pits around Leighton Buzzard, it has not been possible to map their surface distribution because their lithologies are not readily differentiated by the shallow (up to 1.3 m) hand auger method used during the surveys. Nevertheless, it is probable that the silica sands ('Silver Sands') are restricted to the small area around Heath and Reach where they are currently worked, because no unequivocal deposits of similar material of any extent have been proved elsewhere.

Aggregates

Other than the fine aggregates from the Woburn Sands used in mortar, asphalt and concrete tile manufacture, aggregates have been worked extensively but on a very local scale from the glacial sand and gravel and river terrace gravel of the district. These are generally of limited extent, poor quality and variable composition, and so have little economic significance. The presence of relatively high proportions of chalk in the glacial gravels makes them unsuitable for concreting work. There are thus no major sources of high quality aggregate for concreting within the district.

FULLER'S EARTH

There has been a long history of fuller's earth extraction, both by opencast and underground mining, from the Woburn Sands Formation in Bedfordshire (Cameron, 1892; 1893; Cox, 1979b; Robertson 1986) perhaps dating back to Roman times. The earliest written reference to

fuller's earth in Britain is in the Inquisition of the Manor of Aspley, dated 7th February 1295 which relates to the deposits near Woburn.

Fuller's earth is a naturally occurring clay with a waxy, soap-like texture, consisting essentially of calcium smectite. Members of the smectite group of clay minerals, like the micas, have a layered structure, and a particular feature of the group is that internal substitution of Si^{4+} and Al^{3+} by lower valency ions has left variable unsatisfied negative charges within the layers which are balanced by loosely held exchangeable cations, usually calcium, magnesium or sodium, on the interlayer clay surfaces. Ca-smectite may be converted to Na-smectite, or bentonite, by a simple sodium-exchange process involving the addition of a few per cent of sodium carbonate to the raw clay. Another characteristic of the group is their small crystal size and thus very high surface area compared with other clay and non-clay minerals.

Originally fuller's earth clay was used for the cleansing or 'fulling' of woollen cloth, but nowadays the raw earth is processed to produce a number of products used wide-

Plate 12 The main worked fuller's earth seam at Old Wavendon Heath Quarry near Woburn Sands [SP 933 346] (Steetley Minerals Ltd). The seam of high quality fuller's earth is 2 to 3 m thick, olive-green to buff in colour and well jointed (A15113).

ly throughout industry. Some of the major uses are as a bonding agent for foundry sands, in civil engineering, as a fibre and filler retention aid in papermaking, in the refining of edible oils and fats, and as pet litter. The processed earth is also used as a carrier for pesticides and herbicides, in the manufacture of cosmetics, cattle feed binder, oil well drilling fluids, and clay catalysts.

Within the Woburn Sands the fuller's earth occurs as discrete beds which range in thickness from a few centimetres to just under 4 m (Plates 12 and 13). The beds are lenticular and cannot be traced for more than two or three kilometres. Depending on local conditions it is possible for beds of less than one metre thick to be economically recovered, with overburden to mineral thickness ratios greater than 20 to 1 feasible in soft sand.

Within the district fuller's earth deposits of economic importance are known only from the Woburn Sands and Clophill areas. In both areas extraction is restricted to one bed although other, thinner noneconomic beds are also present. At Woburn up to 40 m of overburden are removed to expose the worked bed which averages 2 to 3 m in thickness. At Clophill the maximum overburden is about 20 m, with a maximum bed thickness of about 3.1 m. The latter site, however, is situated within a valley and requires an extensive dewatering programme before extraction can begin.

In the 1880s the fuller's earth in the Woburn area was worked from cylindrical holes known as 'earth wells' dug through the overlying sand. In 1891 the Fuller's Earth Mining Company was set up, shafts were sunk at Aspley Heath, near Woburn Sands and mining from underground galleries commenced in a systematic manner. In 1896 the company was wound up. However, in 1900 the mine was offered for sale as a going concern, and its new owner continued intermittent working, but by 1918 all activity had ceased (Robertson, 1986).

Large-scale opencast extraction, by F W Berk and Co Ltd, commenced in 1950, the quarry was acquired by the Steetley Company in 1970, and has continued up until the present. Initial production was at Aspley Heath, but in 1961 planning consent was obtained to work deposits in Aspley Wood, on the east side of the A5130. In 1978

Plate 13   General view of the fuller's earth workings at Old Wavendon Heath Quarry, near Woburn Sands [SP 933 346] (Steetley Minerals Ltd). Up to 40 m of Woburn Sands is removed as overburden to extract the seam of fuller's earth visible in the floor of the quarry (A15114).

planning consent was granted, on appeal, to exploit the Old Wavendon Heath deposits on the west side of the A5130, and current production is still based on this site. In 1989 Steetley Minerals applied for planning consent to reroute the A5130 and to recover 344 000 tonnes of fuller's earth (dry product) underlying the road and adjacent areas. Planning consent was refused initially in 1990, but granted on appeal in 1992 following a Public Inquiry.

It is estimated that some 1.2 million tonnes of fuller's earth (dry product) have been produced from the Woburn area since 1854. Reserves of fuller's earth with planning consent were about 400 000 tonnes at January 1992.

In 1934, fuller's earth was discovered by BGS at Clophill (Dixon, 1935), some 10 km to the east of Woburn, following its recognition in the log of a water well drilled in 1904. In 1952 The Fuller's Earth Union Ltd (now Laporte Absorbents) obtained planning permission to work the deposit and small-scale production on a trial basis was undertaken in the late 1950s and early 1960s. Large-scale production commenced in 1987, with the raw clay being transported to Redhill, Surrey for processing. An estimated 210 000 tonnes of fuller's earth had been produced from the deposit to the end of 1990 and remaining reserves, all with planning consent, total an estimated 390 000 tonnes (dry product) (Moorlock and Highley, 1991).

Since large-scale extraction commenced at Clophill, Bedfordshire has replaced Surrey as the major source of fuller's earth in Britain.

LIME AND CEMENT

The large Chalk quarries described in Chapter Six were opened to provide the raw material for lime and cement manufacture, with subsidiary output of fill, building stone and flint. Several worked-out pits have taken on a new role as landfill sites.

Lime for agricultural use was formerly produced from the Lower Chalk at Sewell Quarry [SP 995 224] and Barton Quarry [TL 079 296]. Lime is still produced by the Totternhoe Lime and Stone Co. Ltd [SP 981 223], though some lime is brought in from external sources for the manufacture of hydrated lime.

The extensive Kensworth Quarry [TL 017 197] of the Rugby Cement company exploits the upper part of the Middle Chalk and the basal beds of the Upper Chalk (p.74). The quarried chalk is crushed and slurried prior to pumping, via a 90 km pipeline to Rugby and Southam in Warwickshire, where it is mixed with additional clay for cement manufacture. The quarry was opened in 1964, and maximum output of chalk is up to 1.25 million tonnes per annum as dug. For a few years after 1964 an attempt to market the rejected flint from the quarry to the pottery trade was made; the presence of hard rock chalk in the crushed material made it difficult to separate the flint mechanically and the operation was abandoned.

The Lower Chalk, has a relatively high clay content, and is suitable for cement manufacture with little or no requirement for additional clay. It was formerly worked for this purpose at Houghton Regis [TL 005 236] and Sundon [TL 041 267] by the Blue Circle company. Production at these sites ceased in the 1970s. Parts of the Sundon quarry are being used for landfill purposes.

PHOSPHATE

From the mid 19th century up to the early years of the present century, thin beds of phosphatic nodules, incorrectly referred to as coprolites, were dug from the Cretaceous formations in the district. The major worked horizon was the Cambridge Greensand, but other levels in the Upper Gault, Upper Greensand and Woburn Sands were also exploited. The nodules were a source of calcium phosphate for the manufacture of superphosphate fertiliser. The demand for fertilisers was sparked off by the Victorian revolution in farming practice and the concomitant need to improve soil fertility. The industry expanded very quickly to meet the demand and large areas of shallow open-cast diggings were in operation at any one time. Virtually total abstraction was achieved so that little trace of phosphatic material remains over large areas of outcrop. The ground was restored to farming use immediately after working and there is generally little to indicate the extent of former workings in the present landscape, so that historical records are usually the only source of information. The industry declined as the reserves were exhausted, and with the import of guano and higher grade phosphate rock.

Workings in the Cambridge Greensand (p.60) extended over about 70 km south-westward along the strike from Cambridge to Barton-le-Clay, in the district, where the Cambridge Greensand is replaced by a less distinct Glauconitic Marl at the base of the Lower Chalk. The Cambridge Greensand is typically only 0.5 m or less thick and comprises green glauconitic sandy marl with rolled derived phosphatic nodules up to about 70 mm in size. The nodules are commonly phosphatic casts of fossils, but they are not true coprolites (i.e. fossil faeces).

Phosphatic nodules at a high level in the Upper Gault and in the Upper Greensand have also been worked in the southern part of the district. Jukes-Browne and Hill (1900) record coprolite workings near Slapton, Stanbridge and Billington in the district. Settling ponds used to clarify the water for washing the nodules still survive just north of Slapton Lane [SP 945 207] (Aldiss, 1990).

Reworked phosphatic nodules occur in a bed at the base of the Woburn Sands near Heath and Reach, the Brickhills and Woburn and also at other levels within the formation (p.45). They were formerly dug from the basal bed along the foot of the Woburn Sands escarpment between Little Brickhill and Great Brickhill (Horton et al., 1974, p.36 and Keeping, 1875).

BRICKMAKING

Brick manufacture within the district ceased in 1991 with the closure of the Newton Longville works of the London Brick Company. The industry continues at the company's Stewartby works a little to the north. From small beginnings in the Medieval period, brickmaking in the district grew to be important on both local and national scales, ranging from small kilns supplying a village or parish to large modern works supplying mass-produced 'Fletton' bricks nationwide. The history of brickmaking in Bedfordshire has been detailed by Cox (1979a), who gave a gazetteer of 180 known brick and tile making sites in that county. The industry was similarly widespread in Buckinghamshire (Vince, 1968), where two small yards at Stewkley worked up to the outbreak of the 1939–45 war.

Over the centuries a variety of raw materials were used by the small local brickworks, including Upper Jurassic and Lower Cretaceous clays and Quaternary deposits. The costs and difficulties of transporting bricks more than a few miles in earlier times meant that local brickworks used the locally available 'brickearths', even if they were not ideal for the purpose. The clays used were mainly from the weathered zone, extending a few metres below the surface. They were dug and left in heaps over the winter for frost and rain to improve their consistency for moulding. The variety of materials and types of kiln used, and the presence of certain impurities, gave the bricks individual textures and colours characteristic of their localities, in contrast to the bland uniformity of modern mass-produced bricks.

The Oxford Clay was the main source of brick clay within the district, although its outcrop is relatively small. Initially the weathered clay or 'callow' was used in local brickworks, but the introduction of the Fletton process in the 1880s depended on the use of 'green' clay or 'knotts' from the Lower Oxford Clay and the lower part of the Middle Oxford Clay, the 'callow' being rejected for this process. The Fletton process is dependent on five main properties of the 'knotts', namely: the relatively high natural moisture content of about 18 per cent, the low calcium carbonate content, the mainly illite-mica composition of the clay minerals, the high organic content (5 to 7 per cent dry weight) and the general absence of undesirable impurities (Ridgway, 1982). The natural moisture content of the clay removes the need for pugging before pressing the bricks, and is more suitable for the semi-dry pressing technique than other harder clays. The highly carbonaceous nature of the clays makes them partially self firing and so less demanding of fuel in brick manufacture; the bricks also have a somewhat lower firing temperature than those made from other clays. Oxford Clay has been exploited for Fletton brick manufacture in pits at Bletchley [SP 869 325], Loughton [SP 852 364], Newton Longville [SP 859 326] and Ridgmont [SP 967 378]; all are now defunct.

The Ampthill Clay was worked for brickmaking at several localities around Ampthill town from the 17th to the mid-19th century (Cox, 1979a). A brickfield near Nares Gladley Farm [SP 911 276], west of Heath and Reach, active in the late 19th century, used 'Corallian' mudstones and Oxford Clay exposed below the base of the Woburn Sands or possibly sandy head derived from the latter.

The Kimmeridge Clay is present in the south-west of the district, being partially overstepped by the Gault. Two brickfields near Stewkley [SP 846 247; 848 249] were making bricks from Kimmeridge Clay up to 1939 (Vince, 1968) when air-raid precautions necessitated the closing of the open kilns. A third works nearby was obliterated during the construction of the wartime airfield at Wing.

Clays from the Gault were used for brickmaking near Leighton Buzzard at several sites around the town [SP 924 238; 933 264; 934 246] of which little trace now remains.

It is probable that a range of drift deposits were formerly exploited for brickmaking including till and head, but the most important seems to have been the 'brick-earth' associated with karstic collapse structures on the clay-with-flints capping the Chilterns escarpment in the south-east of the district. Around the village of Caddington and Luton town, the production of Luton 'greys' bricks from the brickearth deposits was very important in the Victorian era and up to the 1930s (Cox, 1979a).

BUILDING STONE

Durable natural stone suitable for building purposes is generally scarce within the district. The exceptions are ferruginous 'carstone' from the Woburn Sands, 'Portland Stone' from the outcrops around Stewkley and Totternhoe Stone from the Lower Chalk. Limited amounts of erratic material from the glacial drift have been incorporated in some older buildings.

'Carstone' is an informal name applied to secondarily cemented ferruginous sandstones from the Woburn Sands, which occurs as irregular platy or sheet-like bodies and in more massive form. It is commonly rejected as waste at the sand quarries and has been used for rough masonry in the Leighton Buzzard and Woburn areas. It is also used for rockery stone.

A limited amount of pale, shelly, marly limestone has been worked from the Portland Formation, around Stewkley, where it is seen in some old farm buildings and walls. It was formerly worked in a quarry at Warren Farm [SP 851 243] (p.00 and Plate 3). Some of the limestone was used in the adjacent brickworks, producing lime as a by-product of firing (Vince, 1968).

Totternhoe Stone, a brownish grey calcarenitic freestone, has been worked intermittently in the Totternhoe area over a very long period extending back to Roman times. It is recorded from the remains of a villa near Totternhoe Church and was used as a facing stone at Woburn Abbey in the 18th century and in Dunstable Priory Church, St Alban's Abbey and St Stephen's Chapel, Westminster (Roberts, 1974).

The stone is currently worked at the lowest level of the Totternhoe Lime and Stone Co.'s quarry (p.73) as a separate operation to provide material mainly for the restoration of old buildings. Historically it was worked from a series of adits in the steep slopes between Totternhoe and Sewell, which extended 150 m or more back into the hillside and were 1.8 to 6 m in height (Aldiss, 1990); the latter figure was not entirely within the Totternhoe Stone.

The Totternhoe Stone is susceptible to frost damage, but its properties are enhanced by a period of 'weathering' as sawn blocks, before it is transported to its ultimate destination.

HYDROGEOLOGY

Groundwater levels attain a maximum elevation of over 13 m above OD along the Chalk escarpment within the district. Maximum elevation along the Woburn Sands escarpment is just over 120 m above OD. The broad valley between the two escarpments is drained by the headwaters of the River Ouzel, which then cuts through the Woburn Sands near Leighton Buzzard to flow towards the north-east. The south-west of the district is drained by the River Thame, the south-east by the River Lea and the north-east by tributaries to the River Ivel.

Average annual rainfall varies from below 600 mm in the north-east of the district to nearly 700 mm on the high ground of the Chalk escarpment. Actual evaporation is about 450 to 460 mm/a leaving a potential for infiltration of between 120 and 180 mm/a.

The main aquifers are the Woburn Sands and the Chalk. The Hydrogeological Map of the Area Between Cambridge and Maidenhead (BGS, 1984) shows how the two aquifers relate to regional groundwater flow systems. The potentiometric surface in the Chalk attains a maximum elevation of 130 m above OD beneath the Chalk escarpment at the southern edge of the district. Regional groundwater flow is downdip towards the south-east. Locally groundwater also flows towards the feather edge of the Chalk to the north-west, and north-east towards the River Lea, possibly linked to local reversals of dip. The escarpment is, therefore, an area for recharge to the Chalk aquifer and its continuation to the south-east.

Recharge to the Woburn Sands aquifer is limited to the narrow area of outcrop where boulder clay is thin or absent. Beneath the escarpment the potentiometric surface attains an elevation of 130 m above OD near the Ouzel valley and 90 m above OD near the Ivel valley. Groundwater flows from the escarpment generally down dip to the south-eastwards, becoming confined as it passes beneath the Gault. In the vicinity of Luton the potentiometric surface on the confined Woburn Sands aquifer is about 50 m above OD.

Some groundwater is present within the superficial deposits, principally the glacial sand and gravel and the river terrace deposits.

The Gault, Kimmeridge Clay, 'Corallian' and Oxford Clay are essentially impermeable. Thin limestones within the Upper Jurassic Clay formations are too thin to attain any hydrogeological significance.

The Woburn Sands

The Woburn Sands aquifer has been described previously by Monkhouse (1974) and Anon (1982). The aquifer ranges in thickness up to more than 120 m and is thick-

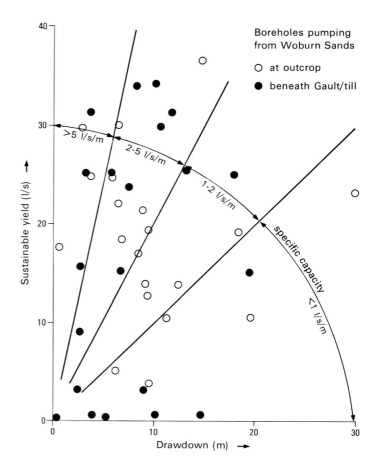

Figure 34 Yield–drawdown relationship in the Woburn Sands.

est around Woburn; the general thickness is about 60 m. Variations in lithology induce a range in hydraulic properties within the aquifer, and vertical layering is sufficient in places to induce perching. All boreholes require to be screened to prevent ingress of sand. Artificial filter packs are usually necessary.

Few detailed pumping tests have been carried out on the Woburn Sands. Available evidence suggests that the transmissivity ranges from 10 to $10^3 \, m^2/d$. This range provides a scattered distribution of specific capacity values (borehole yield divided by near equilibrium drawdown), albeit derived under a variety of different pumping constraints (including sand screens of different efficiency), and which bear no relationship to the presence or thickness of either the Gault or till (Figure 34). Nor is there any apparent correlation between specific capacity and aquifer penetration or thickness. However, over 70 per cent of the boreholes which penetrate the Woburn Sands in the district have a specific capacity greater than 1 l/s/m and over 50 per cent a specific capacity greater than 2 l/s/m.

Groundwater flow in the aquifer is entirely intergranular, and there is virtually no fissure flow. Groundwater flowing down gradient beneath the Gault towards the London Basin allows some recharge to the confined aquifer in the south-east part of the district. However, abstraction has tended to exceed the natural replenishment (Mather et al., 1972). Many boreholes which once overflowed at surface now have a static water level well below ground level, reflecting a depressed piezometric head in the confined aquifer. Seasonal variation in water level, however, is small, typically less than 1 m.

Public supply boreholes which draw from the Woburn Sands are located at:

Birchmoor [SP 944 348], Sandhouse [SP 937 300], Stanbridge Road [SP 935 247], Milebush [SP 907 255], Battlesden [SP 960 281], Clophill [TL 096 383] and Barton-le-Clay [TL 080 336].

The other major use is aggregate washing.

Groundwater in the Woburn Sands is of the calcium-bicarbonate type. The water is moderately mineralised with chloride ion concentrations in the range 13–35 mg/l

(Table 4). Much of the water is rich in iron and sulphate due to the dissolution of pyrite within the sand; an iron concentration of 12.9 mg/l has been recorded at Sandhouse [SP 937 300]. No landfill waste-disposal sites have been sanctioned over the aquifer outcrop.

Chalk

Groundwater may be stored both in the intergranular matrix and partly also in the systems of microfissures and macrofissures. Groundwater transport relies on flow along the fissures, which may be one millimetre or so in width, as well as in the smaller microfissures. The density of the fissures is greatest in lower-lying areas where stress release from the removal of overburden and the enlargement of fissures by solution offer the best hydraulic conditions for high-yielding boreholes. In the district, the Lower Chalk is marly, especially within the Chalk Marl

Table 4 Typical chemical analyses of borehole waters from the Woburn Sands and the Chalk.

a Woburn Sands

Location	Stanbridge Road	Ampthill	Birchmore	Leighton Buzzard	Polluxhill	Leighton Linslade
NGR	SP 935 247	TL 081 355	SP 944 348	SP 925 255	TL 080 336	SP 935 238
Date	3/66	28/05/51	27/11/80	27/11/80	28/11/80	27/11/80
pH	6.9	7.0	6.3	6.9	5.9	5.9
SEC (µmho/cc)		385	211	774	382	774
TDS (mg/1)	470					
HCO_3 (Mg/1)		78	27	281	189	338
SO_4	116	47	8	186	51	151
Cl	14	16	33	35	18	31
NO_3-N	2.1	0				0.2
Ca	135	64	15	113	59	139
Mg	10	9.3	2	63	8.8	11.4
Na	12	1	13	18	11	25
K	4		2.7	3.7	4.2	6.3
Fe (total)	1.6	2.3	0.4	2.0	2.0	2.0

b Chalk

Location	Luton	Luton	Dunstable	Old Moat House	Luton	Luton
NGR	TU 108 212	TL 080 223	TL 017 225	TL 077 240	TL 085 264	TL 094 285
Date	2/11/83	4/10/77	9/04/84	19/04/84	19/05/77	15/09/83
pH	7.3	7.1	7.2	7.3	7.6	7.4
SEC (µmho/cc)	608	673	711	738	587	423
TDS (mg/1)						
HCO_3 (Mg/1)	320	268	122	112	249	174
SO_4	24	78	57	103	55	15
Cl	22	38	35	41	25	17
NO_3-N	8.5	15.1	11.5	12.1	10.5	9.1
Ca	118	137	123	136	114	58
Mg	1.8	2.3	4.4	2.6	1.7	2.3
Na	14	15	29	26	10	10
K	2.2	1.2	16.8	4.6	0.8	1.5
Fe (total)	<0.05	0.03	<0.05	<0.05	<0.05	<0.05

below the Totternhoe Stone, and the Middle Chalk has a number of thin but persistent marl seams. Thus, in general, these divisions of the Chalk may offer slightly inferior hydraulic properties to those of the Upper Chalk. Only the lower 35 m of the latter are present within the district, capping the Chilterns escarpment, and are mostly above the water table.

The yield-drawdown characteristics of boreholes in the Chalk are highly variable and depend both on well construction, in particular diameter, and the intersection of favourable fissures. Production boreholes will, however, stand open within the Chalk.

The highest yielding borehole is at the Albert Road pumping station at Luton [TL 0941 2090] where pumping at 66 l/s for 10 days produced a drawdown of only 10 m. This borehole has a diameter of 610 mm. At the Runley Wood pumping station [TL 0645 2171] a 375 mm-diameter borehole gave 52 l/s for 9 m drawdown over a 7 day test. Other pumping stations are Periwinkle Lane in Dunstable [TL 024 211] and Crescent Road, Luton [TL 096 216]. Other boreholes are typically only 150–300 mm in diameter and yield from 2 to 20 l/s with a specific capacity normally in the range 0.5 to 2.0 l/s/m.

Groundwater in the Chalk is considerably more mineralised than in the Woburn Sands , and is also of the calcium-bicarbonate type Table 4). Chloride concentrations range from 17 to 41 mg/l. The aquifer is vulnerable to diffuse pollution, particularly from agricultural activity wherever cover such as clay-with-flints is absent. Nitrate concentrations are high and in places exceed the maximum admissible concentration of 11.3 mg NO_3-N/l for potable supplies. The Chalk aquifer is at considerable risk to urban and industrial pollution in the vicinity of Dunstable and Luton.

There are two operational landfill sites on the Chalk aquifer: Sundon [TL 038 280] and Barton Quarry [TL 078 296]. There are eight other landfill sites which were closed between 1974 and 1989 over the Chalk.

REFERENCES

Most of the references listed below are held in the Library of the British Geological Survey at Keyworth, Nottingham. Copies of the references can be purchased subject to the current copyright legislation.

ALDISS, D T. 1990. Geological notes and local details for 1:10 000 Sheet SP92SE (Totternhoe) and part of Sheet SP91NE (Edlesborough). *British Geological Survey Technical Report*, WA/90/70.

ALLSOP, J M. 1984. Geophysical appraisal of a Carboniferous Basin in north-east Norfolk, England. *Proceedings of the Geologists' Association*, Vol. 95, 175–180.

— 1985a. Evaluation of gravity and magnetic anomalies in the Warboys area, north of Cambridge. *Proceedings of the Geologists' Association*, Vol. 96, 263–273.

— 1985b. Geophysical investigations into the extent of the Devonian rocks beneath East Anglia. *Proceedings of the Geologists' Association*, Vol. 96, 371–379.

— 1988. Deep resistivity surveys in the English Midlands. *Deep Geology Research Group Report, British Geological Survey*, 88/10.

— and SMITH, N J P. 1988. The deep geology of Essex. *Proceedings of the Geologists' Association*, Vol. 99, 249–260.

ANON. 1982. Report on the Hydrogeology of the Lower Greensand aquifer (Leighton Buzzard–Ely). (London: Binnie and Partners.)

ARKELL, W J. 1933. The Jurassic System in Great Britain. (Oxford: Clarendon Press.)

— 1939. Derived ammonites from the Lower Greensand of Surrey and their bearing on the tectonic history of the Hog's Back. *Proceedings of the Geologists' Association*, Vol. 50, 22–25.

— 1947. *The geology of Oxford.* (Oxford: Clarendon Press.)

AVERY, B W, BULLOCK, P, CATT, J A, RAYNER, J H, and WEIR, A H. 1982. Composition and origin of some brickearths on the Chiltern Hills, England. *Catena*, Vol. 9, 153–174.

BAILEY, H W, GALE, A S, MORTIMORE, R N, SWIECICKI, A, and WOOD, C J. 1983. The Coniacian–Maastrichtian stages of the United Kingdom, with particular reference to southern England. *Newsletters on Stratigraphy*, Vol. 12, 19–42.

— 1984. Biostratigraphical criteria for the recognition of the Coniacian to Maastrichtian stage boundaries in the Chalk of north-west Europe, with particular reference to southern England. *Bulletin of the Geological Society of Denmark*, Vol. 33, 31–39.

BARKER, D. 1966. Ostracods from the Portland and Purbeck beds of the Aylesbury district. *Bulletin of the British Museum (Natural History), Geology*, Vol. 11, 459–487.

BARRON, A J M. 1988. Geological notes and local details for 1:10 000 Sheet SP81NW (Bierton). *British Geological Survey Technical Report*, WA/88/42.

BGS. 1984. *Hydrogeological map of the area between Cambridge and Maidenhead*, 1:100 000 scale. (Keyworth: British Geological Survey.)

BLAKE, J H, and HUDLESTON, W H. 1877. On the Corallian rocks of England. *Quarterly Journal of the Geological Society of London*, Vol. 33, 260–405.

BOWEN, D Q, ROSE, J, McCABE, A M, and SUTHERLAND, D G. 1987. Correlation of Quaternary glaciations in England, Ireland, Scotland and Wales. *Quaternary Science Reviews*, Vol. 5, 299–340.

BRANDON, A, SUMBLER, M G, and IVIMEY-COOK, H C. 1990. A revised lithostratigraphy for the Lower and Middle Lias (Lower Jurassic) east of Nottingham, England. *Proceedings of the Yorkshire Geological Society*, Vol. 48, 121–141.

BRISTOW, C R. 1963. The stratigraphy and structure of the Upper Jurassic and Lower Cretaceous rocks in the area between Aylesbury (Bucks.) and Leighton Buzzard (Beds.). Unpublished PhD thesis, University of London.

— 1968. Portland and Purbeck Beds. 300–311 in *The geology of the East Midlands*. SYLVESTER-BRADLEY, P C, and FORD, T D (editors). (Leicester: Leicester University Press.)

BRIDGES, P J. 1982. Sedimentology of a tidal sea: the Lower Greensand of southern England. 183–189 in *Offshore tidal sands*. STRIDE, A H (editor). (London: Chapman and Hall.)

BROMLEY, R G, and GALE, A S. 1982. The lithostratigraphy of the English Chalk Rock. *Cretaceous Research*, Vol. 3, 273–306.

BUCKINGHAMSHIRE COUNTY MUSEUM. 1980. *Gazetteer of Buckinghamshire brickyards 1800–1980.* (Aylesbury: Buckinghamshire County Museum.)

BUCK, S G. 1985. Sand-flow cross strata in tidal sands of the Lower Greensand (Early Cretaceous), Southern England. *Journal of Sedimentary Petrology*, Vol. 55, 895–906.

BUCKMAN, S S. 1922. *Type ammonites*. Vol. 4. (Thame and London.)

— 1926. *Type ammonites*. Vol. 6. (Thame and London.)

— 1927. *Type ammonites*. Vol. 6. (Thame and London.)

BULMAN, O M B, and RUSHTON, A W. 1973. Tremadoc faunas from boreholes in Central England. *Bulletin of the Geological Survey of Great Britain*, No. 43.

CALLOMON, J H. 1968. The Kellaways Beds and the Oxford Clay. 264–290 in *The geology of the East Midlands*. SYLVESTER-BRADLEY, P C, and FORD, T D (editors). (Leicester: Leicester University Press.)

CAMERON, A C G. 1892. Excursion to Woburn Sands and Sandy. *Proceedings of the Geologists' Association*, Vol. 12, 395–403.

— 1893. Geology, mining and economic uses of fuller's earth. *Transactions of the Federated Institution of Mining Engineers*, Vol. 6, 204–209.

— 1897. Excursion to Leighton Buzzard. *Proceedings of the Geologists' Association*, Vol. 15, 183–185.

CARTER, D J, and HART, M B. 1977. Aspects of mid-Cretaceous stratigraphical micropalaeontology. *Bulletin of the British Museum (Natural History), Geology*, Vol. 29, 1–135.

CASEY, R. 1961. The stratigraphical palaeontology of the Lower Greensand. *Palaeontology*, Vol. 3, 487–621.

— 1963. The dawn of the Cretaceous period in Britain. *Bulletin of the South Eastern Union of Scientific Societies*, No. 117.

CATT, J A. 1981. Quaternary history of the Hertfordshire area. *Transactions of the Hertfordshire Natural History Society*, Vol. 28, 27–53.

— 1986.   The nature, origin and geomorphological significance of clay-with-flints.   151–159 in *The scientific study of flint and chert: papers from the Fourth International Flint Symposium*, SIEVEKING, G G, and HART, M B (editors). (Cambridge University Press.)

— KING, D W, and WEIR, A H. 1974.   The soils of Woburn Experimental Farm.   Rothamsted report for 1974, Part 2, 5–29.

COCKS, L R M, HOLLAND, C H, RICKARDS, R B, and STRACHAN, I. 1971.   A correlation of Silurian rocks in the British Isles. *Geological Society of London Special Report*, No. 1.

COPE, J C W. 1967.   The palaeontology and stratigraphy of the lower part of the Upper Kimmeridge Clay of Dorset. *Bulletin of the British Museum (Natural History). Geology*. Vol. 15, No. 1.

— 1978.   The ammonite faunas and stratigraphy of the upper part of the Upper Kimmeridge Clay of Dorset.   *Palaeontology*, Vol. 21, 469–533.

COWPERTHWAITE, I A, FITCH, F J, MILLER, J A, MITCHELL, J G, and ROBERTSON, R H. 1972.   Sedimentation, petrogenesis and radio isotopic age of the Cretaceous fuller's earth of Southern England.   *Clay Minerals*, Vol. 9, 309–327.

COX, A. 1979a.   *Survey of Bedfordshire: brickmaking; a history and gazetteer*.   (Bedfordshire County Council.)

— 1979b.   Fuller's earth working in Bedfordshire. *Bedfordshire Magazine*, Vol. 17, 91–95.

COX, B M. 1990.   Lower Greensand ammonoids from Clophill, Bedfordshire.   *British Geological Survey Technical Report*, WH/90/276R.

— 1991.   The stratigraphy of Jurassic clay sequences proved beneath Woburn Sands in boreholes near Leighton Buzzard, Bedfordshire.   *British Geological Survey Technical Report*, WH/91/181C.

— and GALLOIS, R W. 1979.   Description of the standard stratigraphical sequences of the Upper Kimmeridge Clay, Ampthill Clay and West Walton Beds.   *Report of the Institute of Geological Sciences*, No. 78/19, 68–72.

— — 1981.   The stratigraphy of the Kimmeridge Clay of the Dorset type area and its correlation with some other Kimmeridgian sequences.   *Report of the Institute of Geological Sciences*, No. 80/4.

CRUX, J A. 1991.   Albian calcareous nannofossils from the Gault Clay of Munday's Hill (Bedfordshire, England).   *Journal of Micropalaeontology*, Vol. 10, 203–222.

DAVIES, A M. 1901.   Excursion to Leighton Buzzard, Wing and Stewkley.   *Proceedings of the Geologists' Association*, Vol. 17, 139–141.

— 1915.   Report of an excursion to Soulbury, Stewkley and Wing.   *Proceedings of the Geologists' Association*, Vol. 26, 90–92.

— 1916.   The zones of the Oxford and Ampthill Clays in Buckinghamshire and Bedfordshire.   *Geological Magazine*, Dec. 6, Vol. 3, 395–400.

DAVIES, G M. 1914.   *Geological excursions round London*. (London: Thomas Murby & Co.)

DE RANCE, C E. 1868.   On the Albian, or Gault, of Folkestone. *Geological Magazine*, Vol. 5, 163–171.

DESTOMBES, J-P, and SHEPHARD-THORN, E R. 1971.   Geological results of the Channel Tunnel site investigation 1964-65. *Report of the Institute of Geological Sciences*, No. 71/11.

DINES, H G, and CHATWIN, C P. 1930.   Pliocene sandstone from Rothamsted (Hertfordshire).   *Summary of Progress of the Geological Survey of Great Britain*, for 1929, 1–7.

DIXON, E E L. 1935.   On the discovery of fuller's earth at Clophill.   *Summary of Progress of the Geological Survey of Great Britain for 1934*, 49.

DIXON, J C, FITTON, J G, and FROST, R T C. 1981.   The tectonic significance of post-Carboniferous igneous activity in the North Sea Basin.   In *Petroleum geology of the continental shelf of North-West Europe*. ILLING, L V, and HOBSON, G D (editors). (London: Heyden and Son.)

DONOVAN, D T, HORTON, A, and IVIMEY-COOK, H C. 1979. The transgression of the Lower Lias over the northern flank of the London Platform.   *Journal of the Geological Society of London*, Vol. 136, 165–173.

DUFF, K L. 1974.   Studies on the palaeontology of the Lower Oxford Clay of southern England.   Unpublished PhD thesis, University of Leicester.

EDMONDS, C N. 1983.   Towards the prediction of subsidence risk upon the Chalk outcrop.   *Quarterly Journal of Engineering Geology*, Vol. 16, 261–266.

ERNST, G, SCHMID, F, and SIEBERTZ, E. 1983.   Event-Stratigraphie im Cenoman und Turon von NW-Deutschland. *Zitteliana*, Vol. 10, 531–554.

EYERS, J. 1991.   The influence of tectonics on early Cretaceous sedimentation in Bedfordshire, England.   *Journal of the Geological Society of London*, Vol. 149, 405–414.

EVANS, C J, and ALLSOP, J M. 1987.   Geophysical aspects of the deep geology of eastern England.   *Proceedings of the Yorkshire Geological Society*, Vol. 46, 321–333.

FITTON, W H. 1836.   Observations on some of the strata between the Chalk and the Oxford Oolite, in the south-east of England.   *Transactions of the Geological Society of London*, 2nd series, Vol. 4, 103–378, 379*–388*.

FLETCHER, B N. 1989.   Foraminifera from the Upper Albian of the Sundon Borehole.   *British Geological Survey Technical Report*, WH/89/344R.

FRANCIS, J. 1896.   On the dip of the underground Palaeozoic rocks at Ware and Cheshunt.   *Report of the British Association for 1895*, 441–454.

GALE, A S. 1989.   Field meeting at Folkestone Warren, 29th November, 1987.   *Proceedings of the Geologists' Association*, Vol. 100, 78–82.

— and FRIEDRICH, S. 1989.   Occurrence of the ammonite genus Sharpeiceras in the Lower Cenomanian Chalk Marl of Folkestone.   80–82 in Field meeting at Folkestone Warren, 29th November, 1987. GALE, A S (editor). *Proceedings of the Geologists' Association*, Vol. 100, 78–82.

GALLOIS, R W, and COX, B M. 1976.   The stratigraphy of the Lower Kimmeridge Clay of eastern England.   *Proceedings of the Yorkshire Geological Society*, Vol. 41, 13–26.

— — 1977.   The stratigraphy of the Middle and Upper Oxfordian sediments of Fenland.   *Proceedings of the Geologists' Association*, Vol. 88, 207–228.

— and MORTER, A A. 1982.   The stratigraphy of the Gault of East Anglia.   *Proceedings of the Geologists' Association*, Vol. 93, 351–368.

GAUNT, G D, FLETCHER, T P, and WOOD, C J. 1992.   Geology of the country around Kingston upon Hull and Brigg.   *Memoir of the British Geological Survey*, Sheets 80 and 89 (England and Wales).

HALLSWORTH, C R. 1986.   Grain-size profiles through two BGS boreholes in the Lower Cretaceous Woburn Sands and the mineralogy of the clay horizons.   *BGS Stratigraphy and Sedimentology Research Group Report*, No. SRG/86/19.

HANCOCK, J M. 1958. The Lower Cretaceous near Leighton Buzzard. *Geologists' Association Guide No. 30A, The London Region*, 36–40.

— 1991. Ammonite scales for the Cretaceous system. *Cretaceous Research*, Vol. 12, 259–291.

HART, M B. 1973. Foraminiferal evidence for the age of the Cambridge Greensand. *Proceedings of the Geologists' Association*, Vol. 84, 65–82.

— BAILEY, H W, CRITTENDEN, S, FLETCHER, B N, PRICE, R J, and SWIECICKI, A. 1989. Chapter 7. Cretaceous. 273–371 in *Stratigraphical atlas of fossil Foraminifera* (2nd edition). JENKINS, D G, and MURRAY, J W (editors). (Chichester: Ellis Horwood.)

HILL, W. 1886. On the beds between the Upper and Lower Chalk of Dover, and their comparison with the Middle Chalk of Cambridgeshire. *Quarterly Journal of the Geological Society of London*, Vol. 42, 232–248.

— and JUKES-BROWNE, A J. 1886. The Melbourn Rock and the Zone of *Belemnitella plena* from Cambridge to the Chiltern Hills. *Quarterly Journal of the Geological Society of London*, Vol. 42, 216–231.

HODGE, C A H, BURTON, R G O, CORBETT, W M, EVANS, R, and SEALE, R S. 1984. Soils and their use in Eastern England. *Bulletin of the Soil Survey of England and Wales* No. 13.

HOPSON, P M. 1991. Geology of the Barkway, Reed, Therfield and Kelshall district. *British Geological Survey Technical Report*, WA/91/06.

HORTON, A, IVIMEY-COOK, H C, HARRISON, R K, and YOUNG, B R. 1980. Phosphatic ooids in the Upper Lias (Lower Jurassic) of central England. *Journal of the Geological Society of London*, Vol. 137, 731–740.

— SHEPHARD-THORN, E R, and THURRELL, R G. 1974. The geology of the new town of Milton Keynes. *Report of the Institute of Geological Sciences*, No. 74/16.

— SUMBLER, M G, and COX, B M. In press. Geology of the country between Oxford and Aylesbury. *Memoir of the British Geological Survey*, Sheet 237 (England and Wales).

HOWARTH, M K. 1978. The stratigraphy and ammonite fauna of the Upper Lias of Northamptonshire. *Bulletin of the British Museum (Natural History); Geology Series*. Vol. 29, 235–288.

— 1980. The Toarcian age of the upper part of the Marlstone Rock Bed of England. *Palaeontology*. Vol. 23, 637–656.

JEANS, C V, MERRIMAN, R J, and MITCHELL, J G. 1977. Origin of Middle Jurassic and Lower Cretaceous fuller's earths in England. *Clay Minerals*, Vol. 12, 11–44.

JEFFERIES, R P S. 1963. The stratigraphy of the *Actinocamax plenus* Sub-zone (Turonian) in the Anglo-Paris Basin. *Proceedings of the Geologists' Association*, Vol. 74, 1–33.

JOHNSON, H D, and LEVELL, B K. 1980. Sedimentology of Lower Cretaceous subtidal sand complex, Woburn Sands, Southern England. *Bulletin of the American Association of Petroleum Geologists*, Vol. 64, 728–729.

JUKES-BROWNE, A J. 1875. On the relations of the Cambridge Gault and Greensand. *Quarterly Journal of the Geological Society of London*, Vol. 31, 256–315.

— 1889. The occurrence of granite in a boring at Bletchley. *Geological Magazine*, Dec. 3, Vol. 6, 356–361.

— 1900. The Cretaceous rocks of Britain. Vol. 1. The Gault and Upper Greensand of England. *Memoir of the Geological Survey of Great Britain*.

— and HILL, W. 1903. The Cretaceous rocks of Britain. Vol. 2. The Lower and Middle Chalk of England. *Memoir of the Geological Survey of Great Britain*.

— — 1904. The Cretaceous rocks of Britain. Vol. 3. The Upper Chalk of England. *Memoir of the Geological Survey of Great Britain*.

KAPLAN, U. 1986. Ammonite stratigraphy of the Turonian of NW-Germany. *Newsletters on Stratigraphy*, Vol. 17, 9–20.

KEEN, M C. 1968. The Cretaceous system. 312–323 in *The geology of the East Midlands*. SYLVESTER-BRADLEY, P C, and FORD, T D (editors). (Leicester: Leicester University Press.)

KEEPING, W. 1875. On the occurrence of Neocomian sands with phosphatic nodules at Brickhill, Bedfordshire. *Geological Magazine*, Dec. 2, Vol. 2, 372–375.

— 1883. The fossils and palaeontological affinities of the Neocomian deposits of Upware and Brickhill. *Sedgwick Prize Essay for 1879*. Cambridge.

KENNEDY, W J. 1969. The correlation of the Lower Chalk of south-east England. *Proceedings of the Geologists' Association*, Vol. 80, 459–551.

KIRKALDY, J F. 1947. The provenance of the pebbles in the Lower Cretaceous rocks. *Proceedings of the Geologists' Association*, Vol. 58, 223–241.

LAKE, R D, and SHEPHARD-THORN, E R. 1985. The stratigraphy and geological structure of the Hog's Back, Surrey and adjoining areas. *Proceedings of the Geologists' Association*, Vol. 96, 7–21.

— YOUNG, B, WOOD, C J, and MORTIMORE, R N. 1987. Geology of the country around Lewes. *Memoir of the British Geological Survey*, Sheet 319 (England and Wales).

LAMPLUGH, G W. 1915. Report of an excursion to Leighton Buzzard. *Proceedings of the Geologists' Association*, Vol. 26, 310–313.

— 1922. On the junction of the Gault and Lower Greensand near Leighton Buzzard (Bedfordshire). *Quarterly Journal of the Geological Society of London*, Vol. 78, 1–81.

— and WALKER, J F. 1903. On a fossiliferous band at the top of the Lower Greensand near Leighton Buzzard (Bedfordshire). *Quarterly Journal of the Geological Society of London*, Vol. 59, 234–265.

LEWIS, W V. 1949. The Pegsdon dry valleys. *Compass*, Vol. 1, 53–70. (Cambridge Geographical Society.)

MARTILL, D M, and HUDSON, J D (editors). 1991. Fossils of the Oxford Clay. *Palaeontological Association Field Guide to Fossils*, No. 4.

MATHER, J D, GRAY, D A, ALLEN, R A, and SMITH, D B. 1973. Groundwater recharge in the Lower Greensand of the London Basin — results of tritium and carbon-14 determinations. *Quarterly Journal of Engineering Geology*, Vol. 6, 141–152.

MIDDLEMISS, F A. 1962. Brachiopod ecology and Lower Greensand palaeogeography. *Palaeontology*, Vol. 5, 253–267.

MOFFAT, A J, and CATT, J A. 1983. A new excavation in Plio-Pleistocene deposits at Little Heath. *Transactions of the Hertfordshire Natural History Society*, Vol. 29, 5–10.

MONKHOUSE, R A. 1974. An assessment of the groundwater resources of the Lower Greensand in the Cambridge–Bedford area. Report of the Water Resources Board, Reading.

MOORLOCK, B S P, and HIGHLEY, D E. 1991. An appraisal of fuller's earth resources in England and Wales. *British Geological Survey Technical Report*, WA/91/75.

— and WYATT, R J. 1986. Leighton Buzzard Project — Boreholes 1986. *Technical Report of the British Geological Survey*, WA/VG/86/3.

MORTER, A A. 1986. Regional stratigraphy of the Lower Greensand. 72–78 in An outline study of the Lower Greensand of parts of south-east England. SHEPHARD-THORN, E R, HARRIS, P M, HIGHLEY, D E, AND THORNTON, M H. *Technical Report of the British Geological Survey*, WF/MN/86/1.

— and WOOD, C J. 1983. The biostratigraphy of Upper Albian — Lower Cenomanian *Aucellina* in Europe. *Zitteliana*, Vol. 10, 515–529.

MORTIMORE, R N. 1986. Stratigraphy of the Upper Cretaceous White Chalk of Sussex. *Proceedings of the Geologists' Association*, Vol. 97, 97–139.

— and WOOD, C J. 1986. The distribution of flint in the English Chalk, with particular reference to the 'Brandon Flint Series' and the high Turmian flint maximum. 7–20 in *The scientific study of flint and chert*: papers from the Fourth International Flint Symposium, SIEVEKING, G G, and HART, M B (editors). (Cambridge University Press.)

MURRAY, K H. 1986. Correlation of electrical resistivity marker bands in the Cenomanian and Turonian Chalk from the London Basin to east Yorkshire. *Report of the British Geological Survey*, Vol. 17, No. 8.

NARAYAN, J. 1963. Cross-stratification and palaeogeography of the Lower Greensand of south-east England and Bas-Boulonnais, France. *Nature, London*, Vol. 199, 1246–1247.

OATES, M J. 1991. Upper Kimmeridgian stratigraphy of Aylesbury, Bucks. *Proceedings of the Geologists' Association*, Vol. 102, 185–199.

OWEN, H G. 1971. Middle Albian stratigraphy in the Anglo-Paris Basin. *Bulletin of the British Museum (Natural History), Geology*, Supplement 8.

— 1972. The Gault and its junction with the Woburn Sands in the Leighton Buzzard area, Bedfordshire and Buckinghamshire. *Proceedings of the Geologists' Association*, Vol. 83, 287–312.

— 1976. The stratigraphy of the Gault and Upper Greensand of the Weald. *Proceedings of the Geologists' Association*, Vol. 86, 475–498.

— 1988. The ammonite zonal sequence and ammonite taxonomy in the *Douvilleiceras mammillatum* Superzone (Lower Albian) in Europe. *Bulletin of the British Museum (Natural History), Geology*, Vol. 44, 177–231.

PAGE, K N. 1989. A stratigraphical revision for the English Lower Callovian. *Proceedings of the Geologists' Association*, Vol. 100, 363–382.

PATTISON, J, BERRIDGE, N G, ALLSOP, J M, and WILKINSON, I P. 1993. The geology of the country around Sudbury (Suffolk). *Memoir of the British Geological Survey*, Sheet 206 (England and Wales).

PHELPS, M C. 1985. A refined biostratigraphy for the Middle and Upper Carixian (ibex and davoei Zones, Lower Jurassic) in north-west Europe and stratigraphical details of the Carixian–Domerian boundary. *Geobios*, No. 18, 321–362.

PRICE, F G H. 1874. On the Gault of Folkestone. *Quarterly Journal of the Geological Society of London*, Vol. 30, 342–366.

— 1877. On the beds between the Gault and Upper Chalk near Folkestone. *Quarterly Journal of the Geological Society of London*, Vol. 33, 431–448.

RADLEY, J D. 1980. A new look at Portlandian strata exposed at Warren Farm, Stewkley, Buckinghamshire. *Records of Buckinghamshire*, Vol. 22, 125–128.

RASTALL, R H. 1919. The mineral composition of the Lower Greensand Series of Eastern England. *Geological Magazine*, Vol. 56, 211–220; 265–272.

REID, A B, ALLSOP, J M, GRANSER, G, MILLETT, A J, and SOMERTON, I W. 1990. Magnetic interpretation in three dimensions using Euler deconvolution. *Geophysics*, Vol. 55, 80–91.

RIDGWAY, J M. 1982. Common clay and shale. *Mineral Dossier Mineral Resources Consultative Committee*, No. 22.

ROBERTS, E. 1974. Totternhoe Stone and flint in Hertfordshire churches. *Medieval Archaeology*, Vol. 18, 66–89.

ROBERTSON, R H S. 1986. Fuller's earth. A history of calcium montmorillonite. *Mineralogical Society Occasional Publication*. 421 pp.

ROBINSON, N D. 1986a. Lithostratigraphy of the Chalk Group of the North Downs, south-east England. *Proceedings of the Geologists' Association*, Vol. 97, 141–170.

— 1986b. Fining-upward microrhythms with basal scours in the Chalk of Kent and Surrey, England and their stratigraphical importance. *Newsletters on Stratigraphy*, Vol. 17, 21–28.

RUFFELL, A H, and WACH, G D. 1991. Sequence stratigraphic analysis of the Aptian-Albian Lower Greensand in southern England. *Marine and Petroleum Geology*, Vol. 8, 341–353.

— and WIGNALL, P B. 1990. Depositional trends in the Upper Jurassic–Lower Cretaceous of the northern margin of the Wessex Basin. *Proceedings of the Geologists' Association*, Vol. 101, 279–288.

SAMPSON, C G. 1978. *Paleoecology and archeology of an Acheulian site at Caddington, England*. (Department of Anthropology, Southern Methodist University, Texas.)

SEELEY, H G. 1869. *Index to the fossil remains of Aves, Ornithosauria, and Reptilea from the Secondary System of strata, arranged in the Woodwardian Museum of the University of Cambridge*. (Cambridge.)

SHACKLETON, N J, and OPDYKE, N D. 1973. Oxygen isotope and palaeomagnetic stratigraphy of equatorial Pacific core V28-238: oxygen isotope temperatures and ice volumes on a 10^5 and 10^6 year scale. *Quaternary Research*, Vol. 3, 39–55.

SHEPHARD-THORN, E R. 1988. Geology of the country around Ramsgate and Dover. *Memoir of the British Geological Survey*, Sheets 274 and 290 (England and Wales).

— HARRIS, P M, HIGHLEY, D E, and THORNTON, M H. 1986. An outline study of the Lower Greensand of parts of south-east England. *Technical Report of the British Geological Survey*, WF/MN/86/1.

SMART, J G O, BISSON, G, and WORSSAM, B C. 1966. Geology of the country around Canterbury and Folkestone. *Memoir of the Geological Survey of Great Britain*.

SMART, P J. 1957. Palaeontology report for 1956. *Bedfordshire Naturalist*, Vol. 11, 23–25.

— 1958. Palaeontology report for 1957. *Bedfordshire Naturalist*, Vol. 12, 16–27.

— 1960. Palaeontology report for 1959. *Bedfordshire Naturalist*, Vol. 14, 27–39.

— 1990. A large ammonite from Barton in the Clay. *Bedfordshire Magazine*, Vol. 22, 270–272.

SMITH, N J P, and 15 others. 1985a. Map 1. Pre-Permian geology of the United Kingdom (south). (British Geological Survey.)

— and 15 others. 1985b. Map 2. Contours on the top of the pre-Permian surface of the United Kingdom (south). (British Geological Survey.)

SMITH, W G. 1894. *Man the primeval savage: his haunts and relics from the hill-tops of Bedfordshire to Blackwall.* (London: Edward Stanford.)

— 1916. Notes on the Palaeolithic floor near Caddington. *Archaeologia*, Vol. 67, 49–74.

SOIL SURVEY OF ENGLAND AND WALES. 1983. 1:250 000 Soil Map Series. Sheet 4. Eastern England.

SPARKS, B W, and LEWIS, W V. 1957. Escarpment dry valleys near Pegsdon, Hertfordshire. *Proceedings of the Geologists' Association*, Vol. 68, 26–38.

SPATH, L F. 1923–43. A monograph of the Ammonoidea of the Gault. *Monograph of the Palaeontographical Society.*

STOKES, R B. 1977. The echinoids *Micraster* and *Epiaster* from the Turonian and Senonian of England. *Palaeontology*, Vol. 20, 805–821.

TEALL, J J H. 1875. The Potton and Wicken phosphatic deposits. *Sedgwick Prize Essay for 1873.* (Cambridge.)

TOOMBS, H A. 1935. Field meeting at Leighton Buzzard, Bedfordshire. *Proceedings of the Geologists' Association*, Vol. 46, 432–436.

TORRENS, H S. 1968. The Great Oolite Series. 227–263 in *The geology of the East Midlands.* SYLVESTER-BRADLEY, P C, and FORD, T D (editors). (Leicester: Leicester University Press.)

TUCKER, R D, and PHARAOH, T C. 1991. U-Pb zircon ages for Late Precambrian igneous rocks in southern Britain. *Journal of the Geological Society of London*, Vol. 148, 435–443.

VACQUIER, V, STREELAND, N C, HENDERSON, R G, and ZEITZ, I. 1957. Interpretation of aeromagnetic maps. *Memoir of the Geological Society of America*, No. 47.

VINCE, J N T. 1968. The brickmakers of Langley and Stewkley. *Buckinghamshire Life*, January 1968, 12–14.

WARD, W H, BURLAND, J B, and GALLOIS, R W. 1968. Geotechnical assessment of a site at Mundford, Norfolk, for a large proton accelerator. *Géotechnique*, Vol. 18, 399–431.

WEEKS, A G. 1969. The stability of natural slopes in south-east England as affected by periglacial activity. *Quarterly Journal of Engineering Geology*, Vol. 2, 49–61.

WHITAKER, W. 1865. On the Chalk of Buckinghamshire and on the Totternhoe Stone. *Quarterly Journal of the Geological Society of London*, Vol. 21, 398–400.

— 1872. The geology of the London Basin. *Memoir of the Geological Survey of Great Britain.*

WHITAKER, W, and JUKES-BROWNE, A J. 1894. On deep borings at Culford and Winkfield, with notes on those at Ware and Cheshunt. *Quarterly Journal of the Geological Society of London*, Vol. 50, 488–514.

WHITTAKER, A (editor). 1985. *Atlas of onshore sedimentary basins in England and Wales. Post Carboniferous tectonics and stratigraphy.* (Glasgow: Blackie.)

WIEDMANN, J, KAPLAN, U, LEHMANN, J, and MARCZINOWSKI, R. 1989. Biostratigraphy of the Cenomanian of NW Germany. 931–948 in *Cretaceous of the Western Tethys.* Proceedings of the 3rd International Cretaceous Symposium, Tubingen, 1987. Stuttgart.

WIGNALL, P B. 1990. Benthic palaeoecology of the late Jurassic Kimmeridge Clay of England. *Special Papers in Palaeontology*, No. 43.

WILKINSON, I P. 1988. Ostracoda across the Albian/Cenomanian boundary in Cambridgeshire and western Suffolk, eastern England. 1229–1244 in *Evolutionary biology of ostracoda, its fundamentals and applications.* HANAI, T, IKEYA, N, and ISHIZAKI, K (editors). Developments in Palaeontology and Stratigraphy, Volume 11. (Barking, Essex: Elsevier.)

— 1989. Foraminifera from the Lower Chalk of the Sundon Borehole. *British Geological Survey Technical Report*, WH/89/31R.

— 1990a. The micropalaeontology of a suite of samples from the Totternhoe area. *British Geological Survey Technical Report*, WH/90/122R.

— 1990b. The biostratigraphical application of Ostracoda to the Albian of eastern England. *Courier Forschungsinstitut Senckenberg*, Vol. 123, 239–258.

— 1991. Late Cretaceous foraminifera from the Totternhoe Lime and Stone Quarry. *British Geological Survey Technical Report*, WH/91/114R.

— and MORTER, A A. 1981. The biostratigraphical zonation of the East Anglian Gault by Ostracoda. 163–176 in *Microfossils from Recent and fossil shelf seas.* NEALE, J W, and BRASIER, M D (editors). (Chichester: Ellis Horwood.)

WIMBLEDON, W A. 1980. Portlandian correlation chart. *Special Report of the Geological Society of London*, No. 15, 85–93.

— and COPE, J C W. 1978. The ammonite faunas of the English Portland Beds and the zones of the Portlandian Stage. *Journal of the Geological Society*, Vol. 135, 183–190.

WOOD, C J. 1990a. The stratigraphy of the Lower Chalk of the Chilterns: observations on the Barton, Sundon, Houghton Regis and Totternhoe quarries. *British Geological Survey Technical Report*, WH/90/397R.

— 1990b. Determinations of macrofossils from the Lower Chalk and Middle Chalk of the area around Totternhoe, Beds., collected by D T Aldiss and C J Wood. *British Geological Survey Technical Report*, WH/90/283R.

— 1990c. The stratigraphy of the Middle and Upper Chalk of the Rugby Portland Cement Co. working quarry at Kensworth, Bedfordshire. *British Geological Survey Technical Report*, WH/90/99R.

WOODLAND, A W. 1970. The buried tunnel-valleys of East Anglia. *Proceedings of the Yorkshire Geological Society*, Vol. 37, 521–578.

WOODS, H. 1896. The Mollusca of the Chalk Rock. I. *Quarterly Journal of the Geological Society of London*, Vol. 52, 68–98.

— 1897. The Mollusca of the Chalk Rock. II. *Quarterly Journal of the Geological Society of London*, Vol. 53, 377–404.

WOODS, M A. 1991. Interpretation of Gault fossils from an area between Aston Abbotts and Bierton, Buckinghamshire. *British Geological Survey Technical Report*, WH/91/297R.

WOODWARD, H B. 1895. The Jurassic rocks of Britain. Vol. 5. The Middle and Upper Oolitic rocks of England (Yorkshire excepted). *Memoir of the Geological Survey of Great Britain.*

WORSSAM, B C, and TAYLOR, J H. 1969. Geology of the country around Cambridge. *Memoir of the Geological Survey of Great Britain.*

WRAY, D J, and GALE, A S. 1993. Geochemical correlation of marl bands in Turonian chalks of the Anglo-Paris Basin. In

Geological Society of London Special Publication: high resolution stratigraphy. KIDD, R V, and HAILWOOD, E A (editors).

WRIGHT, C W. 1979. The ammonites of the English Chalk Rock. *Bulletin of the British Museum (Natural History), Geology,* Vol. 31, 281–332.

— and KENNEDY, W J. 1984. The Ammonoidea of the Lower Chalk, Part 1. *Monograph of the Palaeontographical Society.*

— and WRIGHT, E V. 1947. The stratigraphy of the Albian beds at Leighton Buzzard. *Geological Magazine,* Vol. 84, 161–168.

WRIGHT, J K. 1980. Oxfordian correlation chart. *Special Report of the Geological Society of London,* No. 15, 61–76.

WYATT, R J, and AMBROSE, K. 1988. Geological notes and local details for 1:10 000 Sheets SP51NW and SP51SW: Weston-on-the-Green and Islip. *British Geological Survey Technical Report,* WA/88/27.

— MOORLOCK, B S P, LAKE, R D, and SHEPHARD-THORN, E R. 1988. Geology of the Leighton Buzzard–Ampthill district. *British Geological Survey Technical Report,* WA/88/1.

WYMER, J J. 1985. *Palaeolithic sites of East Anglia.* (Norwich: Geo Books.)

APPENDIX 1

The macrofauna of the Lias Group in the Tattenhoe Borehole [SP 8289 3437]

Identifications by H C Ivimey-Cook and M K Howarth
(Middle and Upper Lias ammonites)

See also Chapter Two, pp.9–12.

THE FAUNA OF THE UPPER LIAS

Zone of *Hildoceras bifrons* (79.18 to 83.49 m)

Peronoceras fibulatum Subzone (79.18 to 82.73 m)
    gastropod indet. juv.
    Entolium lunare (Roemer)
    Dactylioceras cf. *commune* (J Sowerby)
    Dactylioceras sp.
    Hildoceras bifrons (Bruguière)
    Hildoceras sp.
    belemnite indet.
    fish fragments

Dactylioceras commune Subzone (82.73 to 83.49 m)
    Astarte sp.
    Entolium sp.
    Palaeoneilo?
    Placunopsis sp.
    Propeamussium sp.
    Pseudomytiloides dubius (J. de C. Sowerby)
    Dactylioceras commune (J Sowerby)
    Dactylioceras sp.
    Harpoceras sp.
    Hildoceras cf. *sublevisoni* Fucini
    Hildoceras sp.
    belemnite indet.
    crinoid columnals indet.

Zone of *Harpoceras falciferum* (83.49 to ?86.00 m)

Harpoceras falciferum Subzone (83.49 to 84.72 m)
    serpulids indet.
    Entolium sp.
    Eopecten sp.
    Pseudomytiloides?
    Dactylioceras sp.
    Harpoceras falciferum (J Sowerby)
    Harpoceras sp.
    pseudohastitid belemnite

Cleviceras exaratum Subzone (84.72 to 86.09 m)
    wood fragments
    Discinisca sp.
    rhynchonellid fragments
    Plicatula?
    Pseudomytiloides sp.
    Dactylioceras sp.
    Cleviceras elegans (J Sowerby)
    Harpoceras cf. *serpentinum* (Schlotheim)
    crustacean fragments
    fish fragments and coprolites

THE FAUNA OF THE MARLSTONE ROCK BED (FORMATION)

Zone of *Pleuroceras spinatum* (c.86.09 to 87.12 m)
    belemnite indet.

THE FAUNA OF THE BRANT MUDSTONE FORMATION

Zone of *Amaltheus margaritatus* (87.12 to 93.66 m)

Amaltheus gibbosus Subzone: not proved

Amaltheus subnodosus Subzone
    plant fragments and rootlets
    foraminiferan indet.
    Amberleya sp.
    Camptonectes subulatus (Münster)
    Camptonectes sp.
    Entolium?
    Grammatodon sp.
    Oxytoma sp.
    Palaeoneilo sp.
    Pseudolimea sp.
    Protocardia truncata (J de C. Sowerby)
    Pseudopecten equivalvis (J Sowerby)
    Amaltheus subnodosus (Young & Bird) between 87.65 and 88.62 m
    Amaltheus sp.
    belemnite indet.
    Chondrites and other burrows

Amaltheus stokesi Subzone
    Dentalium sp.
    Camptonectes subulatus (Münster)
    Camptonectes sp.
    Chlamys?
    Entolium lunare (Roemer)
    Goniomya hybrida (Münster)
    Grammatodon sp.
    Lucina sp.
    Meleagrinella?
    Modiolus subcancellatus Buvignier
    Modiolus sp.
    Palaeoneilo galatea (d'Orbigny)
    P. oviformis Troedsson
    Palmoxytoma sp.
    Pleuromya sp.
    Plicatula sp.
    Protocardia sp.
    Pseudopecten equivalvis (J Sowerby)
    Pseudopecten sp.
    Rollieria bronni (Andler)
    Ryderia sp.
    Tutcheria sp.

Amaltheus cf. *stokesi* (J Sowerby) between 89.09 and 92.48 m
Amaltheus sp.
Amauroceras sp.
Tragophylloceras?
belemnites indet.
Balanocrinus sp.
Isocrinus sp.
crinoid debris
fish debris
Chondrites-type burrows

Zone of *Prodactylioceras davoei* (93.66 to c.99.40 m)

Amberleya (Eucyclus) sp.
cerithiids indet.
Dentalium sp.
Camptonectes subulatus (Münster)
Goniomya hybrida (Münster)
Grammatodon?
ostreids indet.
Oxytoma sp.
Palaeoneilo galatea (d'Orbigny)
P. oviformis Troedsson
Palaeoneilo sp.
Parainoceramus ventricosus (J de C Sowerby)
Parainoceramus sp.
Pleuromya sp.
Protocardia truncata (J de C Sowerby)
Pseudopecten sp.
Ryderia graphica (Tate)
Tutcheria richardsoni Cox
Tutcheria sp.
Aegoceras cf. *crescens* (Hyatt) at 93.84 m
Aegoceras sp.
Androgynoceras cf. *maculatum* (Young & Bird) at 99.27 m
Androgynoceras cf. *sparsicosta* (Trueman) at 99.27 m
Liparoceras?
ostracods
Balanocrinus sp.
Hispidocrinus sp.
Isocrinus sp.
Eodiadema sp. [tests and spines]
fish fragments

Zone of *Tragophylloceras ibex* (c.99.40 to c.142.50 m)

Discinisca holdeni (Tate)
Discinisca sp.
Rimirhynchia anglica (Rollier)
Rimirhynchia sp.
Cincta?
Lobothyris sp.
Amberleya?
Dentalium sp.
Camptonectes subulatus (Münster)
Camptonectes sp.
Cardinia attenuata (Stutchbury)
Cardinia sp.
Cucullaea sp.
Dacryomya minor (Simpson)
Goniomya hybrida (Münster)

Grammatodon sp.
Gryphaea gigantea J de C Sowerby
Gryphaea sp.
Laevitrigonia? troedssoni Melville
Laevitrigonia?
Mactromya?
Meleagrinella?
Modiolus cf. *scalprum* J. Sowerby
Modiolus sp.
Oxytoma inequivalve (J Sowerby)
Oxytoma sp.
Palaeoneilo galatea (d'Orbigny)
Palaeoneilo oviformis Troedsson
Palaeoneilo sp.
Parainoceramus ventricosus (J de C Sowerby)
Parainoceramus sp.
Parallelodon buckmani (G F Richardson)
Parallelodon sp.
Pinna sp.
Plagiostoma sp.
Plicatula spinosa J Sowerby
Plicatula sp.
Pleuromya costata (Young & Bird)
Pleuromya sp.
Protocardia truncata (J de C Sowerby)
Protocardia sp.
Pseudolimea acuticostata (Münster)
Pseudolimea sp.
Pseudopecten sp.
Rollieria bronni (Andler)
Ryderia graphica (Tate)
Ryderia sp.
Steinmannia?
Aegoceras (Beaniceras) cf. *luridum* (Simpson) at 100.80 and 109.45 m
A. (B.) sp. down to 119.09 m
Androgynoceras ('Beaniceras')? sp. cf. *A. centaurus* (d'Orbigny) at 125.08 m
Liparoceras sp.
Lytoceras sp.
Tragophylloceras sp.
Hastites sp.
belemnites indet.
Balanocrinus subterroides (Quenstedt)
Balanocrinus sp.
Isocrinus sp.
ophiuroid fragments
Eodiadema sp. [test and spines]
ostracods
fish fragments
Chondrites-type and other burrows

Zone of *Uptonia jamesoni* (c.142.50 to c.149.23 m)

Piarorhynchia sp.
Rimirhynchia sp.
lobothyrid indet.
Chlamys?
lucinids indet.
Apoderoceras?
Uptonia jamesoni (J de C Sowerby) at 142.85 m
hastitid belemnite

APPENDIX 2

Abridged logs of BGS boreholes

Ascott Farm Sand Pit Borehole   SP92SW/42
[SP 9078 2408] Surface level c.+102 m

	Thickness m	Depth m
Lower Cretaceous		
GAULT		
Upper Gault		
Open-holed in grey clay	5.00	5.00
Clay, greenish grey with yellowish brown mottling, fissured	1.00	6.00
Clay, grey, slightly silty, fissured, with phosphatic nodules	0.60	6.60
Sand, yellowish brown, fine- and medium-grained, pebbly	0.40	7.00
Clay, pale to medium grey, slightly silty, fissured, with phosphatic nodules	1.60	8.60
Lower Gault		
Clay, dark grey to olive-grey, slightly silty micaceous	5.05	13.65
Lower Gault ('Junction Beds')		
Clay, medium grey, sandy, slightly pebbly	0.52	14.17
Sand, olive- and rusty-brown, medium- and coarse-grained, clayey, pebbly, sandy	1.03	15.20
WOBURN SANDS		
Sand, yellowish orange, fine- to coarse-grained	0.75	15.95
Sand, yellowish orange, dominantly medium-grained, pebbly, laminated silty clay below 22.1 m	6.80	22.75
Clay, greyish black, silty, sandy, cementstone fragments at base	0.91	23.66
Sand, dark brown to olive-grey, fine-grained, with wisps and laminae of greyish black clay below 24.60 m; dark greenish grey below 25.40 m; cementstone nodules at 25.90 m	2.94	26.60

Upper Jurassic (see also pp.00–00)

	Thickness m	Depth m
KIMMERIDGE CLAY		
Mudstone, pale to medium grey, shelly	1.90	28.50
AMPTHILL CLAY		
Cementstone, pale grey	0.20	28.70
Mudstone, pale to medium grey, shelly, intensely burrowed at top, phosphatic nodules at 31.15 m and 31.75–31.80	3.60	32.30

Woburn Sands A Borehole   SP93SW/174   [SP 9308 3438]
Surface level (base of working pit) c.+96 m

	Thickness m	Depth m
Lower Cretaceous		
WOBURN SANDS		
Sand, orange-brown, fine- and medium-grained	2.50	2.50
Fuller's earth, mudstone, greyish yellow	1.70	4.20
Sand, orange-brown to yellowish grey, fine- to medium-grained, with pellets and thin lenses of clay	9.23	13.43
Clay, greyish yellow	0.13	13.56
Sand, orange-brown, fine- to coarse-grained; orange-brown mudstone at 21.75–21.77 m	21.44	35.00

Woburn Sands B Borehole   SP93NW/62   [SP 9323 3526]
Surface level c.+123 m

	Thickness m	Depth m
Lower Cretaceous		
WOBURN SANDS		
Sand, orange-brown, medium-grained	0.50	0.50
Fuller's earth, mudstone, greyish yellow	2.30	2.80
Sand, fawn-grey, and orange-brown, fine- and medium-grained; grey clay lenses and sponge spicules at some levels; 0.05 m band of smooth grey clay at 13.95 m; 0.05 m yellowish orange and olive-brown laminated clay at 15.90 m; hardpan at base	16.93	19.73
Fuller's earth, mudstone, greyish yellow	1.25	20.98
Sand, fawn-grey and orange-brown, fine- and medium-grained, with clay lenses or pellets some levels	7.55	28.53
Clay, greenish grey, passing down into	0.07	28.60
Sand, as above	3.01	31.61
Fuller's earth, mudstone, yellowish grey	0.28	31.99
Sand, fawn-grey, and orange-brown, fine- to medium-grained	3.01	35.00

Birchmoor Farm Borehole   SP03NW/161   [SP 9494 3518]
Surface level c.+95 m

	Thickness m	Depth m
Lower Cretaceous		
WOBURN SANDS		
Sand, fine- to coarse-grained, grey to orange-brown, and locally turquoise-green, shelly near base	50.30	50.30
Sand, pebbly, grey-brown, very glauconitic	0.36	51.02
Sand, pebbly, blue-green/grey-brown	0.26	51.28
Clay, sandy, pebbly, greenish grey	0.69	51.97
Conglomerate, cemented, pale grey phosphatic chips and pebbles	0.39	52.36
Middle Jurassic		
MIDDLE OXFORD CLAY		
Clay, grey, variably silty	7.30	59.66

Birchmoor Pumping Station No. 1 Borehole   SP93SW/253
[SP 9423 3491] Surface level c.+100 m

	Thickness m	Depth m
Lower Cretaceous		
WOBURN SANDS		
Sand, mainly fine- to medium-grained, red-brown to yellow-brown	6.25	6.25
Fuller's earth, buff, waxy	1.05	7.30
Sand, sandstone, red-brown mainly fine- to medium-grained	2.90	10.20
Fuller's earth, siltstone and sandstone	0.,75	10.95
Sand, fine- to medium-grained, khaki, with occasional fragments of fuller's earth	3.75	14.70
Sand and sandstone, fine- to coarse-grained, glauconitic	0.50	15.20
Sand, sandstone, blue-green, and fuller's earth	0.50	15.70
Sand, fine- to medium-grained, blue-green to olive-green	3.30	19.00
Sand, fine- to medium-grained, yellow-brown to khaki	6.00	25.00
Clay, sandy, rusty-orange	4.20	29.30
Sandstone, dark purple-brown, mainly fine- to medium-grained	0.30	29.60
Sand, fine- to medium-grained, yellow-brown to khaki	10.40	40.00

Birchmoor Pumping Station No. 2 Borehole
SP93SW/254   [SP 9455 3493] Surface level c.+95 m

	Thickness m	Depth m
Lower Cretaceous		
WOBURN SANDS		
Sand, fine- to medium-grained, reddish brown to greyish yellow	4.32	4.32
Fuller's earth, slightly sandy, pale cream	0.13	4.45
Ironstone, dark orange-brown	0.10	4.55
Sand, mainly fine- to medium-grained, red-brown to grey, partings of fuller's earth, some ironstone	11.95	16.50
Clay, pale bluish greenish grey	0.10	16.60
Sand, as above, with sandstone fragments, locally bright blue-green	16.40	33.00

Birchmoor Pumping Station No. 3 Borehole
SP93SW/255 [SP 9445 3498] Surface level c.+99 m

	Thickness m	Depth m
Lower Cretaceous		
WOBURN SANDS		
Sand, fine-grained, orange	2.80	2.80
Clay, possible fuller's earth, very sandy, grey-brown	0.04	2.84
Sand, fine-grained, variably clayey, orange to reddish orange	2.36	5.20
Clay, possible fuller's earth, grey-brown to olive-grey, sandy	0.20	5.40

	Thickness m	Depth m
Sand, fine- to medium-grained, orange to pale grey, glauconitic	0.90	6.30
Clay, very sandy, pale grey	0.05	6.35
Sand, fine- to medium-grained, slightly clayey, silty, glauconitic, orange-tinged khaki	1.35	7.70
Fuller's earth, clay, sandy in top, olive-grey to greenish greyish brown	0.75	8.45
Sand, fine- to medium-grained, variably clayey and silty, grey-brown to khaki	0.75	9.20
Clay, possible fuller's earth, grey-brown	0.03	9.23
Sand, medium- to fine-grained, pale orange-grey to grey, variably silty and clayey, glauconitic	5.77	15.00

Potsgrove Borehole   SP93SW/256 [SP 9406 3066]
Surface level c.+130 m

	Thickness m	Depth m
Quaternary		
Clay, chalky pebbly	4.00	4.00
Sand, fine- to medium-grained, orange-brown to biscuit	2.60	5.60
Clay, pale grey-brown	0.15	5.75
Sand, as above, but with scattered coarse grains	0.69	6.44
Clay, orange-brown, slightly silty, passing down into grey clay, with mica	5.78	12.22
Sand, orange, pebbly	0.21	12.43
Clay, grey to grey-brown	0.70	13.13
Core missing	0.49	13.62
Clay, grey, sandy, pebbly partings	0.27	13.89
Gravel, sandy, clayey, passing down into sand, orange-brown, medium- to coarse-grained, with scattered pebbles	1.06	14.95
Lower Cretaceous		
WOBURN SANDS		
Sand, fine- to medium-grained, glauconitic, yellow-orange to brown, variably pebbly between 19.46 to 20.56 and between 29.34 and 30.81	15.51	30.46
Core missing	2.64	33.10
Sand, clayey, grey-brown, gritty, pebbly	0.07	33.17
Sand, medium-grained, pale cream-beige, boxstone fragments	0.68	33.85
Core missing	1.18	35.03
Clay, sandy, soft	0.18	35.21
Sand, deep orange, boxstone fragments	0.22	35.43
Open-holed, no core	8.73	44.16
Sand, fine- to coarse-grained slightly clayey at top, orange, greyish orange, grey-beige, ironstone fragments, locally cemented, pebbly at 57.48	19.93	64.09
Clay, pale brown, plastic	0.05	64.14
Sand, medium- to fine-grained, orange to grey	0.46	64.60
Clay, silty, brownish grey	0.42	65.02
Clay, very sandy, pebbly	0.12	65.14
Sand, fine- to medium-grained, grey to orange, ironstone fragments, locally clayey	27.13	92.27
Conglomerate, phosphatic pebbles, blue-green, ammonite fragments	0.37	92.64

Middle Jurassic

MIDDLE OXFORD CLAY
Clay, hard, grey to pale grey, fossiliferous   3.01   95.65

Froxfield Borehole   SP93SE/8   [SP 7937 3337]
Surface level c.+115 m

	Thickness m	Depth m
Lower Cretaceous		
WOBURN SANDS		
Not cored, sandy	3.80	3.80
Sand, mainly fine- to medium-grained, orange-brown to cream, variably clayey and silty	1.65	5.45
Open-holed, no core, soft sand	5.56	11.01
Clay, pale grey-brown, sandy	0.14	11.15
Sand, pale cream, locally clayey	0.63	11.78
Clay, sandy, pale orange-brown	0.12	11.90
Sand, pale grey-brown, laminated, passing down into sandy clay, with clay partings	0.19	12.17
Sand, slightly clayey, pale beige	0.35	12.52
Open-holed, sand	11.59	24.11
Conglomerate, sandy, in varicoloured clay matrix, with pebbles of quartz, quartzite chert and phosphate	0.27	24.38
Sand, orange to orange-brown	0.32	24.70
Conglomerate, clay matrix, pebbles as in conglomerate above	0.13	24.83
Sand, orange-brown, mainly fine- to medium-grained, some cemented horizons and ironstone bands, some cemented calcareous bands, some thin clay seams	37.87	62.70
Sandstone, calcareous and argillaceous, shelly	0.31	63.01
Sand, grey-green, mainly fine-grained, locally calcareous	3.09	66.10

Not seen	10.27	76.37
Sand, fine- to medium-grained, pale grey to olive-green	1.21	77.58
Open-holed, no core, greenish sand and 0.30 m of conglomeratic material	3.47	81.05

Middle Jurassic

MIDDLE OXFORD CLAY
Clay (mudstone), medium grey to pale grey, with shell fragments   2.47   83.52

Clophill Quarry Borehole   TL03NE/64   [TL 0966 3830]
Surface level c.+57 m

	Thickness m	Depth m
Made ground	1.0	1.0
Lower Cretaceous		
WOBURN SANDS		
Sand, fine- to medium-grained, locally coarse-grained and gritty, orange-brown, locally cemented, with scattered fine pebbles including 'lydites', lignite fragments at base	14.10	15.10
Fuller's earth, clay, bluish green	0.30	15.40
Sand, fine- to medium-grained, blue-green	2.30	17.70
Fuller's earth, clay, pale bluish, greenish grey	1.50	19.20
Sand, fine- to medium-grained, blue-green, some clay partings	4.60	23.80
Silt, clayey, and fine sandy, dull grey-brown, small sandstone fragments recovered	4.60	28.40
Sand, clayey and silty, bluish green-grey	0.60	29.00
Silt, sandy, clayey, grey-brown	0.20	29.20
Sand, fine-grained, clayey, bluish green-grey	0.80	30.00

INVENTORY OF CITED FOSSILS

GENERAL INDEX

BRITISH GEOLOGICAL SURVEY

Keyworth, Nottingham NG12 5GG
(0602) 363100

Murchison House, West Mains Road, Edinburgh
EH9 3LA   031-667 1000

London Information Office, Natural History Museum
Earth Galleries, Exhibition Road, London SW7 2DE
071-589 4090

The full range of Survey publications is available through the Sales Desks at Keyworth and at Murchison House, Edinburgh, and in the BGS London Information Office in the Natural History Museum Earth Galleries. The adjacent bookshop stocks the more popular books for sale over the counter. Most BGS books and reports are listed in HMSO's Sectional List 45, and can be bought from HMSO and through HMSO agents and retailers. Maps are listed in the BGS Map Catalogue, and can be bought BGS approved stockists and agents as well as direct from BGS.

The British Geological Survey carries out the geological survey of Great Britain and Northern Ireland (the latter as an agency service for the government of Northern Ireland), and of the surrounding continental shelf, as well as its basic research projects. It also undertakes programmes of British technical aid in geology in developing countries as arranged by the Overseas Development Administration.

The British Geological Survey is a component body of the Natural Environment Research Council.

HMSO publications are available from:

HMSO Publications Centre
(Mail, fax and telephone orders only)
PO Box 276, London SW8 5DT
Telephone orders 071-873 9090
General enquiries 071-873 0011
Queueing system in operation for both numbers
Fax orders 071-873 8200

HMSO Bookshops
49 High Holborn, London WC1V 6HB
(counter service only)
071-873 0011   Fax 071-873 8200
258 Broad Street, Birmingham B1 2HE
021-643 3740   Fax 021-643 6510
33 Wine Street, Bristol BS1 2BQ
0272-264306   Fax 0272-294515
9 Princess Street, Manchester M60 8AS
061-834 7201   Fax 061-833 0634
16 Arthur Street, Belfast BT1 4GD
0232-238451   Fax 0232-235401
71 Lothian Road, Edinburgh EH3 9AZ
031-228 4181   Fax 031-229 2734

HMSO's Accredited Agents
(see Yellow Pages)

And through good booksellers